Gear Handbook

Design and Calculations

Alec Stokes

INTERNATIONAL

UTTERWORTH
EINEMANN

24590351

Butterworth-Heinemann Ltd
Linacre House, Jordan Hill, Oxford OX2 8DP

◉ PART OF REED INTERNATIONAL BOOKS

OXFORD   LONDON   BOSTON
MUNICH   NEW DELHI   SINGAPORE   SYDNEY
TOKYO   TORONTO   WELLINGTON

First published 1992

British Library Cataloguing in Publication Data

Stokes, Alec
  Gear handbook: design and calculations
  I. Title
  621.8
  ISBN 0 7506 1149 9

Library of Congress Cataloguing in Publication Data

Stokes, Alec
  Gear handbook: design and calculations/Alec Stokes.
  p.   cm.
  Includes bibliographical references and index.
  ISBN 1 5609 1 257 X
  1. Gearing—Handbooks, manuals, etc.   I. Title.
  TJ185.S74   1992
  621.8′33—dc20

                                                          91–36304
                                                          CIP

Typeset by Vision Typesetting, Manchester
Printed and bound in Great Britain

Contents

Gear Handbook

By the same author

Manual Gearbox Design (Butterworth-Heinemann 1992)

Preface

The idea of producing this data handbook arose over the years that I have spent in the gear and transmission design business. During the design stages my desk was covered with various books and papers through which I had to plough in order to find the information I required. I quickly realized the need for a book containing all the design calculations for gear manufacture and inspection, and when the opportunity arose during my five years at Lotus Engineering, where I spent four nights per week in lodgings, I decided to start what turned out to be a very interesting, time-consuming but rather large task. Some three years after starting the project I arrived at the format and presentation, where each gear in both its imperial diametral pitch and metric module form is treated as a complete entity, and which will be of great use to anyone engaged in the gear design field, whether they be engineers, designers or students.

A. Stokes

Foreword

A.C. Rudd, Technical Director, Group Lotus

More than 20 years ago, frustrated by the contradictory books on gear design, I asked Alec Stokes to write down, for his colleagues to use, a set of guidelines on gear design drawn from his then 25 years' experience of high-performance gear systems. His first book *High Performance Gear Design* was the result.

When he paid me the great compliment of once more asking me to write the Foreword to his next book I was at first in something of a quandary. Then, working on a new engine design, I noticed how well thumbed my copy of his first book had become and I realized how much I had relied upon it during the past 20 years when involved in five four-wheel-drive projects, variable speed, variable geometry, 55 000 rpm axial compressors, several racing transmissions and innumerable engine projects ranging from four to eight or more cylinders. It was nearly always the first, certainly the second, reference book the scores of designers involved reached for in the course of these projects.

I am sure therefore that this book, incorporating as it does, much more than double the experience and knowledge of the first, will be of inestimable value to leading designers at the top of their profession as well as the next generation seeking guidance as they start up the ladder of knowledge.

Acknowledgements

In the preparation and writing of this book I am very aware of the assistance, both direct and indirect, received over the past 40 years. It is impossible to mention the names of everyone. But the major forces involved include the following:

1   The Directors of Lotus Cars and Engineering, in particular Mr A.C. Rudd, for presenting me with the type of challenges, since I joined the company, which rekindled the urge to pass on some of the knowledge on gear and transmission design which has been accumulated over more than 40 years.

2   My family, who encouraged me to accept the offer when Lotus invited me to join their design team and have given me their full backing ever since.

3   Colleagues at Lotus, among whom I feel I have made many friends and who are always willing to provide advice and support when situations arise that require teamwork and maximum effort.

4   Special mention must also be made of the authors whose books and work in the gear and transmission fields were the basis of my introduction into the gear and transmission business. The authors include the following: Professor W.A. Tuplin, Dr H.E. Merritt, Earl Buckingham and Darle Dudley. Mention must also be made of the British Standards Institution, who endeavour to keep designers up to date with modern gear technology, and the Gleason Gear Co. whose work on bevel and hypoid gear design provide all the information the designer requires.

5   Another group of people who must take much credit for any success I have achieved are the management and colleagues with whom I worked at B.R.M. Many happy years were spent with the Formula One racing team at Bourne and it was here that I had my introduction into gear and transmission design and where my first efforts in Formula One gearbox design were produced.

6   The final acknowledgement goes to fellow transmission designers and the personnel of the many gear manufacturers whom I have been fortunate to meet and who have always been willing to help and advise when problems have arisen.

1

Introduction

The intention of this book is to provide the engineer, gear designer or student with the necessary formulae needed to calculate the data required on a gear detail drawing for both manufacturing and inspection purposes. In most chapters a brief explanation of the gear form has been included to help with the design assessment, although an attempt has been made to reduce to a minimum the amount of reading matter included in the book.

Each chapter contains the full range of formulae for the particular gear in question. A brief description of each of the chapters is as follows.

Chapter 2, Spur Gear Calculations, gives the formulae for full-depth straight-cut spur gears – the term spur gears refers to cylindrical gears having straight teeth cut parallel to the axis of the gear which are used to connect parallel shafts which rotate in opposite directions. Being of simple form, a spur gear can be produced accurately and in use they give high efficiency. Tooth contact at any instant occurs along a line parallel to the axis of the gear, and the tooth load produces no axial thrust.

Spur gears give excellent results at moderate peripheral speeds, but tend to be noisy at high speeds unless manufactured to the highest degree of accuracy.

If stub tooth gears are to be calculated, the formulae can be modified to suit; for example, an 8/10 DP stub tooth gear has all the dimensions calculated as for an 8 DP gear except for the following:

1 Addendum
2 Dedendum
3 Whole depth
4 Bottom clearance

This also affects the outside diameter and root diameter, and items 1–4 inclusive are calculated as for a 10 DP gear. The resultant information will be for an 8/10 DP stub tooth gear, and the calculation for metric module stub tooth gears is carried out in the same manner.

The formulae given in Chapter 1 are for diametral pitch and metric module gears and cover gears running at standard centres, extended addendum gears, long and short addendum gears and non-standard centre distance gears. The formulae are also included for the calculation of the necessary inspection dimensions, and finally the recommended backlash is included.

Chapter 3, Internal Spur Gears, includes a simple explanation of the uses of internal spur gears, along with the formulae for calculating the data required for manufacturing and inspection purposes. Also included is an explanation of addendum modification and the terminology used with internal spur gears. Both diametral pitch and metric module gear calculations are included and the chapter is completed with the recommended backlash for internal spur gears.

Chapter 4, Helical Gears, gives a brief explanation of the helical gear tooth form and the method used to decide the hand of the helix. The calculations for the manufacturing and inspection data for both diametral pitch and metric module gears are given in detail, along with the formulae for corrected or addendum-modified gears, and the chapter finishes with the recommended backlash for helical gears.

Chapter 5, Straight Bevel Gears, opens with an explanation of the tooth form and uses of straight bevel gears and continues with the calculations for the manufacturing and inspection data for both diametral pitch and metric module straight bevel gears with shafts at 90° angle.

The calculations for straight-cut bevel gears with shafts at both less than 90° angle and greater than 90° angle follow and the chapter is concluded with the recommended backlash for both diametral pitch and metric module straight bevel gears.

Chapter 6, Spiral Bevel Gears, opens with a description of the tooth form and an explanation of how a spiral angle and the direction of rotation are decided. The calculations for the manufacturing and inspection data for spiral bevel gears with shafts at 90° angle covering both diametral pitch and metric module gears follows and then come the formulae for spiral bevel gears with shafts at both less than 90° angle and greater than 90° angle. The chapter concludes with the recommended backlash for both diametral pitch and metric module spiral bevel gears.

Chapter 7, Zerol Bevel Gears, starts with a description of the Zerol bevel tooth form which is followed by the formulae for the manufacturing and inspection data for both diametral pitch and metric module Zerol bevel gears with shafts at 90° angle. Then follow the formulae for Zerol bevel gears at both less than 90° angle and greater than 90° angle. The chapter concludes with the recommended backlash for both diametral pitch and metric module Zerol bevel gears.

Chapter 8, Hypoid Bevel Gears, opens with a brief description of the hypoid bevel gear and its tooth form, followed by the method of denoting the hand of spiral and the direction of thrust due to the direction of rotation. Then come the calculations for diametral pitch and metric module hypoid gears which give the manufacturing and inspection data. These calculations are for ratios operating at 90° shaft angles.

Hypoid bevels were introduced by the Gleason Gear Co. and are a cross between a spiral bevel gear and a worm gear. The axes of a pair of hypoid bevel gears are non-intersecting and the distance between the axes are referred to as the 'offset'.

Chapter 9, Worm Gears, opens with an appraisal of the format of the worm gear pair and their uses, then gives the British Standard method for calculating the manufacturing and inspection data for both diametral pitch and metric module worm gears.

The next four chapters deal with the stress calculations for the various types of gears covered in the previous chapters.

Chapter 10, Spur and Helical Gear Tooth Stress Calculations, covers the various formulae available for calculating the stress and expected life of spur and helical gears. The formulae covered are as follows:

1   Lewis stress formula
2   Buckingham stress formula
3   Tuplin stress formula
4   Hertz stress formula
5   BS 436: 1940, Stress Calculations for Spur and Helical Gears
6   BS 436: 1986, Stress Calculations for Spur and Helical Gears

   (*Note*: This British Standard supersedes BS 436: 1940 and is a far more comprehensive method of arriving at the strength of the gear teeth.)

Chapter 11, Bevel Gear Stress Formulae, covers the various formulae available for stressing bevel gears. The formulae covered are as follows:

1   Spiral bevel gears (BS 545: 1949).
2   Modified Lewis formulae for bevel gears
3   Gleason stress formula

Chapter 12, Hypoid Gear Stress Formulae, is devoted to the Gleason method for calculating the bending and contact stresses in hypoid gear teeth calculated to the Gleason hypoid gear system.

Chapter 13, Worm Gear Stress Formula, covers the British Standard method for the stress calculations for both diametral pitch and metric module worm gears.

Chapter 14, Summary, lists other Standards that are used in the gearing industry and gives guidance to the designer on how to eliminate vibration and noise from the gear train drives, especially as he gains more experience.

Also included in this chapter is a résumé of the differences between the various stressing formulae for spur and helical gears. This includes the safety factors that have been used with the formulae to design a manually operated gearbox used in a well-known and owner-proven passenger car which has been on the market for some years. The design formulae covered in this comparison exercise are as follows:

1   Lewis formula
2   Buckingham formula
3   British Standard 436: 1986
4   AGMA 170.01: 1976

It will be seen from the figures given in this comparison that the answer given by the formulae must be correctly interpreted unless gears that are grossly overweight are not to become the order of the day. The ISO Standard and finite element analysis are briefly discussed in the final pages of the chapter.

2
Spur gear calculations

The following calculations give the dimensions required to manufacture spur gears (Figure 2.1).

Some dimensions or details of the gear pair must be known and should be used as a starting point, and calculation sheets or a computer program can be prepared based on the following formulae.

The formulae are given for calculating both diametral pitch (Imperial) and metric module spur gears.

Diametral pitch spur gears

1   No. of teeth – pinion
    No. of teeth – wheel
2   Diametral pitch
3   Pressure angle
Note: 20° is the normal standard pressure angle
4   Circular pitch

$$= \frac{\pi}{DP} = \frac{3.14159}{DP}$$

5   Pitch circle diameter

$$= \frac{\text{No. of teeth}}{DP}$$

6   Base circle diameter = PC dia. × cos Pressure angle
7   Dedendum – standard:

$$\text{Minimum} = \frac{1.157}{DP} \qquad \text{Maximum} = \frac{1.35}{DP}$$

8   Addendum – standard

$$= \frac{1}{DP}$$

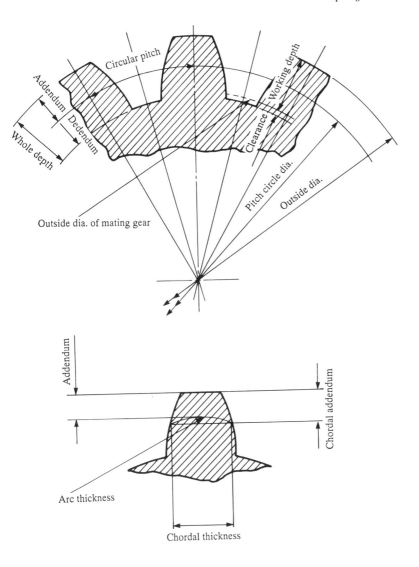

Figure 2.1   Gear terminology – spur gear

9   Whole depth:

$$\text{Minimum} = \frac{2.157}{\text{DP}} \qquad \text{Maximum} = \frac{2.35}{\text{DP}}$$

10   Bottom clearance:

$$\text{Minimum} = \frac{0.157}{\text{DP}} \qquad \text{Maximum} = \frac{0.35}{\text{DP}}$$

11   Outside diameter – standard = PC dia. + (2 × Addendum – standard)

12   Root diameter:

Minimum = OD – (2 × Max. whole depth)
Maximum = OD – (2 × Min. whole depth)

13   Backlash – standard between gears

14   *Gear centres.* If the gear centres to be used are standard, they are calculated as follows:

$$\frac{\text{PC dia. (pinion)} + \text{PC dia. (wheel)}}{2}$$

If the centres to be used are non-standard, a correction must be applied.

Correction may also be used to balance the strength between the pinion and the wheel, which is relative to the operating pitch circle diameters of the gears, calculated as follows:

Std PC dia. ± (Corr. on gear × 2)

14A   Correction on centres

$$= \text{Actual centres} - \frac{\text{PC dia. (pinion)} + \text{PC dia. (wheel)}}{2}$$

= Actual centres – Standard centres

15   Actual centres – corrected (close meshing)

$$= \frac{\text{Std gear CRS} \times \cos \text{ Press. angle}}{\cos \text{ PA of engagement}}$$

∴ cos PA of engagement

$$= \frac{\text{Std gear CRS} \times \cos \text{ Press. angle}}{\text{Actual CRS – Corrected}}$$

∴ Pressure angle of engagement can be found and ultimately the involute of the pressure angle or engagement.

16   Check: Actual centres – corrected:
Involute of pressure angle of engagement

$$= \frac{\text{No. of teeth (pinion) [Corr. arc thick } (P) + \text{Corr. arc thick } (W)] - \pi \times \text{PC dia. } (P)}{\text{PC dia. (pinion)} \times \text{Total no. of teeth (pinion + wheel)}} + A$$

where A = Involute of pressure angle

17   Arc thickness – corrected

$$= \frac{1.5708}{\text{DP}} + (2 \times \text{Corr. on gear} \times \tan \text{ Press. angle})$$

Note: By using calculations 15 to 17 in various orders, the specific correction required can be found.

18 Corrected addendum can now be calculated as follows:

$$\text{Corr. addendum} = \text{Std add.} \pm \text{Corr. on gear}$$

Using the corrected addendum, the corrected outside diameter can be calculated as follows:

19 Corrected outside diameter $= \text{PC dia.} + (2 \times \text{Corr. addendum})$

Having calculated the corrected outside diameter, the root diameter can be calculated using calculation 12.

20 Chordal thickness – corrected

$$= \text{PC dia.} \times \sin\left(\frac{90 \times \text{Corr. arc thickness}}{\text{PC radius} \times \pi}\right)$$

Note: For inspection purposes, the backlash allowance on the gear should be taken away from the chordal thickness. The backlash allowance per gear is usually taken as half the total backlash between the gear pair – see calculation 13.

21 Chordal addendum

$$= \text{Corr. addendum} + \left(\frac{\text{Corr. arc thickness}^2}{4 \times \text{PC dia.}}\right)$$

Note: Calculations 20 and 21 are for use with a gear tooth micrometer, but a more practical method of checking the gear teeth for accuracy of spacing is by using the chordal dimension over a specific number of teeth. A table giving the number of teeth which should be used to measure over is given in calculation 22.

22 Chordal dimension over no. of teeth (N)

$$= \text{PC rad.} \times \cos \text{PA}\left(\frac{\text{Corr. arc thick.}}{\text{PC rad.}} + \frac{6.2832 \times \text{No. of spaces}}{\text{No. of teeth on gear}} + 2 \times \text{Inv. PA}\right)$$

where $N = $ standard number of teeth to be used to measure over.

$$\text{PC rad.} = \frac{\text{PC dia.}}{2} \text{ or } \frac{\text{Calculation 5}}{2}$$

No. of spaces = no. of spaces between number of teeth being measured over: No. of spaces $= N - 1$.

Notes:

(a) For corrected arc thickness, see calculation 17.

(b) The standard number of teeth used to measure over is given in the table below.

No. of teeth N to gauge over	$14\frac{1}{2}°$ press. angle (No. of teeth on gear)	20° press. angle (No. of teeth on gear)
2	12–18	12–18
3	19–37	19–27
4	38–50	28–36
5	51–62	37–45
6	63–75	46–54

(c) The backlash allowance on the gear should be taken away from the calculated chordal dimension for inspection purposes.

23   If correction is used on the gear teeth, the following check should be made to ensure that the involute form of the tooth does not create a pointed tooth when using positive correction or a severe undercut when using negative correction, thus weakening the tooth root strength – see calculations 24 and 25.

24   *Positive correction – tooth pointing*, where ϕ_3 = pressure angle at tooth point:

$$\text{Inv. } \phi_3 = \frac{\text{Corr. arc thickness}}{\text{PC dia.}} + \text{Involute press. angle}$$

$$\text{Diameter when pointed} = 2 \times \left(\frac{\text{PC radius} \times \cos. \text{ Press. angle}}{\cos \phi_3}\right)$$

25   *Negative correction – undercutting.* The maximum amount of negative correction that can be used without undercutting can be calculated as follows:

(a) Where total number of teeth on both gears is greater than 59, then

$$K_p = 0.4(1 - t/T) \text{ for IDP gears}$$

or

$$K_p = 0.02(30 - t \sec^3\sigma)$$

Using whichever is the greater, this gives full involute action with pinions having a small number of teeth and ensures better zone and strength factors,

where $K_w = -K_p$ (IDP gears)
 K_p = corr. factor – pinion
 K_w = corr. factor – wheel
 t = no. of teeth – pinion
 T = no. of teeth – wheel
 σ = spiral or helix angle

Values of $\sec^3\sigma$	
Spiral angle, σ	$\text{Sec}^3\sigma$
0° (spur)	1.000
$22\frac{1}{2}$°	1.268
30°	1.540
45°	2.830

(b) Where total number of teeth on both gears is less than 60, the centre distance should be extended by an amount equal to Δ/DP in inches,

where Δ = extension in centre distance factor – see Figure 2.2

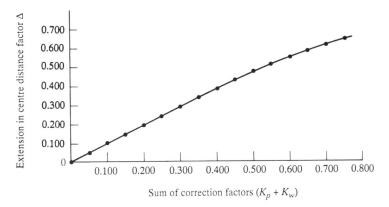

Figure 2.2   Extension in centre distance

Then:

$$K_p(\text{IDP gears})=0.02(30-t\ \sec^3\sigma)$$
$$K_w(\text{IDP gears})=0.02(30-T\ \sec^3\sigma)$$

26   Some designs require the maximum possible length of contact between the mating gears, which when properly designed and accurately manufactured will result in a smoother rolling action between adjacent teeth.

Normally, gears are designed to roll on standard centre distances with standard tooth thicknesses and backlash requirements. By using extended addendums on both the mating gears, this results in a longer radial working depth and smaller root diameters. The length of the addendum extension is limited by the minimum allowable top land width of the teeth, which must be decided by the designer.

There could also be a loss of beam strength due to the extra tooth length and possible undercut of the tooth flank.

Such gears are referred to as 'extended addendum gears'.

27   *Long and short addendum gears.* Occasionally a design will require a gear pair where one of the gears is considerably smaller than its mate. If standard tooth proportions are used, the root fillet conditions produced in the small pinion and its mating gear contacts will result in a poorly operating pair of gears.

As all profile action stops at the base circle, the larger gear addendum extending beyond the line of action represents a loss of contact between the gears.

Further, if the pinion flank is not excessively undercut, which would weaken the pinion teeth, the mating gear tooth tips would find fillet metal interfering with its trochoidal sweep.

The long and short addendum gears running as pairs were found to alleviate this type of problem. Normally the positive and negative correction method is used to relieve undesirable conditions, when running standard gears together show up the problem. The pinion outside diameter can be increased (long addendum) and the gear outside decreased (short addendum) by an equal amount; thus the numbers of teeth, the gear ratio, the working depth and the gear centres remain unchanged.

The amount by which the outside diameter can be varied is dependent on the number of teeth and the pressure angle, and the limiting factors include the minimum acceptable top land width on the pinion teeth, excessive profile sliding and the beam strength requirements of the gear. These design parameters must be checked after the preliminary tooth proportions have been established.

The actual amount of 'correction or profile shift' that can be applied to a pinion without creating the problem of the outside diameter of the gear extending beyond the limit of the involute profile on the pinion, can be arrived at by calculating the maximum outside diameter of the gear as follows:

Maximum theoretical outside diameter without involute interference

$$= \sqrt{D_b^2 + (2C \sin \phi_{tR})^2}$$

where

$$\cos \phi_{tR} = \frac{D_b \text{ pinion} + D_b \text{ gear}}{2C}$$

D_b = base diameter
C = gear centres

The difference between this new outside diameter, which should have a tolerance of -0.010–0.020 in, applied in practice, and the standard outside diameter divided by two is the 'correction or profile shift'. Calculations 17 to 22 must be repeated at this stage to give the new manufacturing and inspection dimensions.

This method is based on maintaining standard centre distances where the generating pitch circle diameters are the actual rolling pitch diameters.

28   *Non-standard centre distance gears.* When a pair of gears are required to operate on other than standard centres, it is usual to use centres greater than standard to give a more efficient gear pair, even though the involute gear form lends itself readily to either increased or decreased gear centres.

From the previous notes it is obvious that to operate on other than standard centres the gear tooth data can no longer be standard and must be calculated by inserting the relevant centres and known data in calculations 15 to 22.

Oversized and undersized gear designs of this type are quite common. In the speed reducer and automotive transmission fields it is much more expedient to change the gear tooth design for a ratio change than to involve the designer in large design modifications and the subsequent increase in tooling cost to change the gear housing centre distance.

This ability to modify physically the shape of the teeth and still have an efficiently operating gear pair is one of the main assets of the involute gear system.

29   Having completed the gear tooth correction calculations, the final task is to check that the minimum bottom clearance (calculation 10) is maintained. This can be calculated as follows:

Loss of tooth tip clearance

$$= \text{Actual centres} - (\text{Std centres} + \text{Total corr. on gear pair})$$

If any loss of clearance (minimum bottom clearance must be maintained) is found, it is possible to reduce the outside diameter of the larger gear as a final operation after gear cutting.

Note: The outside diameter reduction will reduce the contact ratio – see calculation on page 20.
30 Having completed the calculations for the manufacturing dimensions, the inspection dimensions must be calculated for the diametral pitch gears.

The British Standard methods of arriving at these dimensions are given in the following pages and cover the dimensional limits for the following:

(a) Pitch tolerance
(b) Tooth profile tolerance
(c) Tooth alignment tolerance
(d) Radial run-out tolerance

The tolerances are given for varying grades of gear tooth finishes in each of the above, and it is the gear designer's task to suit the purpose and life for which the gears have been designed to the correct grade of finish. Figures quoted are from BS 436.
31 *Pitch tolerance.* The limits of tolerance on transverse pitch, both adjacent and cumulative, should be in accordance with the requirements of the table below and appropriate to the particular grade of gear.

The tolerance is calculated in units of 0.001 in, where $l =$ any selected length of arc in inches, including an arc length of one pitch, but not greater than $(\pi d) \times 0.5$, where $d =$ pitch circle diameter.

Grade of gear	Limits of tolerance
1	$0.05\sqrt{l} + 0.025$
2	$0.08\sqrt{l} + 0.04$
3	$0.12\sqrt{l} + 0.06$
4	$0.20\sqrt{l} + 0.10$
5	$0.32\sqrt{l} + 0.16$
6	$0.50\sqrt{l} + 0.25$
7	$0.71\sqrt{l} + 0.35$
8	$1.00\sqrt{l} + 0.50$
9	$1.40\sqrt{l} + 0.71$
10	$2.00\sqrt{l} + 1.00$
11	$2.80\sqrt{l} + 1.40$
12	$4.00\sqrt{l} + 2.00$

32 *Tooth profile tolerance.* The tolerance is calculated in units of 0.001 in, and $\theta_t =$ tolerance factor

$$= \frac{25.4}{DP} + 0.5\sqrt{PC \text{ dia.}}$$

The profile tolerance is calculated as shown in the table below, and the grade of gear must be the same as used for the pitch tolerance – calculation 31.

Grade of gear	Limits of tolerance
1	$0.00250_t + 0.080$
2	$0.00400_t + 0.100$
3	$0.00630_t + 0.125$
4	$0.0100_t + 0.160$
5	$0.0160_t + 0.200$
6	$0.0250_t + 0.250$
7	$0.0400_t + 0.320$
8	$0.0630_t + 0.400$
9	$0.1000_t + 0.630$
10	$0.1600_t + 1.000$
11	$0.2500_t + 1.600$
12	$0.4000_t + 2.500$

33   *Tooth alignment tolerance.* The tolerance is calculated in units of 0.001 in, and b = tooth facewidth, in inches.

The tooth alignment tolerance is calculated as shown in the table below, and the grade must be the same as used for the pitch tolerance and the tooth profile tolerance – calculations 31 and 32.

Grade of gear	Tooth alignment tolerance
1	$0.063\sqrt{b} + 0.063$
2	$0.08\sqrt{b} + 0.080$
3	$0.10\sqrt{b} + 0.100$
4	$0.125\sqrt{b} + 0.125$
5	$0.16\sqrt{b} + 0.16$
6	$0.20\sqrt{b} + 0.20$
7	$0.25\sqrt{b} + 0.25$
8	$0.40\sqrt{b} + 0.40$
9	$0.63\sqrt{b} + 0.63$
10	$1.00\sqrt{b} + 1.00$
11	$1.60\sqrt{b} + 1.60$
12	$2.50\sqrt{b} + 2.50$

34   *Radial run-out tolerance.* The tolerance is calculated in units of 0.001 in and θ_p = tolerance factor

$$= \frac{25.4}{DP} + 1.25\sqrt{PC \ \text{dia}}$$

The radial run-out tolerance is calculated as shown in the table below, and the grade used must be the same as used for the pitch tolerance, the tooth profile tolerance and the tooth alignment tolerance – calculations 31 to 33.

Grade of gear	Radial run-out tolerance
1	$0.009\theta_p + 0.11$
2	$0.014\theta_p + 0.18$
3	$0.0224\theta_p + 0.28$
4	$0.036\theta_p + 0.45$
5	$0.056\theta_p + 0.7$
6	$0.090\theta_p + 1.1$
7	$0.125\theta_p + 1.6$
8	$0.16\theta_p + 2.0$
9	$0.20\theta_p + 2.5$
10	$0.25\theta_p + 3.2$
11	$0.32\theta_p + 4.0$
12	$0.40\theta_p + 5.0$

Metric module spur gears

1 No. of teeth – pinion
No. of teeth – wheel
2 Module
3 Pressure angle:
Note: 20° is the normal standard pressure angle.
4 Circular pitch

$$= \pi \times \text{Module}$$
$$= 3.14159 \times \text{Module}$$

5 Pitch circle diameter = No. of teeth × Module
6 Base circle diameter = PC dia. × cos Pressure angle
7 Dedendum – standard:

Minimum = 1.157 × Module
Maximum = 1.35 × Module

8 Addendum – standard = Module
9 Whole depth:

Minimum = 2.157 × Module
Maximum = 2.35 × Module

10 Bottom clearance:

Minimum = 0.157 × Module
Maximum = 0.35 × Module

11   Outside diameter – standard = PC dia + (2 × Addendum – std)

12   Root diameter:

$$\text{Minimum} = \text{OD} - (2 \times \text{Max. whole depth})$$
$$\text{Maximum} = \text{OD} - (2 \times \text{Min. whole depth})$$

13   Backlash – standard between gears

14   *Gear centres*. If the gear centres to be used are standard, these are calculated as follows:

$$\frac{\text{PC dia. (pinion)} + \text{PC dia. (wheel)}}{2}$$

If the centres to be used are non-standard, a correction must be applied.

Correction may also be used to balance the strength between the pinion and the wheel, which is relative to the operating pitch circle diameters of the gears, calculated as follows: Std PC dia. ± (Corr. on gear × 2)

14A   Correction on centres:

$$= \text{Actual centres} - \frac{\text{PC dia. (pinion)} + \text{PC dia. (wheel)}}{2}$$

$$= \text{Actual centres} - \text{Standard centres}$$

15   Actual centres – corrected (close meshing)

$$= \frac{\text{Std gear CRS} \times \cos \text{ Press. angle}}{\cos \text{ Pressure angle of engagement}}$$

∴ cos PA of engagement

$$= \frac{\text{Std gear CRS} \times \cos \text{ Pressure angle}}{\text{Actual CRS – corrected}}$$

∴ Pressure angle of engagement can be found and ultimately the involute of the pressure angle of engagement.

16   Check: Actual centres – corrected:

Involute of pressure angle of engagement

$$= \frac{\text{No. of teeth (pinion) [Corr. arc thick. } (P) + \text{Corr. arc thick. } (W)] - \pi \times \text{PC dia. } (W)}{\text{PC dia. (pinion)} \times \text{Total no. of teeth (pinion + wheel)}}$$

+ Involute of pressure angle

17   Arc thickness – corrected = 1.5708 × Module + (2 × Corr. on gear × tan Press. angle)

Note: By using calculations 15, 16 and 17 in various orders, the specific correction required can be found.

18   Corrected addendum can now be calculated as follows: Corr. addendum = Std add. ± Corr. on gear

Using the corrected addendum, the corrected outside diameter can be calculated as follows:

19 Corr. outside diameter $= $ PC dia. $+ (2 \times$ Corr. addendum)

Having calculated the corrected outside diameter, the root diameter can be calculated using calculation 12.

20 Chordal thickness – corrected

$$= \text{PC dia.} \times \sin\left(\frac{90 \times \text{Corr. arc thickness}}{\text{PC radius} \times \pi}\right)$$

Note: For inspection purposes, the backlash allowance on the gear should be taken away from the chordal thickness. The backlash allowance per gear is usually taken as half the total backlash between the gear pair – see calculation 13.

21 Chordal addendum

$$= \text{Corr. addendum} + \left(\frac{\text{Corr. arc thickness}^2}{4 \times \text{PC dia.}}\right)$$

Note: Calculations 20 and 21 are for use with a gear tooth micrometer, but a more practical method of checking the gear teeth for accuracy of spacing is by using the chordal dimension over a specific number of teeth. A table giving the number of teeth which should be used to measure over is given in calculation 22.

22 Chordal dimension over no. of teeth (N)

$$= \text{PC rad.} \times \cos \text{PA}\left(\frac{\text{Corr. arc thick.}}{\text{PC rad.}} + \frac{6.2832 \times \text{No. of spaces}}{\text{No. of teeth on gear}} + 2 \times \text{Inv. PA}\right)$$

where

$N = $ Standard number of teeth to be used to measure over.

$$\text{PC rad.} = \frac{\text{PC dia.}}{2} \quad \text{or} \quad \frac{\text{Calculation 5}}{2}$$

No. of spaces $= $ No. of spaces between number of teeth being measured over: No. of spaces $= N - 1$.

Notes:

(a) For corrected arc thickness see calculation 17.

(b) The standard number of teeth used to measure over is given in the table below.

No. of teeth N to gauge over	$14\frac{1}{2}°$ press. angle (No. of teeth on gear)	$20°$ press. angle (No. of teeth on gear)
2	12–18	12–18
3	19–37	19–27
4	38–50	28–36
5	51–62	37–45
6	63–75	46–54

(c) The backlash allowance on the gear should be taken away from the calculated chordal dimension for inspection purposes.

23   If correction is used on the gear teeth, the following check should be made to ensure that the involute form of the tooth does not create a pointed tooth when using positive correction or a severe undercut when using negative correction, thus weakening the tooth root strength – see calculations 24 and 25.

24   *Positive correction – tooth pointing*, where ϕ_3 = pressure angle at tooth point:

$$\text{Inv. } \phi_3 = \frac{\text{Corr. arc thickness}}{\text{PC dia.}} + \text{Involute press. angle}$$

$$\text{Diameter when pointed} = 2 \times \left(\frac{\text{PC radius} \times \cos \text{ Press. angle}}{\cos \phi_3} \right)$$

25   *Negative correction – undercutting.* The maximum amount of negative correction that can be used without undercutting can be calculated as follows:
(a) Where total number of teeth on both gears is greater than 59, then

$$K_p = 0.4(1 - t/T) - \text{(for IDP gears)}$$

or

$$K_p = 0.02(30 - t \sec^3 \sigma)$$

Using whichever is the greater, this gives full involute action with pinions having a small number of teeth and ensures better zone and strength factors,

where: $K_w = -K_p$(IDP gears)
   K_p = corr. factor – pinion
   K_w = corr. factor – wheel
   t = no. of teeth – pinion
   T = no. of teeth – wheel
   σ = spiral or helix angle

Values of $\sec^3 \sigma$	
Spiral angle, σ	$\text{Sec}^3 \sigma$
0° (spur)	1.000
$22\frac{1}{2}°$	1.268
30°	1.540
45°	2.830

(b) Where total number of teeth on both gears is less than 60, the centre distance should be extended by an amount equal to

$$\frac{\Delta \times \text{Module}}{25.4}$$

in inches, or $\Delta \times$ module in millimetres,

where $\quad \Delta =$ extension in centre distance factor – see Figure 2.2 (page 9)

Then:

$$K_p(\text{IDP gears}) = 0.02(30 - t \ \sec^3\sigma)$$
$$K_w(\text{IDP gears}) = 0.02(30 - T \ \sec^3\sigma)$$

26 Some designs require the maximum possible length of contact between the mating gears, which when properly designed and accurately manufactured will result in a smoother rolling action between adjacent teeth.

Normally, gears are designed to roll on standard centre distances with standard tooth thicknesses and backlash requirements. By using extended addendums on both the mating gears, this results in a longer radial working depth and smaller root diameters. The length of the addendum extension is limited by the minimum allowable top land width of the teeth, which must be decided by the designer.

There could also be a loss of beam strength due to the extra tooth length and possible undercut of the tooth flank.

Such gears are referred to as 'extended addendum gears'.

27 Long and short addendum gears – see item 27 (page 9).

28 Non-standard centre distance gears – see item 28 (page 10).

29 Having completed the gear tooth correction calculations, the final task is to check that the minimum bottom clearance (calculation 10) is maintained. If any loss is detected using the formula shown in item 29 (page 10), the corrective action shown after the above formula should be taken.

30 Having completed the calculations for the manufacturing dimensions, there remain the inspection dimensions for metric module spur gears as the final information required to complete the drawing.

The British Standard methods of arriving at these dimensions are given in the following pages and cover the dimensional limits for the following:

(a) Pitch tolerance
(b) Tooth profile tolerance
(c) Tooth alignment tolerance
(d) Radial run-out tolerance

The tolerances are given for varying grades of gear tooth finishes in each of the above, and the gear designer must decide which grade of finish is most suitable for the gear pair, while taking into account the purpose and life expectation for which the gears have been designed.

The tolerances quoted are from BS 436.

31 *Pitch tolerance.* The limits of tolerance on transverse pitch, both adjacent and cumulative, should be in accordance with the requirements of the table below and appropriate to the particular grade of gear.

The tolerance is calculated in units of 0.001 mm, where $l =$ any selected length of arc in millimetres, including an arc length of one pitch, but not greater than $(\pi d) \times 0.5$, where $d =$ pitch circle diameter.

Grade of gear	Limits of tolerance
1	$0.25\sqrt{l}+0.63$
2	$0.4\sqrt{l}+1.00$
3	$0.63\sqrt{l}+1.60$
4	$1.0\sqrt{l}+2.50$
5	$1.6\sqrt{l}+4.00$
6	$2.5\sqrt{l}+6.30$
7	$3.55\sqrt{l}+9.00$
8	$5.0\sqrt{l}+12.50$
9	$7.1\sqrt{l}+18.00$
10	$10.0\sqrt{l}+25.00$
11	$14.0\sqrt{l}+35.50$
12	$20.0\sqrt{l}+50.00$

32 *Tooth profile tolerance.* The tooth profile tolerance is calculated in units of 0.001 mm and the tolerance factor $(\theta_t)=\text{module}+0.1\sqrt{\text{PC dia}}$.

The profile tolerance is calculated as shown in the table below, and the grade of gear must be the same as used for the pitch tolerance – calculation 31.

Grade of gear	Limits of tolerance
1	$0.063\theta_t+2.00$
2	$0.10\theta_t+2.50$
3	$0.16\theta_t+3.15$
4	$0.25\theta_t+4.00$
5	$0.40\theta_t+5.00$
6	$0.63\theta_t+6.30$
7	$1.00\theta_t+8.00$
8	$1.60\theta_t+10.00$
9	$2.50\theta_t+16.00$
10	$4.00\theta_t+25.00$
11	$6.30\theta_t+40.00$
12	$10.00\theta_t+63.00$

33 *Tooth alignment tolerance.* The tooth alignment tolerance is calculated in units of 0.001 mm, and $b=$ tooth facewidth, in millimetres.

The tooth alignment tolerance is calculated as shown in the table below, and the grade must be the same as used for the pitch tolerance and the tooth profile tolerance – calculations 31 and 32.

34 *Radial run-out tolerance.* The tolerance is calculated in units of 0.001 mm and $\theta_p=$ tolerance factor

$$=\text{Module}+0.25\sqrt{\text{PC dia}}.$$

Grade of gear	Tooth alignment tolerance
1	$0.315\sqrt{b}+1.60$
2	$0.40\sqrt{b}+2.00$
3	$0.50\sqrt{b}+2.50$
4	$0.63\sqrt{b}+3.15$
5	$0.80\sqrt{b}+4.00$
6	$1.00\sqrt{b}+5.00$
7	$1.25\sqrt{b}+6.30$
8	$2.00\sqrt{b}+10.00$
9	$3.15\sqrt{b}+16.00$
10	$5.00\sqrt{b}+25.00$
11	$8.00\sqrt{b}+40.00$
12	$12.50\sqrt{b}+63.00$

The radial run-out tolerance is calculated as shown in the following table, and the grade used must be the same as used for the pitch tolerance, the tooth profile tolerance and the tooth alignment tolerance – calculations 31 to 33.

Grade of gear	Radial run-out tolerance
1	$0.224\theta_p+2.80$
2	$0.355\theta_p+4.50$
3	$0.56\theta_p+7.10$
4	$0.90\theta_p+11.20$
5	$1.40\theta_p+18.00$
6	$2.24\theta_p+28.00$
7	$3.15\theta_p+40.00$
8	$4.00\theta_p+50.00$
9	$5.00\theta_p+63.00$
10	$6.30\theta_p+80.00$
11	$8.00\theta_p+100.00$
12	$10.00\theta_p+125.00$

35   The foregoing formulae are designed for use with full-depth spur gear teeth, but can also be used to calculate the dimensions for the stub tooth system.

Both the full-depth and stub tooth systems use standard cutters which produce a 20° pressure angle.

The stub tooth diametral pitch is designated by a fraction, e.g. 6/8.

The numerator of the fraction indicates the pitch of the gear, i.e. 6, and determines the number of teeth and the tooth thickness, while the denominator indicates the pitch used for determining the tooth depth, addendum and dedendum.

The stub tooth system allows pinions with small numbers of teeth to be made to standard proportions without the danger of undercutting at the tooth roots; while the undercutting is eliminated, the contact length is reduced and thus the gears tend to be noisy. Although the shorter tooth depth appears to give a stronger tooth, this is more than offset by the reduction in contact length and contact ratio when compared with the full-depth tooth system.

Spur gears – recommended backlash

The backlash figures given in the following table are for gears assembled ready to run, and the backlash should be shared equally between the pinion and wheel.

Diametrical pitch	Backlash (in)
1	0.025–0.040
$1\frac{1}{2}$	0.018–0.027
2	0.014–0.020
$2\frac{1}{2}$	0.011–0.016
3	0.009–0.014
4	0.007–0.011
5	0.006–0.009
6	0.005–0.008
7	0.004–0.007
8–10	0.004–0.006
10–13	0.003–0.005
14–32	0.002–0.004
Metric module	Backlash (mm)
25	0.65–1.00
20	0.50–0.75
15	0.40–0.55
10	0.28–0.40
8	0.20–0.30
6	0.15–0.25
5	0.15–0.225
4	0.125–0.200
3	0.100–0.175
3.00–2.50	0.100–0.150
2.50–2.00	0.075–0.125
2.00–0.75	0.050–0.100

$$\text{Contact ratio} = \frac{\sqrt{d_a^2 - d_o^2} + \sqrt{D_a^2 - D_o^2} - 2C \ \sin \ \theta}{2 \times \text{circular pitch} \times \cos \ \theta}$$

where d_a = tip circle dia. – pinion
d_o = base circle dia. – pinion
D_a = tip circle dia. – wheel
D_o = base circle dia. – wheel
θ = pressure angle

3
Internal spur gears

Internal spur gears (Figure 3.1) provide a compact drive for transmitting motion between parallel shafts which rotate in the same direction.

A gear pair consists of a standard spur gear pinion meshing with an internal wheel which has teeth cut on the inside of its rim. The pinion is therefore housed inside the wheel and the driving and driven members rotate in the same direction at relative speeds inversely proportional to their numbers of teeth.

The following calculations give the dimensions required to manufacture the internal gear.

Some dimensions or details of the gear pair must be known and should be used as a starting point. The chapter gives formulae for the calculation of both diametral pitch (Imperial) and metric module spur gears.

Internal spur gears – diametral pitch

1   No. of teeth
2   Diametral pitch
3   Pressure angle
Note: 20° pressure angle is the normal standard
4   Circular pitch

$$= \frac{\pi}{DP} = \frac{3.14159}{DP}$$

5   Pitch circle diameter

$$= \frac{\text{No. of teeth}}{DP}$$

6   Base circle diameter = PC dia. × cos Pressure angle
7   Dedendum – standard:

$$\text{Minimum} = \frac{1.157}{DP} \qquad \text{Maximum} = \frac{1.35}{DP}$$

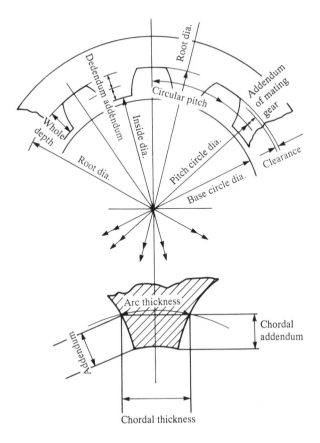

Figure 3.1   Gear terminology – internal gear

8   Addendum – standard

$$\frac{1}{DP}$$

9   Whole depth:

$$\text{Minimum} = \frac{2.157}{DP} \qquad \text{Maximum} = \frac{2.35}{DP}$$

10   Bottom clearance:

$$\text{Minimum} = \frac{0.157}{DP} \qquad \text{Maximum} = \frac{0.35}{DP}$$

11   Outside (root) diameter – standard = PC dia. + (2 × Dedendum – standard)
12   Inside diameter: PC dia. – (2 × Addendum – standard)
13   Backlash – standard between gears

14 *Gear centres.* If the gear centres to be used are standard, these are calculated as follows:

$$\frac{\text{PC dia. (internal gear)} - \text{PC dia. (spur gear)}}{2}$$

If the centres to be used are non-standard, a correction must be applied either to the internal gear or to the spur gear pinion. The amount of correction required is calculated as follows:

14A Correction required

$$= \text{Actual centres} - \text{Standard centres}$$

$$= \text{Actual CRS} - \left[\frac{\text{PC dia. (int. gear)} - \text{PC dia. (spur gear)}}{2} \right]$$

If correction is required, calculations 4 to 12 inclusive should be recalculated as follows:

15 Corrected PC dia. $= \text{Std PC dia.} \pm (2 \times \text{Correction})$

16 Corrected circular pitch

$$= \frac{\text{Corr. PC dia.} \times \pi}{\text{No. of teeth}}$$

17 Corrected base circle dia. $= \text{Corr. PC dia.} \times \cos \text{Press. angle}$

18 Circular tooth thickness

$$= \frac{\text{Corr. circular pitch}}{2}$$

Note: For circular tooth thickness calculations use circular pitch calculation 4 for dimension at standard PC dia. and calculation 16 for dimension at corrected PC dia.

19 Corrected addendum

$$= \text{Std addendum} \pm \left(\frac{\text{Corr. circular tooth thickness}}{4 \times \text{Corr. PC dia.}} \right)$$

20 Whole depth: see calculation 9

21 Corrected dedendum $= \text{Whole depth (min.)} - \text{Corr. addendum}$

22 Bottom clearance: see calculation 10

23 Outside (root) diameter – corrected $= \text{std PC dia.} + (2 \times \text{Corr. dedendum})$

24 Inside diameter – corrected $= \text{std PC dia.} - (2 \times \text{Corr. addendum})$

25 Using the relevant section for either a standard or corrected internal gear, the calculations for the inspection dimensions will continue as follows:

Chordal tooth thickness

$$= \text{Circular tooth thickness} - \left(\frac{\text{Circular tooth thick.}}{4 \times \text{PC dia.} \times \text{No. of teeth}} \right)^2$$

26 Normal circular space $= \text{Circular pitch} - \text{Circular tooth thickness}$

27 The inspection dimensions for internal spur gears comprise the following:

(a) Dimension between 2 balls or pins
(b) Pitch tolerance
(c) Tooth profile tolerance
(d) Tooth alignment tolerance
(e) Radial run-out tolerance

The calculations for these dimensions are made as follows, and the tolerances are given for varying grades of gear tooth finish as shown for spur gears.
28 Dimension between 2 balls or pins:
(a) Ball or pin diameter:

$$= \frac{1.44}{DP}$$

Now the nearest standard ball or pin diameter should be selected and used in the following calculations:
(b) Involute function for pressure angle at ball or pin centre:

Inv. $\phi_w =$

$$\text{Inv. press. angle} - \left[\frac{\text{Ball dia.}/(\cos \text{ Press. angle}) - \text{Circ. space}}{\text{Corr. PC dia.}} \right]$$

(c) For gears with even no. of teeth:
Dimension between 2 balls or pins

$$= \frac{\text{Base dia.}}{\cos \phi_w} - \text{Ball or pin dia.}$$

(d) For gears with odd no. of teeth:
Dimension between 2 balls or pins

$$= \frac{\text{Base dia.} \times \cos \dfrac{90}{\text{No. of teeth}}}{\cos \phi_w} - \text{Ball or pin dia.}$$

29 *Pitch tolerance.* The limits of tolerance on transverse pitch, both adjacent and cumulative, should be in accordance with the requirements of the following table and appropriate to the particular grade of gear.

The tolerance is calculated in units of 0.001 in, where $l =$ any selected length of arc in inches, including an arc length of one pitch, but not greater than $\pi \times d \times 0.5$, where $d =$ pitch circle diameter.

Grade of gear	Limits of tolerance
1	$0.05\sqrt{l}+0.025$
2	$0.08\sqrt{l}+0.04$
3	$0.12\sqrt{l}+0.06$
4	$0.20\sqrt{l}+0.10$
5	$0.32\sqrt{l}+0.16$
6	$0.50\sqrt{l}+0.25$
7	$0.71\sqrt{l}+0.35$
8	$1.00\sqrt{l}+0.50$
9	$1.40\sqrt{l}+0.71$
10	$2.00\sqrt{l}+1.00$
11	$2.80\sqrt{l}+1.40$
12	$4.00\sqrt{l}+2.00$

30 *Tooth profile tolerance*. The tooth profile tolerance is calculated in units of 0.001 in, and θ_t = tolerance factor

$$=\frac{25.4}{DP}+0.5\sqrt{PC\ dia.}$$

The profile tolerance is calculated as shown in the following table, and the grade of gear must be the same as used for the pitch tolerance – calculation 29.

Grade of gear	Limits of tolerance
1	$0.0025\theta_t+0.080$
2	$0.0040\theta_t+0.100$
3	$0.0063\theta_t+0.125$
4	$0.010\theta_t+0.160$
5	$0.016\theta_t+0.200$
6	$0.025\theta_t+0.250$
7	$0.040\theta_t+0.320$
8	$0.063\theta_t+0.400$
9	$0.100\theta_t+0.630$
10	$0.160\theta_t+1.000$
11	$0.250\theta_t+1.600$
12	$0.400\theta_t+2.500$

31 *Tooth alignment tolerance*. The tooth alignment tolerance is calculated in units of 0.001 in, and b = tooth facewidth, in inches.

The tooth alignment tolerance is calculated as shown in the following table, and the grade of gear used must be the same as used for the pitch tolerance and the tooth profile tolerance – calculations 29 and 30.

Grade of gear	Tooth alignment tolerance
1	$0.063\sqrt{b} + 0.063$
2	$0.080\sqrt{b} + 0.080$
3	$0.100\sqrt{b} + 0.100$
4	$0.125\sqrt{b} + 0.125$
5	$0.160\sqrt{b} + 0.160$
6	$0.200\sqrt{b} + 0.200$
7	$0.250\sqrt{b} + 0.250$
8	$0.400\sqrt{b} + 0.400$
9	$0.630\sqrt{b} + 0.630$
10	$1.000\sqrt{b} + 1.000$
11	$1.600\sqrt{b} + 1.600$
12	$2.500\sqrt{b} + 2.500$

32 *Radial run-out tolerance.* The radial run-out tolerance is calculated in units of 0.001 in and θ_p = tolerance factor

$$= \frac{25.4}{DP} + 1.25\sqrt{PC\ dia..}$$

The radial run-out tolerance is calculated as shown in the table below, and the grade of gear used must be the same as used for the pitch tolerance, the tooth profile tolerance and the tooth alignment tolerance – calculations 29 to 31.

Grade of gear	Radial run-out tolerance
1	$0.009\theta_p + 0.11$
2	$0.014\theta_p + 0.18$
3	$0.022\,4\theta_p + 0.28$
4	$0.036\theta_p + 0.45$
5	$0.056\theta_p + 0.7$
6	$0.090\theta_p + 1.1$
7	$0.125\theta_p + 1.6$
8	$0.16\theta_p + 2.0$
9	$0.20\theta_p + 2.5$
10	$0.25\theta_p + 3.2$
11	$0.32\theta_p + 4.0$
12	$0.40\theta_p + 5.0$

Internal spur gears – metric module

1 No. of teeth
2 Module

3 Pressure angle:

Note: 20° pressure angle is normal standard.

4 Circular pitch

$$= \pi \times \text{Module}$$
$$= 3.14159 \times \text{Module}$$

5 Pitch circle diameter = No. of teeth × Module
6 Base circle diameter = PC dia. × cos Pressure angle
7 Dedendum – standard:

Minimum = 1.157 × Module
Maximum = 1.35 × Module

8 Addendum – standard = Module
9 Whole depth:

Minimum = 2.157 × Module
Maximum = 2.35 × Module

10 Bottom clearance:

Minimum = 0.157 × Module
Maximum = 0.35 × Module

11 Outside (root) diameter – standard = PC dia. + (2 × Dedendum – standard)
12 Inside diameter = PC dia. – (2 × Addendum – standard)
13 Backlash – standard between gears
14 *Gear centres*. If the gear centres to be used are standard, these are calculated as follows:

$$\frac{\text{PC dia. (internal gear)} - \text{PC dia. (spur gear)}}{2}$$

If the centres to be used are non-standard, a correction must be applied either to the internal gear or to the spur gear pinion. The amount of correction required is calculated as follows:

14A Correction required = Actual CRS – Standard centres

$$= \text{Actual CRS} - \left[\frac{\text{PC dia. (int. gear)} - \text{PC dia. (spur gear)}}{2} \right]$$

If correction is required, calculations 4 to 12 inclusive should be recalculated as follows:

15 Corrected PC dia. = std PC dia. ± (2 × Correction)
16 Corrected circular pitch

$$= \frac{\text{Corr. PC dia.} \times \pi}{\text{No. of teeth}}$$

17 Corrected base circle diameter = Corr. PC dia. × cos Press. angle
18 Circular tooth thickness = Circular pitch (corr.) × 0.5

Note: For circular tooth thickness calculations use circular pitch calculation 4 for dimension at standard PC dia. and calculation 16 for dimension at corrected PC dia.

19   Corrected addendum

$$= \text{Std adden.} \pm \left(\frac{\text{Corr. circular tooth thickness}}{4 \times \text{Corr. PC dia.}} \right)$$

20   Whole depth – see calculation 9
21   Corrected dedendum = Whole depth (min.) – Corr. addendum
22   Bottom clearance – see calculation 10
23   Outside (root) diameter – corrected = Std PC dia. + (2 × Corr. dedendum)
24   Inside diameter – corrected = Std PC dia. – (2 × Corr. addendum)
25   Using the relevant section for either a standard or corrected internal gear, the calculations for the inspection dimensions will continue as follows:

Chordal tooth thickness

$$= \text{Circular tooth thickness} - \left(\frac{\text{Circular tooth thickness}}{4 \times \text{PC dia.} \times \text{No. of teeth}} \right)^2$$

26   Normal circular space = Circular pitch – Circular tooth thickness
27   The inspection dimensions for internal spur gears comprise the following:

(a) Dimension between 2 balls or pins
(b) Pitch tolerance
(c) Tooth profile tolerance
(d) Tooth alignment tolerance
(e) Radial run-out tolerance

The calculations for these dimensions are made as follows, and the tolerances are given for varying grades of gear tooth finish as shown for spur gears.
28   Dimensions between 2 balls or pins:

(a) Ball or pin diameter = 1.44 × Module

Now the nearest standard ball or pin diameter should be selected and used in the following calculations:
(b) Involute function for pressure angle at ball or pin centre:

Inv. $\phi_w =$

$$\text{Inv. press. angle} - \left[\frac{\text{Ball dia.}/(\cos \text{ Press. angle}) - \text{Circ. space}}{\text{Corr. PC dia.}} \right]$$

(c) For gears with even no. of teeth:

Dimension between 2 balls or pins

$$= \frac{\text{Base dia.}}{\cos \phi_w} - \text{Ball or pin dia.}$$

(d) For gears with odd no. of teeth:

Dimension between 2 balls or pins

$$= \frac{\text{Base dia.} \times \cos 90/(\text{No. of teeth})}{\cos \phi_w} - \text{Ball or pin dia.}$$

29　*Pitch tolerance.* The limits of tolerance on transverse pitch, both adjacent and cumulative, should be in accordance with the requirements of the table below, and appropriate to the particular grade of gear.

The tolerance is calculated in units of 0.001 mm, where l=any selected length of arc in millimetres, including an arc length of one pitch, but not greater than $\pi \times d \times 0.5$, where d=pitch circle diameter.

Grade of gear	Limits of tolerance
1	$0.25\sqrt{l}+0.63$
2	$0.40\sqrt{l}+1.00$
3	$0.63\sqrt{l}+1.60$
4	$1.00\sqrt{l}+2.50$
5	$1.60\sqrt{l}+4.00$
6	$2.50\sqrt{l}+6.30$
7	$3.55\sqrt{l}+9.00$
8	$5.00\sqrt{l}+12.50$
9	$7.10\sqrt{l}+18.00$
10	$10.00\sqrt{l}+25.00$
11	$14.00\sqrt{l}+35.50$
12	$20.00\sqrt{l}+50.00$

30　*Tooth profile tolerance.* The tooth profile tolerance is calculated in units of 0.001 mm, and θ_t=tolerance factor=module+$0.1\sqrt{PC\ dia.}$.

The profile tolerance is calculated as shown in the table below, and the grade of gear must be the same as used for the pitch tolerance – calculation 29.

Grade of gear	Limits of tolerance
1	$0.063\theta_t+2.00$
2	$0.100\theta_t+2.50$
3	$0.160\theta_t+3.15$
4	$0.25\theta_t+4.00$
5	$0.40\theta_t+5.00$
6	$0.63\theta_t+6.30$
7	$1.00\theta_t+8.00$
8	$1.60\theta_t+10.00$
9	$2.50\theta_t+16.00$
10	$4.00\theta_t+25.00$
11	$6.30\theta_t+40.00$
12	$10.00\theta_t+63.00$

31　*Tooth alignment tolerance.* The tooth alignment tolerance is calculated in units of 0.001 mm, and b=tooth facewidth, in millimetres.

The tooth alignment tolerance is calculated as shown in the table below, and the grade of gear must be the same as that used for the pitch tolerance and the tooth profile tolerance – calculations 29 and 30.

Grade of gear	Tooth alignment tolerance
1	$0.315\sqrt{b}+1.60$
2	$0.40\sqrt{b}+2.00$
3	$0.50\sqrt{b}+2.50$
4	$0.63\sqrt{b}+3.15$
5	$0.80\sqrt{b}+4.00$
6	$1.00\sqrt{b}+5.00$
7	$1.25\sqrt{b}+6.30$
8	$2.00\sqrt{b}+10.00$
9	$3.15\sqrt{b}+16.00$
10	$5.00\sqrt{b}+25.00$
11	$8.00\sqrt{b}+40.00$
12	$12.50\sqrt{b}+63.00$

32   *Radial run-out tolerance.* The radial run-out tolerance is calculated in units of 0.001 mm, and $\theta_p=$ tolerance factor $=$ module $+0.25\sqrt{\text{PC dia.}}$.

The radial run-out tolerance is calculated as shown in the table below, and the grade of gear used must be the same as used for the pitch tolerance, the tooth profile tolerance and the tooth alignment tolerance – calculations 29 to 31.

Grade of gear	Radial run-out tolerance
1	$0.224\theta_p+2.80$
2	$0.355\theta_p+4.50$
3	$0.56\theta_p+7.10$
4	$0.90\theta_p+11.20$
5	$1.40\theta_p+18.00$
6	$2.24\theta_p+28.00$
7	$3.15\theta_p+40.00$
8	$4.00\theta_p+50.00$
9	$5.00\theta_p+63.00$
10	$6.30\theta_p+80.00$
11	$8.00\theta_p+100.00$
12	$10.00\theta_p+125.00$

The final calculations for the internal gear when operating with a standard spur gear pinion is to check the following:

(a) Whether interference exists between the tip of the internal gear and the fillet of the pinion tooth – see calculation 33

(b) Whether interference exists between the tip of the pinion tooth and the fillet of the internal gear tooth – see calculation 34

(c) Whether interference exists between the tip of the pinion tooth and the profile of the internal gear tooth as the pinion tooth comes into and goes out of mesh – see calculation 35

33   To check whether interference exists between the tip of the internal gear and the fillet of the pinion tooth, proceed as follows:

where R_{B1} = base radius of pinion
R_{F1} = radius to top of fillet in bottom of pinion tooth (radius to bottom of working depth)
ϕ = pressure angle
C = gear centres
R_{B2} = base radius of internal gear
R_{i2} = minimum internal radius to avoid fillet interference

$$\therefore R_{i2} = \sqrt{(R_{B2})^2 + [C \sin \phi + \sqrt{R_{F1}^2 - R_{B1}^2}]^2}$$

If the inside radius of the internal gear is less than R_{i2}, interference exists between the corner of the internal gear tooth and the fillet of the pinion tooth. In this case the internal radius of the internal gear must be adjusted or the radius to top of fillet in the bottom of the pinion tooth modified.

34   To check whether interference exists between the tip of the pinion tooth and the fillet of the internal gear tooth, proceed as follows:

where R_{B1} = base radius of pinion
R_{B2} = base radius of internal gear
ϕ = pressure angle
C = gear centres
R_{F2} = radius to fillet on internal gear tooth
R_{o1} = maximum outside radius of pinion to avoid fillet interference

$$\therefore R_{o1} = \sqrt{(R_{B1})^2 + \sqrt{[R_{F2})^2 - (R_{B2})^2 - C \sin \phi]^2}}$$

If the outside radius of the pinion is larger than R_{o1}, interference exists between the tip of the pinion tooth and the fillet of the internal gear tooth. If this is so, the outside radius of the pinion should be adjusted if possible, but if this adjustment is too large, the number of teeth on the pinion should be reduced or the number of teeth on the internal gear increased and the above calculation repeated.

35   To check whether interference exists between the tip of the pinion tooth and the profile of the internal gear tooth as the pinion tooth comes into and goes out of mesh, proceed as follows:

where C = gear centres
R_i = inside radius of internal gear
R_{B2} = base radius of internal gear
ϕ_{Ro} = pressure angle at outside radius of pinion
R_o = outside radius of pinion
R_{B1} = base radius of pinion
ϕ = normal pressure angle
ϕ_{Ri} = pressure angle at inside radius of internal gear

and when

$$\cos \phi_{Ro} = \frac{R_{B1}}{R_o}$$

$$\cos \phi_{Ri} = \frac{R_{B2}}{R_i}$$

and arc indicates angle in radians

Then: If the value of 'X' in the following calculation is greater than 'Y', no interference exists; but if 'X' is smaller than 'Y', interference exists and the procedure to eliminate this is the same as shown in calculation 34 to eliminate interference between the tip of the pinion tooth and the fillet of the internal gear tooth.

35A

$$X = C(\sin \phi - \cos \phi \ \text{arc} \ \phi) + R_{B1}\left[\text{arc} \cos\frac{R_i^2 - R_o^2 - C^2}{2C \times R_o} + \text{inv} \ \phi_{Ro}\right]$$

35B

$$Y = R_{B2}\left[\text{arc} \cos\frac{R_i^2 + C^2 - R_o^2}{2C \times R_i} + \text{inv} \ \phi_{Ri}\right]$$

36 *Interference.* The teeth of internal gears are usually generated by means of a pinion-type cutter, and in the design stages of the gears it is necessary to consider the engagement of the pinion cutter with the internal gear in addition to the engagement of the pinion with the internal gear.

When generating the internal gear teeth with the pinion-type cutter, which has to be fed into depth in a radial direction, a portion of the internal tooth involute surface will be removed unless there is sufficient difference between the number of teeth on the cutter and in the internal gear. This type of interference is called trimming.

37 To determine whether trimming takes place, given the proportions of both the cutter and the internal gear, requires the following range of calculations (see calculations 38 to 40).

38 If a chord drawn between the intersections of the outside diameter of the cutter and the inside diameter of the internal gear is tangential to or outside the base circle of the gear, no trimming will take place; thus

where R_o = outside radius of cutter
$\quad\quad\quad R_i$ = inside radius of internal gear
$\quad\quad\quad C$ = centre distance of generation
$\quad\quad\quad R_{B2}$ = base radius of internal gear
$\quad\quad\quad Y$ = distance from centre of internal gear to chord between intersections of R_o and R_i.

If Y is equal to or greater than R_{B2}, no trimming will take place; if Y is less than R_{B2}, trimming may or may not take place,

where $Y = \dfrac{R_i^2 + C^2 - R_o^2}{2C}$

39 If Y is less than R_{B2} and the centre of the tooth of the cutter, and the centre of the space of the internal gear tooth represents the direction of feeding to depth,

where N_3 = number of teeth on cutter
$\quad\quad\quad N_2$ = number of teeth in internal gear
$\quad\quad\quad \theta$ = angle from line of feed to intersection of tangent to R_{B2} with R_i.
$\quad\quad\quad \theta_1$ = angle from line of feed to intersection of R_o and R_i
$\quad\quad\quad \theta_2$ = angle from line of feed to tip of internal gear tooth
$\quad\quad\quad \theta_3$ = angle from line of feed to tip of cutter tooth
$\quad\quad\quad T_2$ = arc tooth thickness of internal gear tooth at tip
$\quad\quad\quad T_3$ = arc tooth thickness of cutter tooth at tip

$$\cos\theta = \frac{R_{B2}}{R_i}$$

$$\cos\theta_1 = \frac{Y}{R_i}$$

$$\text{arc } \theta_2 = \frac{\pi}{N_2} - \frac{T_2}{2R_i} \text{ in radians}$$

$$\text{arc } \theta_3 = \frac{T_3}{2R_o} \text{ in radians}$$

As trimming does not take place until the angle θ_2 is greater than θ, it is possible to find successively the angle to the tips of successive teeth on the internal gear, for all values between θ and θ_1:

for the second tip of the internal gear tooth,

$$\text{arc } \theta_2' = \frac{3\pi}{N_2} - \frac{T_2}{R_i}$$

for the third tip,

$$\text{arc } \theta_2'' = \frac{5\pi}{N_2} - \frac{T_2}{R_i}$$

and for each successive tooth as follows:

$$\text{arc } \theta_2''' = \frac{7\pi}{N_2} - \frac{T_2}{R_i} \quad\quad \text{arc } \theta_2'''' = \frac{9\pi}{N_2} - \frac{T_2}{R_i}$$

and so on; for each succeeding tooth, the value of θ_2 is increased by $2\pi/N_2'$.
    When the values of θ_2 between θ and θ_1 are determined, the corresponding values of θ_3 are determined as follows:

$$\text{arc } \theta_3' = \frac{T_3}{2R_o} + \frac{2\pi}{N_3} \quad\quad \text{arc } \theta_3'' = \frac{T_3}{2R_o} + \frac{4\pi}{N_3}$$

$$\text{arc } \theta_3''' = \frac{T_3}{2R_o} + \frac{6\pi}{N_3} \quad\quad \text{arc } \theta_3'''' = \frac{T_3}{2R_o} + \frac{8\pi}{N_3}$$

and so on; for each succeeding tooth, the value of θ_3 is increased by $2\pi/N_3$.

When the requisite values for θ_2 and θ_3 have been calculated, then final calculations for this section can be made:

$X_2 = $ length of chord from centre line to tip of internal gear tooth
$X_2 = R_i \sin \theta_2$
$X_3 = $ length of chord from centre line to tip of cutter tooth
$X_3 = R_o \sin \theta_3$

If X_2 is greater than X_3, no trimming will take place; but if X_2 is less than X_3, trimming will take place.

40   If Y is less than R_{B2} and the centre of the tooth of the internal gear, and the centre of the space of the cutter tooth represents the direction of feeding to depth.

Using symbols as used in calculations 38 and 39:

$$\cos \theta = \frac{R_{B2}}{R_i}$$

$$\cos \theta_1 = \frac{Y}{R_i}$$

$$\text{arc } \theta_2 = \frac{2\pi}{N_2} - \frac{T_2}{2R_i}$$

$$\text{arc } \theta_3 = \frac{\pi}{N_3} + \frac{T_3}{2R_o}$$

The angles to the tips of successive teeth on the internal gear, for all values between θ and θ_1:

For the second tip of internal gear tooth,

$$\text{arc } \theta_2' = \frac{4\pi}{N_2} - \frac{T_2}{2R_i}$$

$$\text{arc } \theta_3' = \frac{3\pi}{N_3} + \frac{T_3}{2R_o}$$

For the third tip,

$$\text{arc } \theta_2'' = \frac{6\pi}{N_2} - \frac{T_2}{2R_i}$$

$$\text{arc } \theta_3'' = \frac{5\pi}{N_3} + \frac{T_3}{2R_o}$$

and for each successive tooth as follows:

$$\text{arc } \theta_2''' = \frac{8\pi}{N_2} - \frac{T_2}{2R_i} \qquad \text{arc } \theta_2'''' = \frac{10\pi}{N_2} - \frac{T_2}{2R_i}$$

$$\text{arc } \theta_3''' = \frac{7\pi}{N_3} + \frac{T_3}{2R_o} \qquad \text{arc } \theta_3'''' = \frac{9\pi}{N_3} + \frac{T_3}{2R_o}$$

and so on for each succeeding tooth until the values of θ_2 and θ_3 between θ and θ_1 are determined.

Using

$$X_2 = R_i \sin \theta_2$$

and

$$X_3 = R_o \sin \theta_3$$

Calculate X_2 and X_3 for each tooth. If X_2 is greater than X_3, no trimming will take place; but if X_2 is less than X_3, trimming will take place.

Whether the amount of trimming that is involved in a design can be accommodated must be decided by the designer. If it cannot be accommodated, the design must be modified.

41   *Addendum modification – internal gears.* The application of addendum modification to internal gear teeth allows some latitude in design, thus enabling standard gear-cutting tools to be used to the best advantage in covering varying sizes of gear design.

Addendum modification is an enlargement or reduction of the gear tooth dimensions produced when the basic generating rack is displaced from its nominal position. The addendum modification coefficient is the displacement of the reference plane of the generating basic rack from the reference diameter of the gear, calculated for gears of unit normal module or diametral pitch.

By taking advantage of the adaptability of the involute system, various tooth design features are available to the designer and the use of addendum modification allows the following points to be covered:

(a) The avoidance of tooth profile undercuts
(b) The adaptation of a pair of standard pitch gears to run at non-standard centres
(c) The achievement of optimum tooth proportions
(d) The control of the proportion of approaching to receding contact
(e) Permits a range of working pressure angles to be achieved using standard geometry cutting tools.

An increase in the total addendum modification coefficient for both the mating gears leads to an increase of the working pressure angle and a reduction of the contact ratio, which leads to a noisier gear pair. However, the higher the value of the total addendum modification coefficient, the higher the bending strength of the gear teeth.

Minimum and maximum values for the total addendum modification coefficient can be calculated to suit certain rational limiting conditions:

(a) Generation by hob or rack form cutter.
(b) Tip to root clearance should not be reduced by more than $0.1 \times$ module or $0.1/DP$ below its nominal value
(c) Extended root fillets, ensuring that curtailment of the path of involute contact is avoided

The limits may be applied to non-critically loaded gear pairs, provided that the addendum modification coefficients for the gears conform approximately to one of the formulae given in calculations 33–40.

Too low a value for the addendum modification coefficient leads to undercut tooth profiles – spur gears having less than 18 teeth and the minimum value of addendum modification coefficient required to avoid undercutting are known as 'standard long addendum pinions'.

Too high a value of addendum modification coefficient leads to excessively narrow tip width, so that the shear strength at the tooth tip is less than the tooth beam strength.

Note: Gears with a high value of addendum modification coefficient require engagement over a long span of generating rack to form the teeth. For example, while engagement over a two-pitch span of generating rack will form the teeth when the addendum modification coefficient is zero, when the addendum modification coefficient is 1.0 then approximately four pitches are required, and if the addendum modification coefficient is 2.0 then approximately $5\frac{1}{2}$ pitches are required.

When using pinion-type generating tools (gear shaping), the limits for gears cut by rack-form tools are generally applicable, provided that the cutter will fully form the tips and roots of the teeth, although this is rarely possible with a cutter which has less than 35 teeth.

The formulae used for evaluating the actual centre distance, the centre distance modification coefficient and the total addendum modification coefficient for external gears are also applicable to internal gears, provided that the following rules are observed:

(a) Diameter and number of teeth of the wheel, together with the centre distance, are given a negative value.

(b) The addendum modification coefficient – wheel is negative when the wheel is being enlarged.
     Note: Negative values for the addendum modification coefficient – pinion, plus addendum modification coefficient – wheel, result in increased pressure angles and vice versa.

(c) The preferred value for the addendum modification coefficient – wheel is −0.4. Other values may prove more convenient for the design of both internal planetary gear trains and internal wheel and pinion pairs of close ratio.

(d) Satisfactory tooth action is obtained when the addendum modification coefficient – pinion, the addendum modification coefficient – wheel and the centre distance modification coefficient values result in pressure angles between 14° and 30°, provided that the path of contact crosses the line of centres well within the working depth of the teeth and the contact ratio is not less than 1 : 1.

(e) The wheel tip circle diameter must conform with one of the formulae shown in calculations 33–40, as applicable, in order that the wheel tooth tips do not foul the pinion root fillets.

(f) Interference between the wheel and pinion tooth tips prevents the use of very close gear ratios if the teeth are designed to standard proportions.

Important. It should be noted that if the centre distance modification coefficient is made equal to the sum of the addendum modification coefficients of both the pinion and wheel, and has either a positive or negative value, other than zero, then the internal gears will have interference problems.

42   Terminology:

Addendum modification
An enlargement or reduction of gear tooth dimensions produced when the generating basic rack is displaced from its nominal position.

Addendum modification coefficient
The displacement of the reference plane of the generating basic rack from the reference cylinder of the gear, for gears of unit normal module or diametrical pitch.

Centre distance modification coefficient
The modification of the gear centre distance, either negative or positive, for gears of unit normal module or diametral pitch.

Notes:
(a)   The addendum modification coefficient establishes a datum tooth thickness at the reference diameter of the gear, but does not necessarily establish the height of either the reference addendum or the working addendum.
(b)   In a pair of gears, the datum tooth thicknesses are those which give zero backlash at the meshing centre distance, in all cases. Allowance for backlash must be made in accordance with normal practice for standard gears.

Metric module gears (dimensions in millimetres)

43   Reference diameter = Module × No. of teeth on gear
44   Centre distance modification coefficient

$$= \frac{\text{Actual centres}}{\text{Module}} - \tfrac{1}{2} \text{ sum of total no. of teeth (pinion and wheel)}$$

or

$$= \frac{1}{\text{Module}} \left(\text{Centres} - \frac{\text{Ref. dia. (pinion)} + \text{Ref. dia. (wheel)}}{2} \right)$$

45   Centre distance – actual

$$= \text{Module} \left(\frac{\text{Total no. of teeth (pinion + wheel)}}{2} + \text{Centre distance modn coeff.} \right)$$

46   Relative values for addendum modification coefficient – pinion and wheel
46A   For general applications:

Addendum modification coefficient – pinion

$$= \frac{1}{3} \left(1 - \frac{1}{\text{Gear ratio}} \right) + \left(\frac{\text{Sum of adden. modn coeff. (pinion + wheel)}}{1 + \text{Gear ratio}} \right)$$

46B   Approximate equality of bending strength for pinion and wheel:

Addendum modification coefficient – pinion

$$= \frac{1}{2}\left(1 - \frac{1}{\text{Gear ratio}}\right) + \left(\frac{\text{Sum of adden. modn coeff. (pinion + wheel)}}{1 + \text{Gear ratio}}\right)$$

46C   Approximate balance of ratios of specific sliding or slide–roll ratio at extremes of contact path:

Addendum modification coefficient – pinion

$$= A\left(1 - \frac{1}{\text{Gear ratio}}\right) + \left(\frac{\text{Sum of adden. modn coeff. (pinion + wheel)}}{1 + \text{Gear ratio}}\right)$$

where

$$A = \frac{2.0}{\sqrt{\text{No. of teeth} - \text{pinion}}}$$

47   Dimension between 2 balls or pins:

(a) Ball or pin diameter $= 1.44 \times$ Module

Note: Having solved the above equation, the nearest standard ball or pin diameter should be selected and used in the following calculations:

(b) Involute function for pressure angle at centre line of ball or pin:

$$\text{Inv. } \phi_w = \frac{2x \times \text{Module} \times \tan \text{ PA} + \text{Pin or ball dia.} \times \sec \text{ PA} - \text{Module} \times 0.5\pi}{\text{No. of teeth on gear} \times \text{Module}} - A$$

where

$$x = \text{addendum modification coefficient}$$
$$\text{PA} = \text{normal pressure angle}$$
$$A = \text{involute normal pressure angle}$$

(c) For gears with even number of teeth:

Dimension between 2 balls or pins

$$= \frac{\text{Reference dia.} \times \cos \text{ PA}}{\cos \phi_w} - \text{Ball or pin dia.}$$

(d) For gears with odd number of teeth:

Dimension between 2 balls or pins

$$= \frac{\text{Reference dia.} \times \cos \text{ PA} \times \cos\dfrac{90}{\text{No. of teeth on gear}}}{\cos \phi_w} - \text{Ball or pin dia.}$$

48   Root diameter $= \text{Module}(z + 1.7 + x_b - x_a + y)$

where

$$z = \text{number of teeth} - \text{internal gear}$$
$$x_b = \text{addendum modification coefficient} - \text{internal gear}$$

x_a = addendum modification coefficient – mating gear
y = centre distance modification coefficient

49 Inside diameter

$$= \text{Module}\left[z - 2\left(1 + \frac{c}{\text{Module}} - x_b\right)\right]$$

where

z = number of teeth – internal gear
c = bottom clearance
x_b = addendum modification coefficient – internal gear

Diametral pitch gears (dimensions in inches)

50 Reference diameter

$$= \frac{\text{Number of teeth on gear}}{\text{Diametral pitch}}$$

51 Centre distance modification coefficient

$$= \text{Actual centres} \times \text{DP} - \tfrac{1}{2} \text{ sum of total no. of teeth (pinion + wheel)}$$

or

$$= \text{DP}\left(\text{Centres} - \frac{\text{Ref. dia. (pinion)} + \text{Ref. dia. (wheel)}}{2}\right)$$

52 Centre distance – actual

$$= \frac{\tfrac{1}{2} \text{ total no. of teeth (pinion + wheel)} + \text{Centre dist. modn coeff.}}{\text{Diametral pitch}}$$

53 Relative values for addendum modification coefficient – pinion and wheel

53A For general applications:

Addendum modification coefficient – pinion

$$= \frac{1}{3}\left(1 - \frac{1}{\text{Gear ratio}}\right) + \left(\frac{\text{Sum of adden. modn coeff. (pinion + wheel)}}{1 + \text{Gear ratio}}\right)$$

53B Approximate equality of bending strength for pinion and wheel:

Addendum modification coefficient – pinion

$$= \frac{1}{2}\left(1 - \frac{1}{\text{Gear ratio}}\right) + \left(\frac{\text{Sum of adden. modn coeff. (pinion + wheel)}}{1 + \text{Gear ratio}}\right)$$

53C Approximate balance of ratios of specific sliding or slide–roll ratio at extremes of contact path:

Addendum modification coefficient – pinion

$$= A\left(1 - \frac{1}{\text{Gear ratio}}\right) + \left(\frac{\text{Sum of adden. modn. coeff. (pinion + wheel)}}{1 + \text{Gear ratio}}\right)$$

where

$$A = \frac{20}{\sqrt{\text{No. of teeth – pinion}}}$$

54   Dimension between 2 balls or pins:

(a) Ball or pin diameter

$$= \frac{1.44}{\text{Diametral pitch}}$$

Note: Having solved the above equation, the nearest standard ball or pin diameter should be selected and used in the following calculations:

(b) Involute function for pressure angle at centre line of ball or pin:

$$\text{Inv. } \phi_w = \frac{2x \times \tan\ \text{PA} + \text{Pin or ball dia.} \times \text{DP} \times \sec\ \text{PA} - \pi/2}{\text{No. of teeth on gear}} - A$$

where

$$x = \text{addendum modification coefficient}$$
$$\text{PA} = \text{normal pressure angle}$$
$$A = \text{involute normal pressure angle}$$

(c) For gears with even number of teeth:

Dimension between 2 balls or pins

$$= \frac{\text{Reference dia.} \times \cos\ \text{PA}}{\cos\ \phi_w} - \text{Ball or pin dia.}$$

(d) For gears with odd number of teeth:

Dimension between 2 balls or pins

$$= \frac{\text{Reference dia.} \times \cos\ \text{PA} \times \cos\dfrac{90}{\text{No. of teeth on gear}}}{\cos\ \phi_w} - \text{Ball or pin dia.}$$

55   Root diameter

$$= \frac{z + 1.7 + x_b - x_a + y}{\text{Diametral pitch}}$$

where

$$z = \text{number of teeth – internal gear}$$
$$x_b = \text{addendum modification coefficient – internal gear}$$
$$x_a = \text{Addendum modification coefficient – mating gear}$$
$$y = \text{centre distance modification coefficient}$$

56   Inside diameter

$$= \frac{z - 2(1 + c \times \text{Diametral pitch} - x_b)}{\text{Diametral pitch}}$$

where

z = number of teeth – internal gear
c = bottom clearance
x_b = addendum modification coefficient – internal gear

Notes:

(a) In calculation 49, the value of c should lie between:

$$0.25 \times \text{Module (min.)}$$

and

$$0.40 \times \text{Module (max.)}$$

(b) In calculation 56, the value of c should lie between:

$$\frac{0.25}{\text{Diametral pitch}} \text{ (min.)}$$

and

$$\frac{0.40}{\text{Diametral pitch}} \text{ (max.)}$$

Internal gears – recommended backlash

The backlash figures given are for gears assembled ready to run, and the backlash should be shared equally between the pinion and wheel.

Diametral pitch	Backlash (in)
1	0.025–0.040
$1\frac{1}{2}$	0.018–0.027
2	0.014–0.020
$2\frac{1}{2}$	0.011–0.016
3	0.009–0.014
4	0.007–0.011
5	0.006–0.009
6	0.005–0.008
7	0.004–0.007
8–10	0.004–0.006
10–13	0.003–0.005
14–32	0.002–0.004

Metric module	Backlash (mm)
25	0.65–1.00
20	0.50–0.75
15	0.40–0.55
10	0.28–0.40
8	0.20–0.30
6	0.15–0.25
5	0.15–0.225
4	0.125–0.200
3	0.100–0.175
3.00–2.50	0.100–0.150
2.50–2.00	0.075–0.125
2.00–0.75	0.050–0.100

4
Helical gears

Single helical gears (Figure 4.1) serve exactly the same purpose as spur gears and provide an alternative drive for connecting parallel shafts. Standards of accuracy being equal, helical gears are superior to spur gears in both load-carrying capacity and quietness during operation.

Helical gears are produced on the same machines that are used to produce spur gears, but the teeth are cut at an angle to the axis of the gear and follow a spiral path.

Any section at right angles to the axis, i.e. transverse, represents a spur, and successive equidistant sections have equal angular displacements.

As a result of these angular displacements, the position of tooth contact with the mating gear will vary at each section.

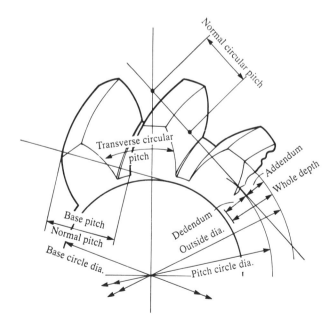

Figure 4.1 Gear terminology – helical gear

As each involute tooth profile occupies an infinite number of successive positions, it traces out the tooth surface, which is called an involute helicoid.

The line of contact along this tooth surface is no longer parallel to the axis as for a spur gear, but is inclined as a result of the different stages of tooth engagement along the tooth face.

Therefore, the tooth engagement and load distribution is gradual with helical gears and they can be used to advantage when the speeds are too high for the successful use of equivalent spur gears.

Since, on a transverse section, a pair of helical gears is similar to a pair of spur gears, the condition of uniform angular velocity ratio is unaffected by variations in centre distance.

Pitch. The pitch of a helical gear measured on the transverse plane is exactly the same as for an equivalent pair of spur gears along with the pitch diameters and centre distance.

Helix angle. The intersection of the tooth surface with the pitch cylinder is a helix. This helix becomes a straight line if the pitch cylinder is cut along a line parallel to the axis and laid out flat. The acute angle which this line makes with the axis is called the helix angle, and the complement of this angle is called the lead angle.

Mating single helical gears must have equal helix angles but of the opposite hand.

Handing. The handing of the helical gears is determined by looking at the teeth on the end-face in the direction of the axis. The teeth then recede in a clockwise direction in a right-hand helix and an anti-clockwise direction in a left-hand helix.

Normal pitch. The normal pitch is the distance between similar faces of adjacent teeth measured at the pitch line – pitch circle diameter – normal to the tooth helix.

Transverse or axial pitch. The transverse or axial pitch is the distance between similar faces of adjacent teeth measured at the pitch line parallel to the axis of the gear.

Lead. The lead is the axial advance which a helical tooth makes in one complete revolution, and is equal to the product of the axial pitch and the number of teeth.

Helix angle. The helix angle should be kept small in order to reduce the amount of side thrust generated. It is usual to keep the helix angle between 15° and 30°, with a general average of 20°.

Facewidth. The facewidth must be sufficient to provide overlap; the necessary ratio of facewidth to normal pitch increases as the helix angle decreases. The overall facewidth should not exceed twice the pinion pitch circle diameter or be less than one-tenth of the wheel pitch circle diameter.

Helical gear calculations

The following calculations give the dimensions required to manufacture helical gears.

Some dimensions or details of the gear pair must be known and should be used as a starting point, and calculation sheets or a computer program can be prepared based on the following formulae.

The formulae are given for calculating both diametrical pitch (Imperial) and metric module helical gears.

Diametral pitch helical gears

1 No. of teeth – pinion
No. of teeth – wheel
2 Normal diametral pitch
3 Pressure angle
Note: 20° is the normal standard pressure angle.
4 Helix angle
5 Hand of helix
6 Transverse diametral pitch = Normal DP × cos Helix angle
7 Transverse pressure angle

$$= \tan^{-1} \frac{\tan \ \text{Pressure} \ \text{angle}}{\cos \ \text{Helix} \ \text{angle}}$$

where $\tan^{-1}$ = the angle whose tangent is equal to . . .
8 Normal circular pitch = π/DP
9 Transverse circular pitch

$$= \frac{\pi}{\text{Transverse} \ \text{DP}}$$

10 Pitch circle diameter

$$= \frac{\text{No. of teeth}}{\text{Normal} \ \text{DP} \times \cos \ \text{Helix} \ \text{angle}}$$

11 Base circle diameter = PC dia. × cos Transverse pressure angle
12 Dedendum – standard:

$$\text{Minimum} = \frac{1.157}{\text{Normal} \ \text{DP}} \qquad \text{Maximum} = \frac{1.35}{\text{Normal} \ \text{DP}}$$

13 Addendum – standard

$$= \frac{1}{\text{Normal} \ \text{DP}}$$

14 Whole depth:

$$\text{Minimum} = \frac{2.157}{\text{Normal} \ \text{DP}} \qquad \text{Maximum} = \frac{2.35}{\text{Normal} \ \text{DP}}$$

15 Bottom clearance:

$$\text{Minimum} = \frac{0.157}{\text{Normal} \ \text{DP}} \qquad \text{Maximum} = \frac{0.35}{\text{Normal} \ \text{DP}}$$

16 Outside diameter – standard = PC dia. + (2 × Addendum – standard)

17   Root diameter:

Minimum = Outs. dia. − (2 × Max. whole depth)
Maximum = Outs. dia. − (2 × Min. whole depth)

18   Backlash – standard between gears

19   Lead

$$= \frac{\pi \times \text{No. of teeth}}{\text{Normal DP} \times \sin \text{ Helix angle}}$$

20   Normal circular thickness

$$= \frac{\text{Normal circular pitch}}{2}$$

21   Centres – standard

$$= \frac{\text{No. of teeth (pinion)} + \text{No. of teeth (wheel)}}{2 \times \text{Normal DP} \times \cos \text{ Helix angle}}$$

22   The first of the inspection dimensions to be calculated is the chordal dimension or base tangent over a specific number of teeth – measured in the transverse plane.

23   *Chordal dimension.* Stage 1 is the calculation to decide the number of teeth to be measured over:

Stage 1. Number of teeth to be measured over

$$= \left(\text{No. of teeth on gear} \times \frac{\text{Press. angle normal}}{180°} \right) + 0.5 + \frac{\text{Helix angle}}{45°}$$

Having calculated stage 1, the nearest absolute number of teeth should be used in stage 2:

Stage 2. Base tangent length over 'X' no. of teeth

$$= \frac{\cos \text{ PA}}{\text{DP}} \left[(\text{'}X\text{'} - 0.5) \times \pi + \text{No. of teeth on gear} \times \text{Inv. trans. PA} \right]$$

where

PA = normal pressure angle
DP = normal diametral pitch
'X' = no. of teeth to be measured over

Stage 3. The backlash allowance on the gear should now be taken away from the calculated base tangent length for inspection purposes.

24   The final inspection tolerances for the gear teeth remain to be calculated.

The British Standard methods of arriving at these tolerances are given in the following pages and cover the dimensional limits for diametral pitch gears for the following:

(a) Pitch tolerance
(b) Tooth profile tolerance
(c) Tooth alignment tolerance
(d) Radial run-out tolerance

The tolerances are given for varying grades of gear tooth finishes in each of the above, and the gear designer must decide which grade of finish is most suitable for the gear pair while taking into account the purpose and life expectation for which the gears have been designed. The tolerances quoted are from BS 436.

25   *Pitch tolerance.* The limits of tolerance on transverse pitch, both adjacent and cumulative, should be in accordance with the requirements of the table below and appropriate to the particular grade of gear.

The tolerance is calculated in units of 0.001 in, where $l=$ any selected length of arc in inches, including an arc length of one pitch, but not greater than $\pi \times d \times 0.5$, where $d=$ pitch circle diameter.

Grade of gear	Limits of tolerance
1	$0.05\sqrt{l}+0.025$
2	$0.08\sqrt{l}+0.04$
3	$0.12\sqrt{l}+0.06$
4	$0.20\sqrt{l}+0.10$
5	$0.32\sqrt{l}+0.16$
6	$0.50\sqrt{l}+0.25$
7	$0.71\sqrt{l}+0.35$
8	$1.00\sqrt{l}+0.50$
9	$1.40\sqrt{l}+0.71$
10	$2.00\sqrt{l}+1.00$
11	$2.80\sqrt{l}+1.40$
12	$4.00\sqrt{l}+2.00$

26   *Tooth profile tolerance.* The tolerance is calculated in units of 0.001 in, and $\theta_t=$ tolerance factor

$$=\frac{25.4}{\text{DP}}+0.5\sqrt{\text{PC dia.}}$$

The profile tolerance is calculated as shown in the table below, and the grade of gear must be the same as used for the pitch tolerance – calculation 25.

Grade of gear	Limits of tolerance
1	$0.0025\theta_t+0.080$
2	$0.0040\theta_t+0.100$
3	$0.0063\theta_t+0.125$
4	$0.010\theta_t+0.160$
5	$0.016\theta_t+0.200$
6	$0.025\theta_t+0.250$
7	$0.040\theta_t+0.320$
8	$0.063\theta_t+0.400$
9	$0.100\theta_t+0.630$
10	$0.160\theta_t+1.000$
11	$0.250\theta_t+1.600$
12	$0.400\theta_t+2.500$

27   *Tooth alignment tolerance.* The tolerance is calculated in units of 0.001 in, and b = tooth facewidth in inches.

The tooth alignment tolerance is calculated as shown in the table below, and the grade must be the same as used for the pitch tolerance and the tooth profile tolerance – calculations 25 and 26.

Grade of gear	Tooth alignment tolerance
1	$0.063\sqrt{b} + 0.063$
2	$0.080\sqrt{b} + 0.080$
3	$0.100\sqrt{b} + 0.100$
4	$0.125\sqrt{b} + 0.125$
5	$0.160\sqrt{b} + 0.160$
6	$0.200\sqrt{b} + 0.200$
7	$0.250\sqrt{b} + 0.250$
8	$0.400\sqrt{b} + 0.400$
9	$0.630\sqrt{b} + 0.630$
10	$1.000\sqrt{b} + 1.000$
11	$1.600\sqrt{b} + 1.600$
12	$2.500\sqrt{b} + 2.500$

28   *Radial run-out tolerance.* The tolerance is calculated in units of 0.001 in, and θ_p = tolerance factor

$$= \frac{25.4}{DP} + 1.25\sqrt{PC \ dia.}$$

The radial run-out tolerance is calculated as shown in the table below, and the grade must be the same as used for the pitch tolerance, the tooth profile tolerance and the tooth alignment tolerance – calculations 25 to 27.

Grade of gear	Radial run-out tolerance
1	$0.009\theta_p + 0.11$
2	$0.014\theta_p + 0.18$
3	$0.0224\theta_p + 0.28$
4	$0.036\theta_p + 0.45$
5	$0.056\theta_p + 0.70$
6	$0.090\theta_p + 1.10$
7	$0.125\theta_p + 1.60$
8	$0.160\theta_p + 2.00$
9	$0.200\theta_p + 2.50$
10	$0.250\theta_p + 3.20$
11	$0.320\theta_p + 4.00$
12	$0.400\theta_p + 5.00$

Metric module helical gears

1   No. of teeth – pinion
   No. of teeth – wheel
2   Module (normal)
3   Pressure angle
Note: 20° is the normal standard pressure angle.
4   Helix angle
5   Hand of helix
6   Transverse module

$$= \frac{\text{Module (normal)}}{\cos \text{ Helix angle}}$$

7   Transverse pressure angle

$$= \tan^{-1} \frac{\tan \text{ Pressure angle}}{\cos \text{ Helix angle}}$$

where $\tan^{-1}$ = the angle whose tangent is equal to . . .
8   Normal circular pitch = $\pi \times$ Module (normal)
9   Transverse circular pitch = $\pi \times$ Transverse module
10   Pitch circle diameter

$$= \frac{\text{No. of teeth} \times \text{Module (normal)}}{\cos \text{ Helix angle}}$$

11   Base circle diameter = PC dia. $\times$ cos Transverse pressure angle
12   Dedendum – standard:

      Minimum = 1.157 $\times$ Module (normal)
      Maximum = 1.35 $\times$ Module (normal)

13   Addendum – standard = Module (normal)
14   Whole depth:

      Minimum = 2.157 $\times$ Module (normal)
      Maximum = 2.35 $\times$ Module (normal)

15   Bottom clearance:

      Minimum = 0.157 $\times$ Module (normal)
      Maximum = 0.35 $\times$ Module (normal)

16   Outside diameter = PC dia. + (2 $\times$ Addendum – standard)
17   Root diameter:

      Minimum = outs. dia. $-$ (2 $\times$ Max. whole depth)
      Maximum = outs. dia. $-$ (2 $\times$ Min. whole depth)

18   Backlash – standard between gears

19 Lead

$$=\frac{\pi \times \text{No. of teeth} \times \text{Module}}{\sin \text{ Helix angle}}$$

20 Normal circular thickness

$$=\frac{\text{Normal circular pitch}}{2}$$

21 Centres – standard

$$=\frac{[\text{No. of teeth (pinion)} + \text{No. of teeth (wheel)}] \times \text{Module}}{2 \times \cos \text{ Helix angle}}$$

22 The first of the inspection dimensions to be calculated is the chordal dimension or base tangent over a specific number of teeth – measured in the transverse plane.
23 *Chordal dimension*. Stage 1 is the calculation to decide the number of teeth to be measured over:

Stage 1. Number of teeth to be measured over

$$=\left(\text{No. of teeth on gear} \times \frac{\text{Press. angle normal}}{180°}\right) + 0.5 + \frac{\text{Helix angle}}{45°}$$

Having calculated stage 1, the nearest absolute number of teeth should be used in stage 2:

Stage 2. Base tangent length over 'X' no. of teeth

$$=\cos \text{ PA} \times \text{Module}[('X' - 0.5) \times \pi + \text{No. of teeth on gear} \times \text{Inv. trans. PA}]$$

where

PA = normal pressure angle
'X' = no. of teeth to be measured over

Stage 3. The backlash allowance on the gear should now be taken away from the calculated base tangent length for inspection purposes.
24 The final inspection tolerances for the gear teeth remain to be calculated.

The British Standard methods of arriving at these tolerances are given in the following pages and cover the dimensional limits for metric module gears for the following:

(a) Pitch tolerance
(b) Tooth profile tolerance
(c) Tooth alignment tolerance
(d) Radial run-out tolerance

The tolerances are given for varying grades of gear tooth finishes in each of the above, and the gear designer must decide which grade of finish is most suitable for the gear pair while taking into account the purpose and life expectation for which the gears have been designed. The tolerances quoted are from BS 436.
25 *Pitch tolerance*. The limits of tolerance on transverse pitch, both adjacent and

cumulative, should be in accordance with the requirements of the table below, and appropriate to the particular grade of gear.

The tolerance is calculated in units of 0.001 mm, where l=any selected length of arc in millimetres, including an arc length of one pitch, but not greater than $\pi \times d \times 0.5$, where d=pitch circle diameter.

Grade of gear	Limits of pitch tolerance
1	$0.25\sqrt{l} + 0.63$
2	$0.40\sqrt{l} + 1.00$
3	$0.63\sqrt{l} + 1.60$
4	$1.00\sqrt{l} + 2.50$
5	$1.60\sqrt{l} + 4.00$
6	$2.50\sqrt{l} + 6.30$
7	$3.55\sqrt{l} + 9.00$
8	$5.00\sqrt{l} + 12.50$
9	$7.10\sqrt{l} + 18.00$
10	$10.00\sqrt{l} + 25.00$
11	$14.00\sqrt{l} + 35.50$
12	$20.00\sqrt{l} + 50.00$

26   *Tooth profile tolerance.* The tooth profile tolerance is calculated in units of 0.001 mm, and the tolerance factor (θ_t)=module$+0.1\sqrt{\text{PC dia.}}$

The profile tolerance is calculated as shown in the following table, and the grade of gear must be the same as used for the pitch tolerance – calculation 25.

Grade of gear	Limits of tooth profile tolerance
1	$0.063\theta_t + 2.00$
2	$0.100\theta_t + 2.50$
3	$0.160\theta_t + 3.15$
4	$0.250\theta_t + 4.00$
5	$0.400\theta_t + 5.00$
6	$0.630\theta_t + 6.30$
7	$1.000\theta_t + 8.00$
8	$1.600\theta_t + 10.00$
9	$2.500\theta_t + 16.00$
10	$4.000\theta_t + 25.00$
11	$6.30\theta_t + 40.00$
12	$10.00\theta_t + 63.00$

27   *Tooth alignment tolerance.* The tooth alignment tolerance is calculated in units of 0.001 mm, and b=tooth facewidth, in millimetres.

The tooth alignment tolerance is calculated as shown in the table below, and the grade must be the same as used for the pitch tolerance and the tooth profile tolerance – calculations 25 and 26.

Grade of gear	Limits of tooth alignment tolerance
1	$0.315\sqrt{b}+1.60$
2	$0.400\sqrt{b}+2.00$
3	$0.500\sqrt{b}+2.50$
4	$0.630\sqrt{b}+3.15$
5	$0.800\sqrt{b}+4.00$
6	$1.000\sqrt{b}+5.00$
7	$1.250\sqrt{b}+6.30$
8	$2.000\sqrt{b}+10.00$
9	$3.150\sqrt{b}+16.00$
10	$5.000\sqrt{b}+25.00$
11	$8.000\sqrt{b}+40.00$
12	$12.500\sqrt{b}+63.00$

28 *Radial run-out tolerance.* The radial run-out tolerance is calculated in units of 0.001 mm, and θ_p = tolerance factor = module + $0.25\sqrt{\text{PC dia.}}$

The radial run-out tolerance is calculated as shown in the table below, and the grade must be the same as used for the pitch tolerance, the tooth profile tolerance and the tooth alignment tolerance – calculations 25 to 27.

Grade of gear	Limits of radial run-out tolerance
1	$0.224\theta_p+2.80$
2	$0.355\theta_p+4.50$
3	$0.560\theta_p+7.10$
4	$0.900\theta_p+11.20$
5	$1.400\theta_p+18.00$
6	$2.240\theta_p+28.00$
7	$3.150\theta_p+40.00$
8	$4.000\theta_p+50.00$
9	$5.000\theta_p+63.00$
10	$6.300\theta_p+80.00$
11	$8.000\theta_p+100.00$
12	$10.000\theta_p+125.00$

29 *Addendum modification – helical gears.* The application of addendum modification to helical gear teeth allows some latitude in design, thus enabling standard gear-cutting tools to be used to the best advantage in covering varying sizes of gear design.

Addendum modification is an enlargement or reduction of the gear tooth dimensions produced when the basic generating rack is displaced from its nominal position, and the addendum modification coefficient is the displacement of the reference plane of the generating basic rack from the reference diameter of the gear, calculated for gears of unit normal module or diametral pitch.

By taking advantage of the adaptability of the involute system, various tooth design features are available to the designer, and the use of addendum modification allows the following points to be covered:

(a) The avoidance of tooth profile undercuts
(b) To adapt a pair of gears of standard pitch to run at non-standard centres
(c) The achievement of optimum tooth proportions
(d) The control of the proportion of approaching to receding contact
(e) Permits a range of working pressure angles to be achieved using standard geometry cutting tools

An increase in the total addendum modification coefficient for both the pinion and wheel leads to an increase of the working pressure angle and a reduction of the contact ratio, which leads to a noisier gear pair, but the higher the value of the total addendum modification coefficient, the higher the bending strength of the gear teeth.

Minimum and maximum values for the total addendum modification coefficient can be calculated to suit certain rational limiting conditions:

(a) Generation by hob or rack form cutter
(b) Tip to root clearance should not be reduced by more than 0.1 × module or 0.1/DP below its nominal value
(c) Extended root fillets, ensuring that curtailment of the path of involute contact is avoided

The limits may be applied to non-critically loaded gear pairs, provided that the addendum modification coefficients for the pinion and wheel conform approximately to one of the formulae given in calculations 36A to 36C (below).

30 *Metric module gears.* Calculation of addendum modification or corrected gear teeth based on the virtual number of teeth in the normal plane.

31 Virtual no. of teeth – normal plane

$$= \frac{\text{Actual no. of teeth on gear}}{\cos^3 \text{Helix angle}}$$

32 Virtual pitch diameter

$$= \frac{\text{PC diameter (equiv. spur gear)}}{\cos^2 \text{Helix angle}}$$

where PC diameter (equiv. spur gear) = Virtual no. of teeth × Module.

33 Reference diameter

$$= \frac{\text{Module} \times \text{No. of teeth (actual)}}{\cos \text{Helix angle}}$$

34   Centre distance modification coefficient

$$= \frac{\text{Actual centres}}{\text{Module}} - \frac{\text{Total no. of teeth (pinion + wheel)}}{2 \times \cos \text{ Helix angle}}$$

or

$$= \frac{1}{\text{Module}} \left(\text{Centres} - \frac{\text{Ref. dia. (pinion) + Ref. dia. (wheel)}}{2} \right)$$

35   Centre distance – actual

$$= \text{Module} \left(\frac{\text{Total no. of teeth (pinion + wheel)}}{2 \times \cos \text{ Helix angle}} + \text{Centre distance modn coeff.} \right)$$

36   Relative values for addendum modification coefficient pinion and wheel

36A   For general applications:

Addendum modification coefficient – pinion

$$= \frac{1}{3} \left(1 - \frac{1}{\text{Gear ratio}} \right) + \left(\frac{\text{Sum of adden. modn coeff. (pinion + wheel)}}{1 + \text{Gear ratio}} \right)$$

36B   Approximate equality of bending strength for pinion and wheel:

Addendum modification coefficient – pinion

$$= \frac{1}{2} \left(1 - \frac{1}{\text{Gear ratio}} \right) + \left(\frac{\text{Sum of adden. modn coeff. (pinion + wheel)}}{1 + \text{Gear ratio}} \right)$$

36C   Approximate balance of ratios of specific sliding or slide–roll ratio at extremes of contact path:

Addendum modification coefficient – pinion

$$= A \left(1 - \frac{1}{\text{Gear ratio}} \right) + \left(\frac{\text{Sum of adden. modn coeff. (pinion + wheel)}}{1 + \text{Gear ratio}} \right)$$

where

$$A = \frac{2.0}{\sqrt{\left(\dfrac{\text{No. of teeth – pinion}}{\cos^3 \text{ Helix angle (ref. dia.)}} \right)}}$$

37   Base tangent (span) dimension

$$= \left[\pi(N - 0.5) + 2x \times \tan \alpha_n + z \text{ inv. } \alpha_t \right] \text{Module} \times \cos \alpha_n$$

where

N = number of teeth within span
x = addendum modification coefficient
α_n = normal pressure angle

α_t = transverse pressure angle
z = no. of teeth on gear

Prior to using the span dimension for inspection purposes, the backlash allowance must be subtracted from the calculated dimension.

38   *Tip diameter.* Three methods for determining the tip diameter are available to the designer, as follows:

38A   Where working depth equals $2 \times$ module:

$$\text{Tip diameter} = \text{Module}\left(\frac{z}{\cos \beta} + 2 + y + x_a - x_b\right)$$

38B   Where tip-to-root clearance is nominal:

$$\text{Tip diameter} = \text{Module}\left(\frac{z}{\cos \beta} + 2(1 + y - x_b)\right)$$

38C   For full-length teeth:

$$\text{Tip diameter} = \text{Module}\left(\frac{z}{\cos \beta} + 2(1 + x_a)\right)$$

when

z = number of teeth on gear
β = helix angle at reference diameter
y = centre distance modification coefficient
x_a = addendum modification coefficient – actual gear
x_b = addendum modification coefficient – mating gear

39   Root diameter = Tip diameter − ($2 \times$ Whole depth)

40   *Diametral pitch gears.* Calculation of addendum modification or corrected gear teeth based on the virtual number of teeth in the normal plane.

41   Virtual no. of teeth – normal plane

$$= \frac{\text{Actual no. of teeth on gear}}{\cos^3 \text{ Helix angle}}$$

42   Virtual pitch diameter

$$= \frac{\text{PC diameter (equiv. spur gear)}}{\cos^2 \text{ Helix angle}}$$

where PC diameter (equiv. spur gear)

$$= \frac{\text{Virtual no. of teeth}}{\text{DP}}$$

43   Reference diameter

$$= \frac{\text{No. of teeth (actual)}}{\text{DP} \times \cos \text{ Helix angle}}$$

44   Centre distance modification coefficient

$$= \text{Actual CRS} \times \text{DP} - \frac{\text{Total no. of teeth (pinion + wheel)}}{2 \times \cos \text{ Helix angle}}$$

or

$$= \text{DP} \left(\text{Centres} - \frac{\text{Ref. dia. (pinion)} + \text{Ref. dia. (wheel)}}{2} \right)$$

45   Centre distance – actual

$$= \frac{(0.5 \times \text{Total no. of teeth (pinion + wheel)} + \text{Centre dist. modn coeff.}}{\cos \text{ Helix angle} \times \text{DP}}$$

46   Relative values for addendum modification coefficient pinion and wheel

46A   For general applications:

Addendum modification coefficient – pinion

$$= \frac{1}{3} \left(1 - \frac{1}{\text{Gear ratio}} \right) + \left(\frac{\text{Sum of adden. modn coeff. (pinion + wheel)}}{1 + \text{Gear ratio}} \right)$$

46B   Approximate equality of bending strength for pinion and wheel:

Addendum modification coefficient – pinion

$$= \frac{1}{2} \left(1 - \frac{1}{\text{Gear ratio}} \right) + \left(\frac{\text{Sum of adden. modn coeff. (pinion + wheel)}}{1 + \text{Gear ratio}} \right)$$

46C   Approximate balance of ratios of specific sliding or slide–roll ratio at extremes of contact path:

Addendum modification coefficient – pinion

$$= A \left(1 - \frac{1}{\text{Gear ratio}} \right) + \left(\frac{\text{Sum of adden. modn coeff. (pinion + wheel)}}{1 + \text{Gear ratio}} \right)$$

where

$$A = - \frac{2.0}{\sqrt{\left(\frac{\text{No. of teeth – pinion}}{\cos^3 \text{ Helix angle (ref. dia.)}} \right)}}$$

47   Base tangent (span) dimension

$$= \left[\pi(N - 0.5) + 2x \times \tan \alpha_n + z \text{ inv. } \alpha_t \right] \frac{\cos \alpha_n}{\text{DP}}$$

where

$N = $ number of teeth within span
$x = $ addendum modification coefficient
$\alpha_n = $ normal pressure angle

α_t = transverse pressure angle
z = no. of teeth on gear

Prior to using the span dimension for inspection purposes, the backlash allowance must be subtracted from the calculated dimension.

48 *Tip diameter*. Three methods are available to the designer for determining the tip diameter, as follows:

48A Where working depth equals 2/DP:

$$\text{Tip diameter} = \frac{(z/\cos\ \beta) + 2 + y + x_a - x_b}{\text{Diametral pitch}}$$

48B Where tip-to-root clearance is nominal:

$$\text{Tip diameter} = \frac{(z/\cos\ \beta) + 2(1 + y - x_b)}{\text{Diametral pitch}}$$

48C For full-length teeth:

$$\text{Tip diameter} = \frac{(z/\cos\ \beta) + 2(1 + x_a)}{\text{Diametral pitch}}$$

when

z = number of teeth on gear
β = helix angle at reference diameter
y = centre distance modification coefficient
x_a = addendum modification coefficient – actual gear
x_b = addendum modification coefficient – mating gear

49 Root diameter = Tip diameter – $(2 \times \text{Whole depth})$

Helical gears – recommended backlash

The backlash figures given are for gears assembled ready to run, and the backlash should be shared equally between the pinion and wheel.

Diametral pitch	Backlash (in)
1	0.025–0.040
$1\frac{1}{2}$	0.018–0.027
2	0.014–0.020
$2\frac{1}{2}$	0.011–0.016
3	0.009–0.014
4	0.007–0.011
5	0.006–0.009
6	0.005–0.008
7	0.004–0.007
8–10	0.004–0.006
10–13	0.003–0.005
14–32	0.002–0.004

Metric module	Backlash (mm)
25	0.65–1.00
20	0.50–0.75
15	0.40–0.55
10	0.28–0.40
8	0.20–0.30
6	0.15–0.25
5	0.15–0.225
4	0.125–0.200
3	0.100–0.175
3.00–2.50	0.100–0.150
2.50–2.00	0.075–0.125
2.00–0.75	0.050–0.100

5
Straight bevel gears

Bevel gears (Figure 5.1) are used to connect two shafts on intersecting axes, and the shaft angle is the angle between the two axes containing the meshing gear teeth. The most commonly used bevel gears and the simplest type have teeth which are radial towards the apex, i.e. straight bevel gears.

The pitch surfaces of bevel gears are cones, and the angle between the axis of the bevel gear and an element of its pitch cone is termed the pitch angle.

It is important to note that, in bevel gears, the face cone apex does not coincide with the pitch cone apex because the face cone of the blank is made parallel to the root cone of the mating gear, in order that uniform clearance is maintained between the tip of the gear teeth and the root of the teeth on the mating gear.

The tooth action of straight bevel gears is analogous to that of spur gears, the teeth making line contact parallel to the pitch line. There is no longitudinal sliding between the teeth, but end-thrust is developed under tooth load acting away from the apex and tending to separate the gears. Therefore, thrust bearings are essential to keep the gears in correct relationship to each other.

The terminology 'pinion and gear' when applied to bevel gears refers to the members with the smaller and larger numbers of teeth in the pair, respectively.

Straight bevel gears produced on modern bevel gear generating machines have a localized tooth bearing which permits a slight amount of latitude in the adjustment of the gears during assembly, and some displacement due to deflections under operating loads without concentrating the load on the ends of the teeth.

Bevel gear cutters are not made to suit any particular pitch. The reason is that the pitch of bevel gear teeth varies along the facewidth and the cutter must therefore be capable of cutting varying pitches.

Straight bevel gears are recommended for peripheral speeds up to 1000 ft/min in cases where maximum smoothness and quietness are not of prime importance.

The first section of this chapter will deal with straight-cut bevel gears with shafts at 90° angle.

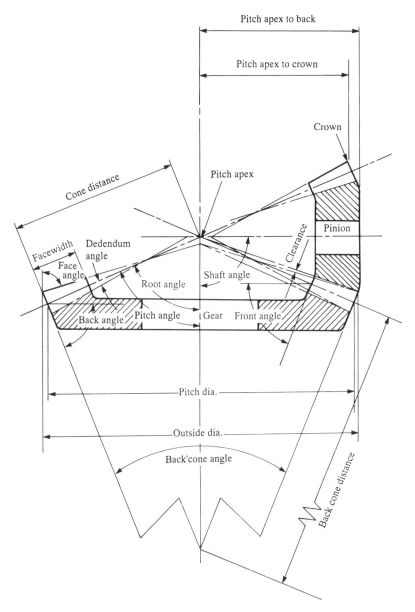

Figure 5.1   Gear terminology – bevel gear

Straight bevel gears – 90° shaft angle

Diametral pitch gears

1 No. of teeth – pinion
2 No. of teeth – wheel

3 Diametral pitch
4 Backlash – standard between gears
5 Pressure angle
6 Circular pitch

$$= \frac{3.14159}{\text{Diametral pitch}}$$

7 Pitch circle diameter

$$= \frac{\text{No. of teeth on gear}}{\text{Diametral pitch}}$$

8 Working depth

$$= \frac{2.000}{\text{Diametral pitch}}$$

9 Whole depth

$$= \frac{2.188}{\text{Diametral pitch}} + 0.002 \text{ in}$$

10 Pitch cone angle – pinion

$$= \tan^{-1} \frac{\text{No. of teeth – pinion}}{\text{No. of teeth – wheel}}$$

where $\tan^{-1}$ = the angle whose tangent is equal to . . .

11 Pitch cone angle – wheel

$$= 90° - \text{pitch cone angle – pinion}$$

12 Cone distance

$$= 0.5\sqrt{\text{PC dia. (pinion)}^2 + \text{PC dia. (wheel)}^2}$$

13 Tooth thickness – tolerance (BS 545):

Class or type of gear	Amount below nominal thickness	
	Maximum	Minimum
A Precision	$(0.2D + 4P + 2)$	$(0.1D + 2P + 1)$
B High-class	$(0.3D + 6P + 3)$	$(0.1D + 2P + 1)$
C Commercial	$(0.4D + 8P + 4)$	$(0.1D + 2P + 1)$
Special cases		
Engine timing gears	$0.075D + 1.5P + 0.75$	$0.037D + 0.75P + 0.37$
Commercial cut diff. or planetary gears	$0.25D + 5P + 2.5$	$0.15D + 3P + 1.50$

In units of 0.001 in

where

D = pitch circle dia. of gear

P = circular pitch

14   Maximum eccentricity – permissible = —— total indicator reading

15   Addendum – wheel

$$= \frac{0.540}{\text{Diametral pitch}} + \frac{0.460}{\text{Diametral pitch} \times (T/t^2)}$$

where

T = no. of teeth – wheel

t = no. of teeth – pinion

16   Addendum – pinion = Working depth − Addendum – wheel

17   Dedendum – wheel = Whole depth − Addendum – wheel

18   Dedendum – pinion = Whole depth − Addendum – pinion.

19   Dedendum angle – wheel

$$= \tan^{-1} \frac{\text{Dedendum – wheel}}{\text{Cone distance}}$$

where

$\tan^{-1}$ = the angle whose tangent is equal to . . .

20   Dedendum angle – pinion

$$= \tan^{-1} \frac{\text{Dedendum – pinion}}{\text{Cone distance}}$$

where

$\tan^{-1}$ = the angle whose tangent is equal to . . .

21   Face angle – blank: pinion = Pitch cone angle – pinion + Dedendum angle – wheel

22   Face angle – blank: wheel = Pitch cone angle – wheel + Dedendum angle – pinion

23   Root angle – pinion = Pitch cone angle – pinion − Dedendum angle – pinion

24   Root angle – wheel = Pitch cone angle – wheel − Dedendum angle = wheel.

25   Outside diameter – pinion = PC dia. (pinion) + (2 × Addendum – pinion × cos Pitch cone angle – pinion)

26   Outside diameter – wheel = PC dia. (wheel) + (2 × Addendum – wheel × cos Pitch cone angle – wheel)

27   Pitch apex to crown – pinion

$$= \frac{\text{PC dia. (wheel)}}{2} - (\text{Addendum – pinion} \times \sin \text{Pitch cone angle – pinion})$$

28   Pitch apex to crown – wheel

$$= \frac{\text{PC dia. (pinion)}}{2} - (\text{Addendum – wheel} \times \sin \text{Pitch cone angle – wheel})$$

29 Circular thickness – wheel

$$= \frac{\text{Circ. pitch}}{2} - (\text{Addendum–pinion} - \text{Addendum–wheel}) \frac{\tan\ \text{PA}}{\cos\ \text{PA}}$$
$$- \frac{\text{Constant}}{\text{DP}}$$

Note: For relevant values of the constant see the table below or Figure 5.2.

							Ratios								
	1.00 to 1.25	1.25 to 1.50	1.50 to 1.75	1.75 to 2.00	2.00 to 2.25	2.25 to 2.50	2.50 to 2.75	2.75 to 3.00	3.00 to 3.25	3.25 to 3.50	3.50 to 3.75	3.75 to 4.00	4.00 to 4.50	4.50 to 5.00	5.00 plus
No. of teeth – pinion							Values of constant								
13	–	0.015	0.040	0.045	0.050	0.060	0.070	0.080	0.090	0.100	0.110	0.120	0.135	0.150	0.165
14	–	0.015	0.030	0.050	0.065	0.080	0.090	0.100	0.110	0.120	0.125	0.130	0.140	0.150	0.160
15–17	–	–	0.010	0.020	0.030	0.045	0.060	0.070	0.080	0.090	0.095	0.100	0.110	0.115	0.120
18–21	–	–	–	–	0.010	0.030	0.045	0.060	0.070	0.080	0.085	0.090	0.095	0.100	0.100
22–29	–	–	–	–	0.010	0.030	0.040	0.050	0.060	0.065	0.070	0.075	0.080	0.085	0.085
30 plus	–	–	–	–	0.010	0.025	0.035	0.040	0.045	0.050	0.055	0.060	0.065	0.070	0.070

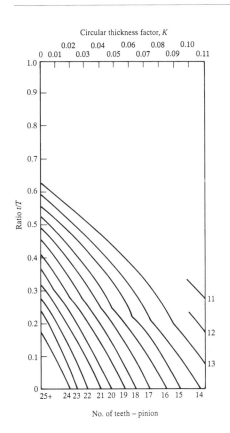

Figure 5.2 Straight bevel gears: 20° pressure angle

30 Circular thickness – pinion = Circular pitch – Circular thickness – wheel

31 Chordal thickness – wheel

$$= \text{Circ. thick. wheel} - \frac{\text{Circ. thick} - \text{wheel}^3}{6 \times \text{PC dia. (wheel)}^2} - \frac{\text{Backlash}}{2}$$

32 Chordal thickness – pinion

$$= \text{Circ. thick.} - \text{pinion} - \frac{\text{Circ. thick} - \text{pinion}^3}{6 \times \text{PC dia. (pinion)}^2} - \frac{\text{Backlash}}{2}$$

33 Chordal addendum – wheel

$$= \text{Adden.} - \text{wheel} + \frac{\text{Circ. thick}^2 \times \cos \text{ Pitch cone angle} - \text{wheel}}{4 \times \text{PC dia. (wheel)}}$$

34 Chordal addendum – pinion

$$= \text{Adden.} - \text{pinion} + \frac{\text{Circ. thick.}^2 \times \cos \text{ Pitch cone angle} - \text{pinion}}{4 \times \text{PC dia. (pinion)}}$$

35 *Pitch errors.* The values of the pitch errors permissible can be calculated to BS 545, as follows:

The permissible errors of indexing or division on the pitch circle should not exceed the values given by the formulae in the table below, where

P = circular pitch (in)
LA = smaller length of arc of pitch circle over which error is to be measured

Class of gear	Maximum permissible pitch error
A Precision	$0.1P + 0.1LA + 0.4$
B High-class	$0.2P + 0.2LA + 1.2$
C Commercial	$0.3P + 0.3LA + 2.0$

In units of 0.001 in

Straight bevel gears – 90° shaft angle

Metric module gears

1 No. of teeth – pinion
2 No. of teeth – wheel
3 Module
4 Backlash – standard between gears
5 Pressure angle
6 Circular pitch = 3.14159 × Module

7   Pitch circle diameter = No. of teeth on gear × Module
8   Working depth = 2.000 × Module
9   Whole depth = (2.188 × Module) + 0.050
10 Pitch cone angle – pinion

$$= \tan^{-1} \frac{\text{No. of teeth } - \text{ pinion}}{\text{No. of teeth } - \text{ wheel}}$$

where

$\tan^{-1}$ = the angle whose tangent is equal to . . .

11 Pitch cone angle – wheel = 90° – Pitch cone angle – pinion
12 Cone distance

$$= 0.5 \sqrt{\text{PC dia. (pinion)}^2 + \text{PC dia. (wheel)}^2}$$

13 Tooth thickness tolerances (BS 545):

Class or type of gear	Amount below nominal thickness	
	Maximum	Minimum
A Precision	0.2D + 4P + 50	0.1D + 2P + 25
B High-class	0.3D + 6P + 75	0.1D + 2P + 25
C Commercial	0.4D + 8P + 100	0.1D + 2P + 25
Special cases		
Engine timing gears	0.075D + 1.5P + 19	0.037D + 0.075P + 10
Commercial cut diff. or planetary gears	0.25D + 5P + 63	0.15D + 3P + 38

Tolerances in units of 0.001 mm

where

D = pitch circle dia. of gear
P = circular pitch

14 Maximum eccentricity – permissible = —— total indicator reading
15 Addendum – wheel

$$= \frac{0.540 \times \text{Module}}{1} + \frac{0.460 \times \text{Module}}{(T/t)^2}$$

16 Addendum – pinion = Working depth – Addendum – wheel
17 Dedendum – wheel = Whole depth – Addendum – wheel
18 Dedendum – pinion = Whole depth – addendum – pinion
19 Dedendum angle – wheel

$$= \tan^{-1} \frac{\text{Dedendum } - \text{ wheel}}{\text{Cone distance}}$$

where

$$\tan^{-1} = \text{the angle whose tangent is equal to} \ldots$$

20   Dedendum angle – pinion

$$= \tan^{-1} \frac{\text{Dedendum} - \text{pinion}}{\text{Cone distance}}$$

where

$$\tan^{-1} = \text{the angle whose tangent is equal to} \ldots$$

21   Face angle – blank: pinion = Pitch cone angle – pinion + Dedendum angle – wheel

22   Face angle – blank: wheel = Pitch cone angle – wheel + Dedendum angle – pinion

23   Root angle – pinion = Pitch cone angle – pinion – Dedendum angle – pinion

24   Root angle – wheel = Pitch cone angle – wheel – Dedendum angle – wheel

25   Outside diameter – pinion = PC dia. (pinion) + (2 × Addendum – pinion × cos Pitch cone angle – pinion)

26   Outside diameter – wheel = PC dia. (wheel) + (2 × Addendum – wheel × cos Pitch cone angle – wheel)

27   Pitch apex to crown – pinion

$$= \frac{\text{PC dia. (wheel)}}{2} - (\text{Addendum} - \text{pinion} \times \sin \text{Pitch cone angle} - \text{pinion})$$

28   Pitch apex to crown – wheel

$$= \frac{\text{PC dia. (pinion)}}{2} - (\text{Addendum} - \text{wheel} \times \sin \text{Pitch cone angle} - \text{wheel})$$

29   Circular thickness – wheel

$$\frac{\text{Circ. pitch}}{2} - (\text{Addendum} - \text{pinion} - \text{Addendum} - \text{wheel}) \frac{\tan \text{PA}}{\cos \text{PA}} - \text{Constant} \times \text{Module}$$

Note: For relevant values of the constant see the table on page 63 or Figure 5.2 (page 63).

30   Circular thickness – pinion = Circular pitch – Circular thickness – wheel

31   Chordal thickness – wheel

$$= \text{Circ. thick. (wheel)} - \frac{\text{Circ. thick.} - \text{wheel}^3}{6 \times \text{PC dia. (wheel)}^2} - \frac{\text{Backlash}}{2}$$

32   Chordal thickness – pinion

$$= \text{Circ. thick.} - \text{pinion} - \frac{\text{Circ. thick.} - \text{pinion}^3}{6 \times \text{PC dia. (pinion)}^2} - \frac{\text{Backlash}}{2}$$

33   Chordal addendum – wheel

$$= \text{Adden.} - \text{wheel} + \frac{\text{Circ. thick.}^2 \times \cos \text{Pitch cone angle} - \text{wheel}}{4 \times \text{PC dia. (wheel)}}$$

34 Chordal addendum – pinion

$$= \text{Adden.} - \text{pinion} + \frac{\text{Circ. thick.}^2 \times \cos \text{ Pitch cone angle } - \text{ pinion}}{4 \times \text{PC dia. (pinion)}}$$

35 *Pitch errors.* The values of the pitch errors permissible can be calculated to BS 545, as follows.

The permissible errors of indexing or division on the pitch circle should not exceed the values given by the formulae in the table below,

where $P = $ PC dia.

$$L = \frac{\pi \times P \times t}{\text{No. of teeth on gear}}$$

$t = $ one adjacent pitch or any whole number up to $0.5 \times$ no. of teeth on gear for cumulative pitch limits.

Class of gear	Maximum pitch tolerance
A Precision	$3.55 \sqrt{L} + 9.00$
B High-class	$7.10 \sqrt{L} + 18.00$
C Commercial	$14.00 \sqrt{L} + 35.50$
	In units of 0.001 mm

36 *Run-out tolerance* (BS 545). The run-out of teeth tolerance – measured normal to the reference cone – should be as given in the following table which is based on the factor θ_p, calculated as follows:

$$\theta_p = \frac{\text{Reference dia.}}{\text{No. of teeth}} + 0.25 \sqrt{\text{Reference dia.}}$$

Class of gear	Run-out of teeth tolerance
A Precision	$3.15\theta_p + 40.0$
B High-class	$5.00\theta_p + 63.00$
C Commercial	$8.00\theta_p + 100.0$
	In units of 0.001 mm

Straight bevel gears with shafts at an acute angle (less than 90°)

Substitute the following calculations for calculations 10 and 11 in the 90° shaft angle straight bevel gear calculations.

1 Pitch cone angle – pinion:

$$= \tan^{-1} \frac{\text{sin Shaft angle}}{\dfrac{\text{No. of teeth} - \text{wheel}}{\text{No. of teeth} - \text{pinion}} + \cos \text{Shaft angle}}$$

where

$\tan^{-1}$ = the angle whose tangent is equal to . . .

2 Pitch cone angle – wheel:

$$= \tan^{-1} \frac{\text{sin Shaft angle}}{\dfrac{\text{No. of teeth} - \text{pinion}}{\text{No. of teeth} - \text{wheel}} + \cos \text{Shaft angle}}$$

where

$\tan^{-1}$ = the angle whose tangent is equal to . . .

3 Check calculation:

Shaft angle = Pitch cone angle – pinion + Pitch cone angle – wheel

Straight bevel gears with shafts at an obtuse angle (greater than 90°)

Substitute the following calculations for calculations 10 and 11 in the 90° shaft angle straight bevel gear calculations.

1 Pitch cone angle – pinion:

$$= \tan^{-1} \frac{\sin(180° - \text{Shaft angle})}{\dfrac{\text{No. of teeth} - \text{wheel}}{\text{No. of teeth} - \text{pinion}} - \cos(180° - \text{Shaft angle})}$$

where

$\tan^{-1}$ = the angle whose tangent is equal to . . .

2 Pitch cone angle – wheel:

$$= \tan^{-1} \frac{\sin(180° - \text{Shaft angle})}{\dfrac{\text{No. of teeth} - \text{pinion}}{\text{No. of teeth} - \text{wheel}} - \cos(180° - \text{Shaft angle})}$$

where

$\tan^{-1}$ = the angle whose tangent is equal to . . .

3 Check calculation:

Shaft angle = Pitch cone angle – pinion + Pitch cone angle – wheel

Straight bevel gears – recommended backlash

The backlash figures given are for gears assembled ready to run, and the backlash should be shared equally between the pinion and crown wheel, i.e. 8 DP gears 0.002–0.003 in backlash on both crown wheel and pinion.

Diametral pitch	Backlash (in)
1.00–1.25	0.020–0.030
1.25–1.50	0.018–0.026
1.50–1.75	0.016–0.022
1.75–2.00	0.014–0.018
2.00–2.50	0.012–0.016
2.50–3.00	0.010–0.013
3.00–3.50	0.008–0.011
3.50–4.00	0.007–0.009
4.00–5.00	0.006–0.008
5.00–6.00	0.005–0.007
6.00–8.00	0.004–0.006
8.00–10.00	0.003–0.005
10.00–16.00	0.002–0.004
16.00–20.00	0.001–0.003
20.00–50.00	0.000–0.002
50.00–64.00	0.000–0.001
Metric module	**Backlash (mm)**
25–20	0.55–0.75
20–16	0.45–0.65
16–12	0.40–0.55
12–10	0.35–0.45
10–8	0.30–0.40
8–6	0.25–0.35
6–5	0.20–0.28
5–4	0.18–0.23
4–3	0.13–0.18
3–2.50	0.076–0.130
2.50–2.00	0.050–0.100
2.00–1.50	0.025–0.075
1.50–1.25	0.000–0.050
1.25–1.00	0.000–0.025

Note: Backlash on bevel gears should always be measured at the outer cone at the tightest point of mesh.

6
Spiral bevel gears

Spiral bevel gears (Figures 6.1 and 6.2) have curved oblique teeth which contact each other gradually and smoothly from one end of the tooth to the other. They mesh with a rolling contact similar to straight bevel gears, but are smoother and quieter in action. Well-designed spiral bevels have two or more teeth in contact at all times. This overlapping tooth action ensures that motion is transmitted smoothly and quietly; hence, spiral bevels are superseding straight bevels in many applications.

Like modern straight bevels, spiral bevel gears are produced with a localized tooth bearing and therefore have the same advantages in assembly and under load. Spiral bevels have lower tooth loading than straight bevels due to the larger radius of curvature on the tooth profile. This, together with the two or more teeth in contact at all times, ensures that tooth loads are more evenly distributed, with the result that spiral bevels can carry more load without surface fatigue.

The normal load on the tooth surfaces of bevel gears can be resolved into two components, one in the direction along the axis of the gear and the other perpendicular to the axis. The axial force produces an axial thrust on the bearings, whereas the force perpendicular to the axis produces a radial load on the bearings. The direction and magnitude of the normal load depend upon the gear ratio, pressure angle, spiral angle, hand of spiral, direction of rotation and whether the gear is the driving or driven member.

The hand of spiral is denoted by the direction in which the teeth curve, i.e. left-hand teeth incline away from the axis in a counter-clockwise direction looking on the small end of the pinion or face of the gear, and right-hand teeth incline away from the axis in a clockwise direction. The hand of spiral of one member is always opposite to that of its mate, and the hand of spiral of the pinion is used to identify the gear pair, i.e. a left-hand spiral pair has a pinion with a left-hand spiral and a gear with a right-hand spiral.

The hand of spiral does not affect the smoothness and quietness of operation or the efficiency of the gear pair, but does affect the thrust loads created. A left-hand spiral pinion driving clockwise, when viewed from the back, i.e. the large end of the pinion or back of the gear, creates an axial thrust that tends to move the pinion out of mesh. This means that if the pinion is set up with too much end-play, additional backlash between the teeth will be introduced which will not prevent

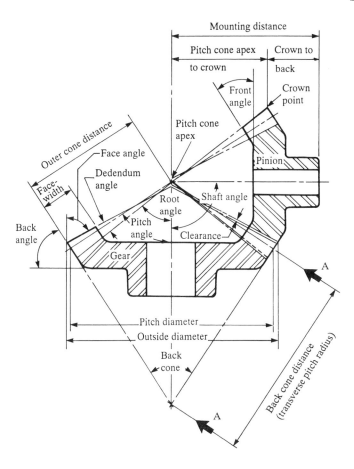

Figure 6.1 Bevel gear nomenclature – axial plane

the gears operating. Alternatively, a right-hand spiral pinion driving clockwise and set up with excess end-play will take up the backlash, thus creating a situation where the teeth may wedge and lead to early failure.

Therefore, the hand of spiral should wherever possible be chosen to give an axial thrust that tends to move the pinion out of mesh.

Notes:
(a) Spiral angles are quoted when looking on the small end of the pinion or face of the gear.
(b) The direction of rotation is quoted when looking on the large end of the pinion or rear of the gear.

Spiral bevel gears have been used successfully at speeds in excess of 8000 ft/min, with the amount of noise being directly related to the finish of the gear teeth.

The first section of this chapter will deal with spiral bevel gears with shafts at 90° angle.

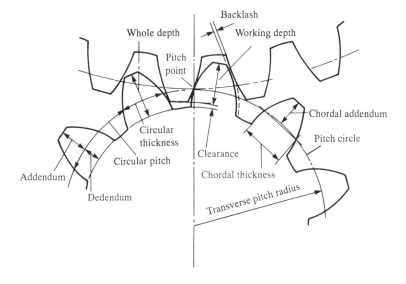

Figure 6.2   Bevel gear nomenclature – transverse section (as viewed in direction A in Figure 6.1)

Spiral bevel gears – 90° shaft angle

Diametral pitch gears

1   No. of teeth – pinion
2   No. of teeth – wheel
3   Diametral pitch
4   Backlash – standard between gears
5   Pressure angle
6   Circular pitch

$$= \frac{3.14159}{\text{Diametral pitch}}$$

7   Pitch circle diameter

$$= \frac{\text{No. of teeth}}{\text{Diametral pitch}}$$

8   Working depth

$$= \frac{1.700}{\text{Diametral pitch}}$$

9   Whole depth

$$= \frac{1.888}{\text{Diametral pitch}}$$

10 Pitch cone angle – pinion:

$$= \tan^{-1} \frac{\text{No. of teeth } - \text{ pinion}}{\text{No. of teeth } - \text{ wheel}}$$

where

$\tan^{-1} =$ the angle whose tangent is equal to . . .

11 Pitch cone angle – wheel $= 90° -$ Pitch cone angle – pinion

12 Outer cone distance

$$= \frac{\text{PC dia. (wheel)}}{2 \times \sin \text{ Pitch cone angle } - \text{ wheel}}$$

13 Addendum – wheel

$$= \frac{0.460}{\text{Diametral pitch}} + \frac{0.390}{\text{Diametral pitch} \times \left(\dfrac{\text{No. of teeth } - \text{ wheel}}{\text{No. of teeth } - \text{ pinion}}\right)^2}$$

14 Addendum – pinion $=$ Working depth $-$ Addendum – wheel

15 Dedendum – wheel $=$ Whole depth $-$ Addendum – wheel

16 Dedendum – pinion $=$ Whole depth $-$ Addendum – pinion

17 Clearance $=$ Whole depth $-$ Working depth

18 Dedendum angle – wheel:

$$= \tan^{-1} \frac{\text{Dedendum } - \text{ wheel}}{\text{Outer cone distance}}$$

where

$\tan^{-1} =$ the angle whose tangent is equal to . . .

19 Dedendum angle – pinion:

$$= \tan^{-1} \frac{\text{Dedendum } - \text{ pinion}}{\text{Outer cone distance}}$$

where

$\tan^{-1} =$ the angle whose tangent is equal to . . .

20 Face angle blank – wheel $=$ Pitch cone angle – wheel $+$ Dedendum angle – pinion

21 Face angle blank – pinion $=$ Pitch cone angle – pinion $+$ Dedendum angle – wheel

22 Root angle – wheel $=$ Pitch cone angle – wheel $-$ Dedendum angle – wheel

23 Root angle – pinion $=$ Pitch cone angle – pinion $-$ Dedendum angle – pinion

24 Outside diameter – wheel $=$ PC dia. (wheel) $+ [2 \times$ Adden. wheel $\times \cos$ Pitch cone angle – wheel]

25 Outside diameter – pinion $=$ PC dia. (pinion) $+ [2 \times$ Adden. pinion $\times \cos$ Pitch cone angle – pinion]

26   Pitch apex to crown – wheel

$$= \frac{\text{PC dia. (pinion)}}{2} - [\text{Adden. wheel} \times \sin \text{Pitch cone angle – wheel}]$$

27   Pitch apex to crown – pinion

$$= \frac{\text{PC dia. (wheel)}}{2} - [\text{Adden. pinion} \times \sin \text{Pitch cone angle – pinion}]$$

28   Circular thickness – wheel

$$= \frac{\text{Circ. pitch}}{2} - (\text{Adden. pinion} - \text{Adden. wheel})\frac{\tan \text{PA}}{\cos \text{PA}} - \frac{\text{Constant}}{\text{DP}}$$

Note: For relevant values of the constant see the table below or Figure 6.3.

	Ratios														
	1.00 to 1.25	1.25 to 1.50	1.50 to 1.75	1.75 to 2.00	2.00 to 2.25	2.25 to 2.50	2.50 to 2.75	2.75 to 3.00	3.00 to 3.25	3.25 to 3.50	3.50 to 3.75	3.75 to 4.00	4.00 to 4.50	4.50 to 5.00	5.00 plus
No. of teeth – pinion							Values of constant								
13	–	0.015	0.04	0.045	0.050	0.060	0.07	0.08	0.09	0.10	0.110	0.120	0.135	0.150	0.165
14	–	0.015	0.03	0.05	0.065	0.080	0.09	0.10	0.11	0.12	0.125	0.130	0.140	0.150	0.160
15–17	–	–	0.01	0.02	0.03	0.045	0.06	0.07	0.08	0.09	0.095	0.100	0.110	0.115	0.120
18–21	–	–	–	–	0.01	0.03	0.045	0.06	0.07	0.08	0.085	0.090	0.095	0.100	0.100
22–29	–	–	–	–	0.01	0.03	0.040	0.05	0.06	0.065	0.070	0.070	0.080	0.085	0.085
30-plus	–	–	–	–	0.01	0.025	0.035	0.04	0.045	0.05	0.055	0.060	0.065	0.070	0.070

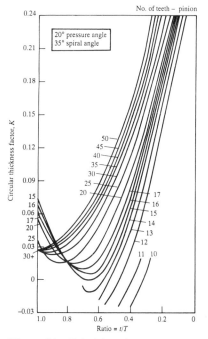

Figure 6.3   Spiral bevel gears

29   Circular thickness – pinion = Circular pitch – Circular thickness – wheel
30   Shaft angle = 90°
31   Spiral angle:
Note: The spiral angle used in the Gleason system is 35°. The use of smaller spiral angles leads to undercutting at the tooth roots and lower contact ratios.
32   *Hand of spiral* – see notes at the beginning of this chapter referring to the hand of spiral.
33   Driving member
34   *Direction of rotation* – see notes at the beginning of this chapter referring to the direction of rotation.
35   *Pitch errors.* The values of the permissible pitch errors can be calculated to BS 545, as follows.

The permissible errors of indexing or division of the pitch circle should not exceed the values given by the formulae in the following table,

where P = circular pitch (in)
   LA = smaller length of arc, in inches, of pitch circle over which error is to be measured

Class of gear	Maximum permissible pitch error
A Precision	$0.1P + 0.1LA + 0.4$
B High-class	$0.2P + 0.2LA + 1.2$
C Commercial	$0.3P + 0.3LA + 2.0$

In units of 0.001 in

36   *Tooth thickness tolerances.* The tooth thickness tolerances calculated to BS 545 give maximum and minimum values below the nominal thickness, as shown in the table below,

where D = pitch diameter of gear (in)
   P = circular pitch (in)
   θ_2 = spiral angle at pitch dia.

Class or type of gear	Amount below nominal thickness	
	Maximum	Minimum
A Precision	$(0.2D + 4P + 2) \cos \theta_2$	$(0.1D + 2P + 1) \cos \theta_2$
B High-class	$(0.3D + 6P + 3) \cos \theta_2$	$(0.1D + 2P + 1) \cos \theta_2$
C Commercial	$(0.4D + 8P + 4) \cos \theta_2$	$(0.1D + 2P + 1) \cos \theta_2$
Special cases		
Engine timing gears	$(0.075D + 1.5P + 0.75) \cos \theta_2$	$(0.037D + 0.75P + 0.375) \cos \theta_2$
Commercial cut differential or planetary gears	$(0.25D + 5P + 2.5) \cos \theta_2$	$(0.15D + 3P + 1.5) \cos \theta_2$

In units of 0.001 in

37 Maximum eccentricity = —— total indicator reading
38 Caliper setting for checking:

where

$$S = \frac{\text{Circ. pitch}}{2} + 2 \tan \text{Press angle} \left(\text{Wheel adden.} \times \sec \text{Spiral angle} - \frac{CP}{\pi} \right)$$

and

$$\mathcal{S} = \text{Circular pitch} - S$$

39 Chordal thickness – wheel

$$= \frac{S}{\sec \left(\text{Spiral angle} + \dfrac{S}{2 \times \text{Cone distance}} \right)}$$

40 Chordal thickness – pinion

$$= \frac{\mathcal{S}}{\sec \left(\text{Spiral angle} + \dfrac{\mathcal{S}}{2 \times \text{Cone distance}} \right)}$$

41 Chordal addendum – wheel

$$= \text{Adden. wheel} + \frac{\text{Chordal thickness – wheel}^2}{4 \times \text{PC dia. (wheel)} \times \sec. \text{Spiral angle}^2 \times \sec. \text{Pitch angle – wheel}}$$

42 Chordal addendum – pinion

$$= \text{Adden. pinion} + \frac{\text{Chordal thickness – pinion}^2}{4 \times \text{PC dia. (pinion)} \times \sec. \text{Spiral angle}^2 \times \sec \text{Pitch angle – pinion}}$$

Spiral bevel gears – 90° shaft angle

Metric module gears

1 No. of teeth – pinion
2 No. of teeth – wheel
3 Module – metric
4 Backlash – standard between gears
5 Pressure angle
6 Circular pitch = $\pi \times$ Module
7 Pitch circle diameter = No. of teeth $\times$ Module
8 Working depth = $1.700 \times$ Module
9 Whole depth = $1.888 \times$ Module
10 Pitch cone angle – pinion:

$$= \tan^{-1} \frac{\text{No. of teeth – pinion}}{\text{No. of teeth – wheel}}$$

where

$\tan^{-1}$ = the angle whose tangent is equal to . . .

11 Pitch cone angle – wheel = 90° – Pitch cone angle – pinion

12 Outer cone distance – pitch cone radius

$$= \frac{\text{Pitch circle dia. (wheel)}}{2 \times \sin \text{ Pitch cone angle } - \text{ pinion}}$$

13 Addendum – wheel

$$= 0.460 \times \text{Module} + \frac{0.390 \times \text{Module}}{\left(\dfrac{\text{No. of teeth } - \text{ wheel}}{\text{No. of teeth } - \text{ pinion}} \right)^2}$$

14 Addendum – pinion = Working depth – Addendum – wheel

15 Dedendum – wheel = Whole depth – Addendum – wheel

16 Dedendum – pinion = Whole depth – Addendum – pinion

17 Clearance = Whole depth – Working depth

18 Dedendum angle – wheel

$$= \tan^{-1} \frac{\text{Dedendum } - \text{ wheel}}{\text{Outer cone distance}}$$

where

$\tan^{-1}$ = the angle whose tangent is equal to . . .

19 Dedendum angle – pinion

$$= \tan^{-1} \frac{\text{Dedendum } - \text{ pinion}}{\text{Outer cone distance}}$$

where

$\tan^{-1}$ = the angle whose tangent is equal to . . .

20 Face angle blank – wheel = Pitch cone angle – wheel + Dedendum angle – pinion

21 Face angle blank – pinion = Pitch cone angle – pinion + Dedendum angle – wheel

22 Root angle – wheel = Pitch cone angle – wheel – Dedendum angle – wheel

23 Root angle – pinion = Pitch cone angle – pinion – Dedendum angle – pinion

24 Outside diameter – wheel = PC dia. (wheel) + [2 × Adden. – wheel × cos Pitch cone angle – wheel]

25 Outside diameter – pinion = PC dia. (pinion) + [2 × Adden. – pinion × cos Pitch cone angle – pinion]

26 Pitch apex to crown – wheel

$$= \frac{\text{PC dia. (pinion)}}{2} - [\text{Adden. } - \text{ wheel} \times \sin \text{ Pitch cone angle } - \text{ wheel}]$$

27   Pitch apex to crown – pinion

$$=\frac{\text{PC dia. (wheel)}}{2}-[\text{Adden.}-\text{pinion}\times\sin\text{Pitch cone angle}-\text{pinion}]$$

28   Circular thickness – wheel

$$=\frac{\text{Circ. pitch}}{2}-(\text{Adden.}-\text{pinion}-\text{Adden.}-\text{wheel})\frac{\tan\text{ PA}}{\cos\text{ PA}}-\text{Module}\times\text{Constant}$$

Note: For the relevant values of the constant see the table on page 74 or Figure 6.3 (page 74).

29   Circular thickness – pinion = Circular pitch – Circular thickness – wheel

30   Shaft angle = 90°

31   Spiral angle:

Note: The spiral angle used in the Gleason system is 35°. The use of smaller spiral angles leads to undercutting at the tooth roots and lower contact ratios.

32   *Hand of spiral* – see notes at the beginning of this chapter referring to the hand of spiral.

33   Driving member

34   *Direction of rotation* – see notes at the beginning of this chapter referring to the direction of rotation.

35   *Pitch errors*. The values of the permissible pitch errors can be calculated to BS 545, as follows.

The permissible errors of indexing or division on the pitch circle should not exceed the values given by the formulae in the table below,

where P = circular pitch (mm)

LA = smaller length of arc, in millimetres, of pitch circle over which error is to be measured

Class of gear	Maximum permissible pitch error
A Precision	$0.1P+0.1LA+10.16$
B High-class	$0.2P+0.2LA+30.48$
C Commercial	$0.3P+0.3LA+50.80$

In units of 0.001 mm

36   *Tooth thickness tolerances*. The tooth thickness tolerances calculated to BS 545 give maximum and minimum values below the nominal thickness, as shown in the table below,

where D = pitch diameter of gear (mm)

P = circular pitch (mm)

θ_2 = spiral angle at pitch dia.

Class or type of gear	Amount below nominal thickness	
	Maximum	Minimum
A Precision	$(0.2D + 4P + 50.8) \cos \theta_2$	$(0.1D + 2P + 25.4) \cos \theta_2$
B High-class	$(0.3D + 6P + 76.2) \cos \theta_2$	$(0.1D + 2P + 25.4) \cos \theta_2$
C Commercial	$(0.4D + 8P + 101.6) \cos \theta_2$	$(0.1D + 2P + 25.4) \cos \theta_2$
Special cases		
Engine timing gears	$(0.075D + 1.5P + 19.05) \cos \theta_2$	$(0.037D + 0.75P + 9.525) \cos \theta_2$
Commercial cut differential or planetary gears	$(0.25D + 5P + 63.5) \cos \theta_2$	$(0.15D + 3P + 38.1) \cos \theta_2$

In units of 0.001 mm

37 Maximum eccentricity = —— total indicator reading

38 Caliper setting for checking:

where

$$S = \frac{\text{Circ. pitch}}{2} + 2 \tan \text{Press. angle} \left(\frac{\text{Wheel adden.}}{\cos \text{Spiral angle}} - \frac{\text{Circ. pitch}}{\pi} \right)$$

and

$$\$ = \text{Circular pitch} - S$$

39 Chordal thickness – wheel

$$= \frac{S}{\sec \left(\text{Spiral angle} + \dfrac{S}{2 \times \text{Cone distance}} \right)}$$

40 Chordal thickness – pinion

$$= \frac{\$}{\sec \left(\text{Spiral angle} + \dfrac{\$}{2 \times \text{Cone distance}} \right)}$$

41 Chordal addendum – wheel

$$= \text{Adden. wheel} + \frac{\text{Chordal thickness} - \text{wheel}^2}{4 \times \text{PC dia. (wheel)} \times \sec \text{Spiral angle}^2 \times \sec \text{Pitch angle} - \text{wheel}}$$

42 Chordal addendum – pinion

$$= \text{Adden. pinion} + \frac{\text{Chordal thickness} - \text{pinion}^2}{4 \times \text{PC dia. (pinion)} \times \sec \text{Spiral angle}^2 \times \sec \text{Pitch angle} - \text{pinion}}$$

Spiral bevel gears with shafts at an acute angle (less than 90°)

Substitute the following calculations for calculations 10, 11, 13, 26 and 27, and substitute the value from item 7 into calculation 28:

1   Pitch cone angle – pinion

$$= \tan^{-1} \frac{\sin \text{ Shaft angle}}{\dfrac{\text{No. of teeth } - \text{ wheel}}{\text{No. of teeth } - \text{ pinion}} + \cos \text{ Shaft angle}}$$

where

$\tan^{-1}$ = the angle whose tangent is equal to . . .

2   Pitch cone angle – wheel = Shaft angle − pitch cone angle – pinion

3   Addendum – wheel. To determine the addendum – wheel, the following ratio for the equivalent 90° shaft bevel gear ratio must be calculated and used in place of the ratio

$$\frac{\text{No. of teeth } - \text{ wheel}}{\text{No. of teeth } - \text{ pinion}}$$

when calculating the addendum – wheel for gears with shafts at less than 90°.
   Equivalent 90° spiral bevel ratio

$$= \sqrt{\frac{\text{No. of teeth } - \text{ wheel} \times \cos \text{ Pitch cone angle } - \text{ pinion}}{\text{No. of teeth } - \text{ pinion} \times \cos \text{ Pitch cone angle } - \text{ wheel}}}$$

$$= \tan \text{ Pitch cone angle } - \text{ wheel at } 90°$$

4   Pitch apex to crown – wheel = Outer cone distance × cos Pitch cone angle – wheel − Adden. – wheel × sin Pitch cone angle – wheel

5   Pitch apex to crown – pinion = Outer cone distance × cos Pitch cone angle – pinion − Adden. – pinion × sin Pitch cone angle – pinion

6   *Pressure angle*. The pressure angle can be taken from Figure 6.4. The point of intersection of the dedendum angle and pitch angle must be on or below the line representing the selected pressure angle.

7   *Circular thickness – wheel*. The formula given remains as given, but value *K* (circular thickness factor) from Figure 6.3 (page 74) must be determined using the number of teeth in the equivalent 90° bevel pinion and the equivalent 90° bevel ratio.
   The equivalent 90° bevel ratio is calculated as shown in item 3, above.
   The number of teeth in the equivalent 90° bevel pinion is calculated as follows:

No. of teeth in equivalent 90° bevel pinion

$$= \frac{\text{No. of teeth } - \text{ pinion} \times \text{Equiv. } 90° \text{ bevel ratio}}{\cos \text{ Pitch cone angle}}$$

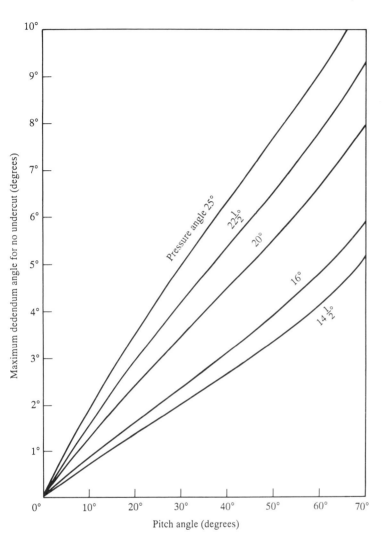

Figure 6.4 Relation between the dedendum angle and pitch angle at which undercut begins to occur in generating spiral bevel gears of 35° spiral angle using sharp-cornered tools

Spiral bevel gears with shafts at an obtuse angle (greater than 90°)

Substitute the following calculations for calculations 10, 11, 13, 26 and 27, and substitute the value from item 7 into calculation 28:

1 Pitch cone angle – pinion

$$= \tan^{-1} \frac{\sin \ (180° - \text{Shaft angle})}{\dfrac{\text{No. of teeth } - \text{ wheel}}{\text{No. of teeth } - \text{ pinion}} - \cos \ (180° - \text{Shaft angle})}$$

where

$\tan^{-1}$ = the angle whose tangent is equal to . . .

2 Pitch cone angle – wheel = Shaft angle – Pitch cone angle – pinion

A pitch cone angle – wheel greater than 90° indicates an internal gear, and a special calculation must be made to determine whether or not the gear can be cut.

In either case, with gears at an acute or obtuse angle the following applies:

$$\frac{\sin \text{ Pitch cone angle } - \text{ pinion}}{\sin \text{ Pitch cone angle } - \text{ wheel}} = \frac{\text{No. of teeth } - \text{ pinion}}{\text{No. of teeth } - \text{ wheel}}$$

3 *Addendum – wheel.* To determine the addendum – wheel, the following ratio for the equivalent 90° shaft bevel gear ratio must be calculated and used in place of the ratio

$$\frac{\text{No. of teeth } - \text{ wheel}}{\text{No. of teeth } - \text{ pinion}}$$

in calculating the addendum – wheel for gears with shafts at more than 90°.

Equivalent 90° spiral bevel ratio

$$= \sqrt{\frac{\text{No. of teeth } - \text{ wheel} \times \cos \text{ Pitch cone angle } - \text{ pinion}}{\text{No. of teeth } - \text{ pinion} \times \cos \text{ Pitch cone angle } - \text{ wheel}}}$$

$$= \tan \text{ Pitch cone angle } - \text{ wheel at } 90°$$

4 Pitch apex to crown – wheel = Outer cone distance × cos Pitch cone angle – wheel – Adden. – wheel × sin Pitch cone angle – wheel

5 Pitch apex to crown – pinion = Outer cone distance × cos Pitch cone angle – pinion – Adden. – pinion × sin Pitch cone angle – pinion

6 *Pressure angle.* The pressure angle can be taken from Figure 6.4. The point of intersection of the dedendum angle and pitch angle must be on or below the line representing the selected pressure angle.

7 *Circular thickness – wheel.* The formula given remains as given, but value K (circular thickness factor) from Figure 6.3 (page 74) must be determined using the number of teeth in the equivalent 90° bevel ratio.

The equivalent 90° bevel ratio is calculated as shown in item 3, above.

The number of teeth in the equivalent 90° bevel pinion is calculated as follows:

No. of teeth in equivalent 90° bevel pinion

$$= \frac{\text{No. of teeth } - \text{ pinion} \times \text{Equiv. } 90° \text{ bevel ratio}}{\cos \text{ Pitch cone angle}}$$

Spiral bevel gears – recommended backlash

The backlash figures given are for gears assembled ready to run, and the backlash should be shared equally between pinion and crown wheel, i.e. 8 DP gears 0.002–0.003 in backlash on both pinion and crown wheel.

Diametral pitch	Backlash (in)
1.00–1.25	0.020–0.030
1.25–1.50	0.018–0.026
1.50–1.75	0.016–0.022
1.75–2.00	0.014–0.018
2.00–2.50	0.012–0.016
2.50–3.00	0.010–0.013
3.00–3.50	0.008–0.011
3.50–4.00	0.007–0.009
4.00–5.00	0.006–0.008
5.00–6.00	0.005–0.007
6.00–8.00	0.004–0.006
8.00–10.00	0.003–0.005
10.00–16.00	0.002–0.004
16.00–20.00	0.001–0.003
20.00–50.00	0.000–0.002
50.00–64.00	0.000–0.001
Module – metric	Backlash (mm)
25–20	0.55–0.75
20–16	0.45–0.65
16–12	0.40–0.55
12–10	0.35–0.45
10–8	0.30–0.40
8–6 ·	0.25–0.35
6–5	0.20–0.28
5–4	0.18–0.23
4–3	0.13–0.18
3–2.50	0.076–0.130
2.50–2.00	0.050–0.100
2.00–1.50	0.025–0.075
1.50–1.25	0.000–0.050
1.25–1.00	0.000–0.025

Note: Backlash on bevel gears should always be measured at the outer cone at the tightest point of mesh.

7
Zerol bevel gears

Zerol bevel gears (Figures 7.1 and 7.2) have curved teeth which lie in the same general direction as straight bevel gears, but should be considered as spiral bevel gears with zero spiral angle. Both spiral and Zerol bevel gears are produced with localized tooth contact which can be controlled for length, width and shape and which permits slight errors in assembly and some displacement due to deflections under load.

Functionally, Zerol bevel gears are similar to straight bevel gears and carry the same ratings; therefore, Zerol bevel gears can be used in mountings designed from straight bevel gears.

Zerol bevel gears should only be used when speeds are less than 1000 ft/min, because at higher speeds they may become noisy.

Considerations of tooth proportions to avoid undercut and loss of contact ratio, as well as to achieve optimum balance of strength, are also similar to those for the straight bevel gear system.

The Zerol system is based on tooth proportions in which the root cone elements do not pass through the pitch cone apex and the face cone element of the mating member is made parallel to the root cone element to produce uniform clearance. The basic pressure angle is 20°, but pressure angles of $22\frac{1}{2}°$ or 25° are also used where necessary to avoid undercutting.

The facewidth is limited to one-quarter of the cone distance because, due to the duplex taper, the small-end tooth depth decreases rapidly as the facewidth increases.

The first section of this chapter will deal with Zerol bevel gears with shafts at 90° angle.

Zerol bevel gears – 90° shaft angle

Diametral pitch gears

1 No. of teeth – pinion
2 No. of teeth – wheel
3 Diametral pitch

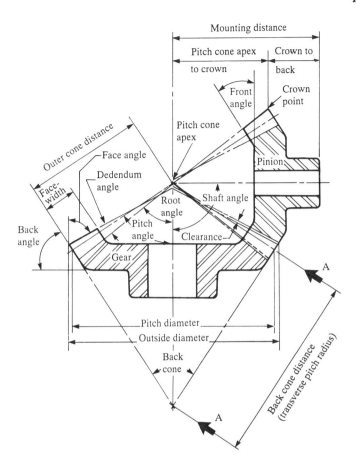

Figure 7.1 Bevel gear nomenclature – axial plane

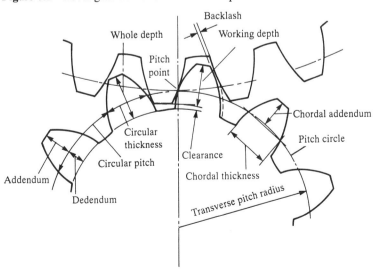

Figure 7.2 Bevel gear nomenclature – transverse section (as viewed in direction A in Figure 7.1)

4   Backlash – standard between gears
5   Pressure angle – see the table on page 88
6   Circular pitch

$$= \frac{3.14159}{\text{Diametral pitch}}$$

7   Pitch circle diameter

$$= \frac{\text{No. of teeth on gear}}{\text{Diametral pitch}}$$

8   Working depth

$$= \frac{2.000}{\text{Diametral pitch}}$$

9   Whole depth

$$= \frac{2.188}{\text{Diametral pitch}} + 0.002 \text{ in}$$

10   Pitch cone angle – pinion

$$= \tan^{-1} \frac{\text{No. of teeth – pinion}}{\text{No. of teeth – wheel}}$$

where

$$\tan^{-1} = \text{the angle whose tangent is equal to } \ldots$$

11   Pitch cone angle – wheel $= 90° -$ Pitch cone angle – pinion
12   Outer cone distance

$$= \frac{\text{Pitch circle diameter – wheel}}{2 \times \sin \text{ Pitch cone angle – wheel}}$$

13   Addendum – wheel

$$= \frac{\text{Value from Table 7.1}}{\text{Diametral pitch}}$$

The addendum given is for 1 diametral pitch.

To obtain the addendum, select from Table 7.1 the value corresponding to the ratio given by the following formula:

$$\text{Ratio} = \frac{\text{No. of teeth – wheel}}{\text{No. of teeth – pinion}}$$

In cases where there is an optional choice, the larger addendum should always be used.

14   Addendum – pinion = Working depth – Addendum – wheel
15   Dedendum – wheel = Whole depth – Addendum – wheel

Table 7.1

Ratios			Ratios		
From	To	Adden.	From	To	Adden.
1.00	1.00	1.000	1.42	1.45	0.760
1.00	1.02	0.990	1.45	1.48	0.750
1.02	1.03	0.980	1.48	1.52	0.740
1.03	1.04	0.970	1.52	1.56	0.730
1.04	1.05	0.960	1.56	1.60	0.720
1.05	1.06	0.950	1.60	1.65	0.710
1.06	1.08	0.940	1.65	1.70	0.700
1.08	1.09	0.930	1.70	1.76	0.690
1.09	1.11	0.920	1.76	1.82	0.680
1.11	1.12	0.910	1.82	1.89	0.670
1.12	1.14	0.900	1.89	1.97	0.660
1.14	1.15	0.890	1.97	2.06	0.650
1.15	1.17	0.880	2.06	2.16	0.640
1.17	1.19	0.870	2.16	2.27	0.630
1.19	1.21	0.860	2.27	2.41	0.620
1.21	1.23	0.850	2.41	2.58	0.610
1.23	1.25	0.840	2.58	2.78	0.600
1.25	1.27	0.830	2.78	3.05	0.590
1.27	1.29	0.820	3.05	3.41	0.580
1.29	1.31	0.810	3.41	3.94	0.570
1.31	1.33	0.800	3.94	4.82	0.560
1.33	1.36	0.790	4.82	6.81	0.550
1.36	1.39	0.780	6.81	–	0.540
1.39	1.42	0.770			

16 Dedendum – pinion = Whole depth – Addendum – pinion

17 *Addendum – wheel*. An alternative method of calculating the addendum – wheel is as follows:

$$\text{Addendum} - \text{wheel} = \frac{0.540}{\text{Diametral pitch}} + \frac{0.460}{\text{Diametral pitch} \times (T/t^2)}$$

where

T = no. of teeth – wheel
t = no. of teeth – pinion

18 Dedendum angle – wheel

$$= \tan^{-1} \frac{\text{Dedendum} - \text{wheel}}{\text{Cone distance}} + \theta$$

where

tan^{-1} = the angle whose tangent is equal to . . ., and θ can be obtained from the table below, where

F = facewidth
d = pitch circle diameter – pinion
P_d = diametral pitch
Γ = pitch cone angle – wheel
N_c = no. of teeth in crown gear
N_c = 2 × diametral pitch × outer cone distance

Pressure angle	Change in dedendum angle, θ (minutes)
20°	$\theta = \dfrac{6668}{N_c} - \dfrac{300\sqrt{d}\ \sin\ \Gamma}{N_c F} - \dfrac{14 P_d}{N_c}$
$22\frac{1}{2}°$	$\theta = \dfrac{4868}{N_c} - \dfrac{300\sqrt{d}\ \sin\ \Gamma}{N_c F} - \dfrac{14 P_d}{N_c}$
25°	$\theta = \dfrac{3412}{N_c} - \dfrac{300\sqrt{d}\ \sin\ \Gamma}{N_c F} - \dfrac{14 P_d}{N_c}$

19   Dedendum angle – pinion

$$= \tan^{-1} \frac{\text{Dedendum} - \text{pinion}}{\text{Cone distance}} + \theta$$

where

tan^{-1} = the angle whose tangent is equal to . . ., and θ is obtained from the preceding table.

20   Face angle – blank: pinion = Pitch cone angle – pinion + Dedendum angle – wheel
21   Face angle – blank: wheel = Pitch cone angle – wheel + Dedendum angle – pinion
22   Root angle – pinion = Pitch cone angle – pinion – Dedendum angle – pinion
23   Root angle – wheel = Pitch cone angle – wheel – Dedendum angle – wheel
24   Outside diameter – pinion = PC dia. (pinion) + (2 × adden. – pinion × cos Pitch cone angle – pinion)
25   Outside diameter – wheel = PC dia. (wheel) + (2 × Adden. – wheel × cos Pitch cone angle – wheel)
26   Pitch apex to crown – pinion

$$= \frac{\text{PC dia. (wheel)}}{2} - (\text{Adden. pinion} \times \sin \text{Pitch cone angle} - \text{pinion})$$

27 Pitch apex to crown – wheel

$$=\frac{\text{PC dia. (pinion)}}{2}-(\text{Adden.} - \text{wheel} \times \sin \text{Pitch cone angle} - \text{wheel})$$

28 Circular thickness – wheel

$$=\frac{\text{Circ. pitch}}{2}-(\text{Adden.} - \text{pinion}-\text{adden.} - \text{wheel}) \tan \text{PA}-\frac{\text{Constant}}{\text{DP}}$$

Note: For relevant values of the constant, see Figures 7.3 and 7.4.

29 Circular thickness – pinion = Circular pitch – Circular thickness – wheel
30

Pressure angle	Gear ratios
20°	15/25 and higher
	16/20 and higher
	17/17 and higher
22$\frac{1}{2}$°	13/15 and higher
	14/14 and higher
	15/15 to 15/24
	16/16 to 16/19
25°	13/13 to 13/14

Zerol bevel gears with shafts at an acute angle (less than 90°)

Substitute the following calculations for calculations 10, 11, 26, 27, 28 and 18, and substitute the value from item 3 (below) into calculations 13 and 17.
1 Pitch cone angle – pinion

$$=\tan^{-1}\frac{\sin \text{Shaft angle}}{\dfrac{\text{No. of teeth} - \text{wheel}}{\text{No. of teeth} - \text{pinion}}+\cos \text{Shaft angle}}$$

where

$\tan^{-1}$ = the angle whose tangent is equal to . . .

2 Pitch cone angle – wheel = Shaft angle – Pitch cone angle – pinion
3 *Addendum – wheel*. To determine the addendum – wheel, the ratio for the equivalent 90° shaft bevel gear ratio must be calculated and substituted for the ratio:

$$\frac{\text{No. of teeth} - \text{wheel}}{\text{No. of teeth} - \text{pinion}}$$

when calculating the addendum – wheel for gears with shafts at less than 90°.

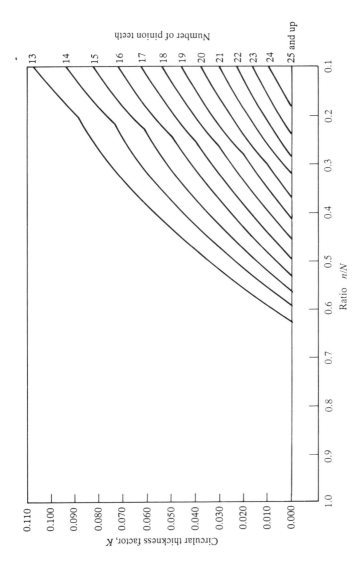

Figure 7.3 Circular thickness factor for Zerol bevel gears with a 20° pressure angle operating at 90° shaft angle

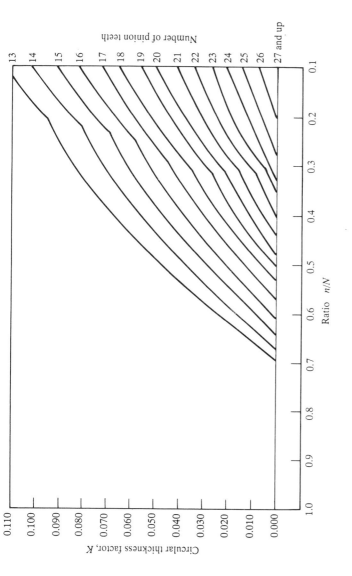

Figure 7.4 Circular thickness factor for Zerol bevel gears with 25° pressure angle operating at 90° shaft angle

Equivalent 90° Zerol gear ratio

$$= \sqrt{\frac{\text{No. of teeth } - \text{ wheel} \times \cos \text{ Pitch cone angle } - \text{ pinion}}{\text{No. of teeth } - \text{ pinion} \times \cos \text{ Pitch cone angle } - \text{ wheel}}}$$

4 Pitch apex to crown – wheel = Outer cone distance × cos Pitch cone angle – wheel – Adden. wheel × sin Pitch cone angle – wheel
5 Pitch apex to crown – pinion = Outer cone distance × cos Pitch cone angle – pinion – Adden. pinion × sin Pitch cone angle – pinion
6 *Circular thickness – wheel.* Except for high ratios, the value of K (constant) may be made equal to zero for angular gears.
7 *Pressure angle.* The pressure angle for angular gears should *not* be taken from the table on page 89, but the minimum pressure angle can be calculated as follows:

Minimum pressure angle

$$= \sin^{-1} \sqrt{\frac{1.15 \times \text{Dedendum } - \text{ pinion}}{\text{Outer cone distance} \times \tan \text{ Pitch cone angle } - \text{ pinion}}}$$

The selected pressure angle should be made equal to or greater than the minimum pressure angle, using one of the standard angles: 20°, $22\frac{1}{2}$° or 25°. If the minimum pressure angle is greater than 25°, the Gleason Gear Co. Rochester, New York, USA, should be consulted.
8 *Dedendum angle – wheel.* Substitute the following value for the change in dedendum angle, where

N_c = no. of teeth in crown gear
N_c = 2 × diametral pitch × outer cone distance
F = facewidth
P_d = diametral pitch
γ = pitch cone angle – pinion
Γ = pitch cone angle – wheel

Pressure angle	Change in dedendum angle, θ (minutes)
20°	$\theta = \dfrac{6668}{N_c} - \dfrac{300}{F} \sqrt{\dfrac{1}{N_c P_d (\tan \gamma + \tan \Gamma)}} - \dfrac{14 P_d}{N_c}$
$22\frac{1}{2}$°	$\theta = \dfrac{4868}{N_c} - \dfrac{300}{F} \sqrt{\dfrac{1}{N_c P_d (\tan \gamma + \tan \Gamma)}} - \dfrac{14 P_d}{N_c}$
25°	$\theta = \dfrac{3412}{N_c} - \dfrac{300}{F} \sqrt{\dfrac{1}{N_c P_d (\tan \gamma + \tan \Gamma)}} - \dfrac{14 P_d}{N_c}$

Zerol bevel gears with shafts at an obtuse angle (greater than 90°)

Substitute the following calculations for calculations 10, 11, 18, 26, 27 and 28, and substitute the value from item 3 (below) into calculations 13 and 17.

1 Pitch cone angle – pinion:

$$= \tan^{-1} \frac{\sin\ (180° - \text{Shaft angle})}{\dfrac{\text{No. of teeth} - \text{wheel}}{\text{No. of teeth} - \text{pinion}} - \cos\ (180° - \text{Shaft angle})}$$

where

$\tan^{-1}$ = the angle whose tangent is equal to . . .

2 Pitch cone angle – wheel = Shaft angle – Pitch cone angle – pinion

If the pitch cone angle – wheel is greater than 90°, this denotes an internal gear and the calculations should be referred to the Gleason Gear Co. to determine whether the gear can be cut.

In either case, with gears at an acute or obtuse angle the following applies:

$$\frac{\sin\ \text{Pitch cone angle} - \text{pinion}}{\sin\ \text{Pitch cone angle} - \text{wheel}} = \frac{\text{No. of teeth} - \text{pinion}}{\text{No. of teeth} - \text{wheel}}$$

3 *Addendum – wheel.* To determine the addendum – wheel, the ratio for the equivalent 90° shaft angle bevel gear ratio must be calculated and substituted for the ratio

$$\frac{\text{No. of teeth} - \text{wheel}}{\text{No. of teeth} - \text{pinion}}$$

when calculating the addendum – wheel for gears with shafts at more than 90°.

Equivalent 90° bevel gear ratio

$$= \sqrt{\frac{\text{No. of teeth} - \text{wheel} \times \cos\ \text{Pitch cone angle} - \text{pinion}}{\text{No. of teeth} - \text{pinion} \times \cos\ \text{Pitch cone angle} - \text{wheel}}}$$

4 Pitch apex to crown – wheel = Outer cone distance × cos Pitch cone angle – wheel – Adden. – wheel × sin Pitch cone angle – wheel

5 Pitch apex to crown – pinion = Outer cone distance × cos Pitch cone angle – pinion – Adden. – pinion × sin pitch cone angle – pinion

6 *Circular thickness – wheel.* Except for high ratios, the value of *K* (constant) may be made equal to zero for angular gears.

7 *Pressure angle.* The pressure angle for angular gears should *not* be taken from the table on page 89, but the minimum pressure angle can be calculated as follows:

Minimum pressure angle

$$= \sin^{-1} = \sqrt{\frac{1.15 \times \text{Dedendum} - \text{pinion}}{\text{Outer cone distance} \times \tan\ \text{Pitch cone angle} - \text{pinion}}}$$

where

$$\sin^{-1} = \text{the angle whose sine is equal to} \dots$$

The selected pressure angle should be made equal to or greater than the minimum pressure angle, using one of the standard angles: $20°$, $22\frac{1}{2}°$ or $25°$. If the minimum pressure angle is greater than $25°$, the Gleason Gear Co. should be consulted.

8 *Dedendum angle – wheel.* Substitute the value from the table below for the change in dedendum angle (in place of the value given in the table on page 88), where

$N_c = $ no. of teeth in crown gear
$N_c = 2 \times \text{diametral pitch} \times \text{outer cone distance}$
$F = $ facewidth
$P_d = $ diametral pitch
$\gamma = $ pitch cone angle – pinion
$\Gamma = $ pitch cone angle – wheel

Pressure angle	Change in dedendum angle, θ (minutes)
$20°$	$\theta = \dfrac{6668}{N_c} - \dfrac{300}{F}\sqrt{\dfrac{1}{N_c P_d(\tan \gamma + \tan \Gamma)}} - \dfrac{14P_d}{N_c}$
$22\frac{1}{2}°$	$\theta = \dfrac{4868}{N_c} - \dfrac{300}{F}\sqrt{\dfrac{1}{N_c P_d(\tan \gamma + \tan \Gamma)}} - \dfrac{14P_d}{N_c}$
$25°$	$\theta = \dfrac{3412}{N_c} - \dfrac{300}{F}\sqrt{\dfrac{1}{N_c P_d(\tan \gamma + \tan \Gamma)}} - \dfrac{14P_d}{N_c}$

Zerol bevel gears – recommended backlash

The backlash figures given are for gears assembled ready to run, and the backlash should be shared equally between pinion and crown wheel, i.e. 8 DP gears, 0.002–0.003 in backlash, on both pinion and crown wheel.

Diametral pitch	Backlash (in)
1.00–1.25	0.020–0.030
1.25–1.50	0.018–0.026
1.50–1.75	0.016–0.022
1.75–2.00	0.014–0.018
2.00–2.50	0.012–0.016
2.50–3.00	0.010–0.013

3.00–3.50	0.008–0.011
3.50–4.00	0.007–0.009
4.00–5.00	0.006–0.008
5.00–6.00	0.005–0.007
6.00–8.00	0.004–0.006
8.00–10.00	0.003–0.005
10.00–16.00	0.002–0.004
16.00–20.00	0.001–0.003
20.00–50.00	0.000–0.002
50.00–64.00	0.000–0.001

Metric module	Backlash (mm)
25–20	0.55–0.75
20–16	0.45–0.65
16–12	0.40–0.55
12–10	0.35–0.45
10–8	0.30–0.40
8–6	0.25–0.35
6–5	0.20–0.28
5–4	0.18–0.23
4–3	0.13–0.18
3–2.50	0.076–0.13
2.50–2.00	0.050–0.100
2.00–1.50	0.025–0.075
1.50–1.25	0.000–0.050
1.25–1.00	0.000–0.025

Note: Backlash on bevel gears should always be measured at the outer cone at the tightest part of mesh.

8
Hypoid bevel gears

Hypoid gears are a cross between spiral bevel gears and worm gears. The axes of a pair of hypoid bevel gears are non-intersecting, the distance between the 'axes' being referred to as the offset.

This offset brings within reach higher ratios of reduction than are normally practicable with bevel gears, as the pitch diameters of hypoid gears are not in a fixed proportion to the numbers of teeth, and it is therefore possible to use a relatively small number of teeth on the pinion, which means that these teeth become stronger than other relative bevel gear teeth.

The spiral angle of the hypoid pinion is usually made either 45° or 50°, but the spiral angle of the wheel is not the same as that of the pinion.

Hypoid bevel gears do not in practice conform strictly to a geometrical prototype in which the engaging members are equivalent to pitch figures such as cylinders or cones. This is because the theoretical basis of engagement is that between hyperboloids of revolution, i.e. figures of the kind generated by rotation around a cylinder of a straight line or 'generatrix' crossing the axis of the cylinder at some angle. Two hyperboloids tangent to each other are in contact at their waists and along a line at which their respective generatrices are in common, the sum of the radii at the waists being the offset between the shaft axes. Since the motions that would be involved in cutting gears to comply with this model are prohibitively complex, it is usual for one member of the pair to be cut in some simple manner and the other to be generated as to be conjugate with it.

Hypoid gears have curved oblique teeth on which contact begins gradually and continues smoothly from one end of the tooth to the other. However, with the gear and pinion axes not being in the same plane, there is lengthwise sliding between the teeth. The hypoid pinion and wheel both have unequal pressure angles on the two sides of the teeth, which ensures that there are equal arcs of action in either direction of rotation, although this means the teeth have an unsymmetrical appearance in their profiles. In the usual hypoid design, the pinion offset is in such a direction that the pinion spiral angle will be larger than the spiral angle of the wheel.

The hypoid gear was introduced in 1925 by the Gleason Gear Co. and is now in widespread use in both industrial and automotive applications.

A very important feature in the design of hypoid gears is the offset of the pinion

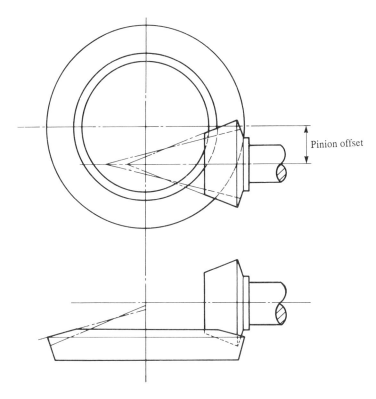

Figure 8.1 Hypoid gear and pinion. Pinion offsets normally do not exceed 40% of the gear cone distance (approximately 20% of the gear pitch diameter), although a few existing applications do exceed this value

axis from the wheel centre line. The offset is designated as being above or below the wheel centre line, as shown in Figures 8.1 and 8.2.

The customary method of deciding whether the offset is above or below centre is with the pinion on the right-hand side of the wheel when looking at the face of the wheel.

The hand of spiral on hypoid gears is denoted by the direction in which the teeth curve, i.e. left-hand teeth incline away from the axis in a counter-clockwise direction when looking at the face of the gear, and right-hand teeth incline away from the axis in a clockwise direction. The hand of spiral of one member of a pair of gears is always opposite to that of its mate.

It is customary practice using the hand of spiral of the pinion to identify the hand of the pair of gears, i.e. a left-hand pair is one with a left-hand spiral on the pinion and a right-hand spiral on the wheel.

The hand of spiral has no effect on the smoothness and noise made by the pair of gears during operation. It also has no effect on the gear efficiency, but the hand of spiral does affect the thrust loading on the bearings. The direction of rotation of a pair of hypoid gears is decided by looking at the large end or back of the pinion, and it is important to remember that a left-hand spiral pinion driving

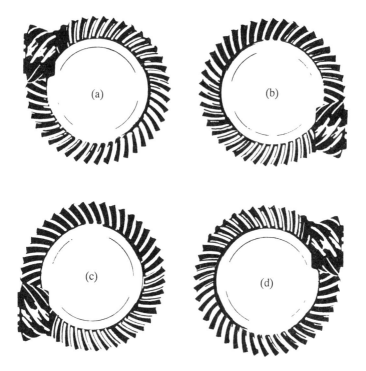

Figure 8.2   Offset relationship of hypoid gears. Both pinions shown in (a) and (b) are referred to as having offset 'below centre' while those in (c) and (d) have offset 'above centre'. In determining direction of offset, it is customary to look at the face of the gear, with pinion at the right

clockwise tends to move axially away from the cone centre, whereas a right-hand spiral pinion would tend to move toward the cone centre due to the oblique direction of the curved teeth of the gears.

If excessive end-float is allowed in the pinion shaft due to faulty assembly or bearing failure, the movement of a right-hand spiral pinion driving clockwise will tend to take up backlash under load, creating a wedging effect between the teeth of the pinion and wheel, whereas a left-hand spiral pinion operating in the same application would tend to increase the backlash between the pinion and wheel.

When the ratio, pressure angle and spiral angle allow, the hand of spiral should be selected to give an axial thrust which tends to move both pinion and wheel out of mesh, otherwise the hand of spiral should be selected to give an axial thrust that tends to move the pinion out of mesh. Often, however, the mounting conditions will dictate the hand of spiral. In a reversible drive there is, of course, no choice unless the pair performs a heavier duty in one direction for a greater part of the time.

In a pair of hypoid gears when the pinion is below centre and to the right when facing the front of the wheel, the hand of spiral of the pinion should always be left hand; and with the pinion above centre and to the right of the wheel, the hand of spiral of the pinion should always be right hand.

The spiral angle or angle of lengthwise inclination of the teeth should be sufficient to give a face contact ratio of at least 1.25, and for maximum smoothness in operation the face contact ratio should be between 1.50 and 2.00.

The design chart in Figure 8.3 may be used to assist in the selection of the spiral angle. The series of curves given on the chart cover face contact ratios between 0.5 and 3.0. The spiral angle is plotted in terms of the product of the facewidth and the diametral pitch.

The first section of this chapter will deal with hypoid bevel gear calculations for diametral pitch gears.

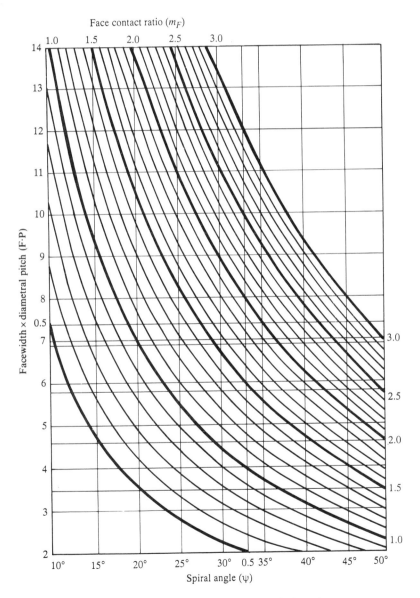

Figure 8.3   Design chart for the selection of the spiral angle

Hypoid bevel gears – diametral pitch

Note: Numbers which are emboldened in the following calculations refer to calculation numbers.

Gears with duplex tooth taper

1 No. of teeth – pinion
2 No. of teeth – wheel
3 **1/2**
4 *Gear facewidth.* Recommended facewidth = 0.3 × Cone distance or 10/DP whichever is smaller.
5 *Hypoid offset.* Passenger cars, light delivery vans and general industrial applications: offset should not exceed 50% of cone distance.

   Trucks, buses, tractors and rail traction: offset should not exceed 20% of cone distance.
6 Wheel pitch circle diameter

$$= \frac{\mathbf{2}}{\text{Diametral pitch}}$$

7 *Cutter radius.* Recommended values:

Gear or wheel PC dia. (in)	Cutter rad. (in)
3 to $5\frac{1}{4}$	$1\frac{3}{4}$
$3\frac{7}{8}$ to $6\frac{3}{4}$	$2\frac{1}{4}$
$4\frac{1}{4}$ to $7\frac{1}{2}$	$2\frac{1}{2}$
$5\frac{1}{8}$ to 9	3
$5\frac{3}{8}$ to $9\frac{3}{8}$	$3\frac{1}{8}$
$6\frac{1}{2}$ to $11\frac{1}{4}$	$3\frac{3}{4}$
$7\frac{3}{4}$ to $13\frac{1}{2}$	$4\frac{1}{2}$
$10\frac{1}{4}$ to 18	6
$13\frac{3}{4}$ to 24	8
18 to $31\frac{1}{2}$	$10\frac{1}{2}$

8 Desired mean pinion spiral angle (degrees)

$$= 25 + 5\sqrt{\frac{\mathbf{2}}{\mathbf{1}}} + 90\frac{\mathbf{5}}{\mathbf{6}}$$

The calculated value for the desired mean pinion spiral angle may be rounded,

but in order to maintain a satisfactory strength value should not be more than 5°
of the calculated value.

9   Tangent – mean pinion spiral angle = tan **8**

10   Cotan $\Gamma_1 = 1.2 \times$ **3**

11   Sin Γ_1

12   Mean gear radius

$$= \frac{\textbf{6} - \textbf{4}\ \textbf{11}}{2.00}$$

13   Sin ε_1^1

$$= \frac{\textbf{5} \times \textbf{11}}{\textbf{12}}$$

14   Cos ε_1^1

15   **14** $+ (\textbf{9} \times \textbf{13})$

16   **3** $\times$ **12**

17   Mean pinion radius $= \textbf{15} \times \textbf{16}$

18   Tooth taper factor:

pinion with less than 12 teeth $= 0.02 \times$ **1** $+ 1.06$
pinion with 12 teeth or more $= 1.30$

19 $\dfrac{\textbf{12}}{\textbf{10}} + \textbf{17}$

20   Tan $\eta = $ **5/19**

21 $\sqrt{1.0 + \textbf{20}^2}$

22   Sin $\eta = $ **20/21**

23   Offset angle in plane of rotation – pinion $= \eta$

24   Sin ε_2

$$= \frac{\textbf{5} - [\textbf{17}\ \textbf{22}]}{\textbf{12}}$$

25   Tan ε_2

26   Tan $\gamma_2 = $ **22/25**

27   Cos γ_2

28   Sin $\varepsilon_2^1 = $ **24/27**

29   Cos ε_2^1

30   Tan ψ_{P2}

$$= \frac{\textbf{15} - \textbf{29}}{\textbf{28}}$$

31   **28**$[\textbf{9} - \textbf{30}]$

32   **3** $\times$ **31**

33   Sin $\varepsilon_1 = $ **24** $- [\textbf{22} \times \textbf{32}]$

34   Tan ε_1

35   Tan $\gamma_1 = $ **22/34**

36 γ_1

37 Cos γ_1

38 Sin $\varepsilon_1' = \mathbf{33/37}$

39 ε_1'

40 Cos ε_1'

41 Tan ψ_{P1}

$$= \frac{\mathbf{15 + 31 - 40}}{\mathbf{38}}$$

42 Pinion spiral angle $= \psi_{P1}$

Should be close to desired mean pinion spiral angle – item 8.

43 Cos ψ_{P1}

44 Gear spiral angle:

$$\psi_{G1} = \mathbf{42 - 39}$$

45 Cos ψ_{G1}

46 Tan ψ_{G1}

47 Cotan $\Gamma_I = \mathbf{20/33}$

48 Gear pitch angle $= \Gamma_I$

49 Sin Γ_I

50 Cos Γ_I

51 $\dfrac{\mathbf{17 + [12 \times 32]}}{\mathbf{37}}$

52 $\mathbf{12/50}$

53 $\mathbf{51 + 52}$

54 $\dfrac{\mathbf{12 \times 45}}{\mathbf{49}}$

55 $\dfrac{\mathbf{43 \times 51}}{\mathbf{35}}$

56 $-$ Tan ϕ_{01}

$$= \frac{\mathbf{[41 \times 55] - [46 \times 54]}}{\mathbf{53}}$$

57 Pitch limit pressure angle $= -\phi_{01}$

58 Cos ϕ_{01}

59 $\dfrac{\mathbf{41 \times 56}}{\mathbf{51}}$

60 $\dfrac{\mathbf{46 \times 56}}{\mathbf{52}}$

61 $\mathbf{54 \times 55}$

62 $\dfrac{54-55}{61}$

63 $59+60+62$

64 $\dfrac{41-46}{63}$

65 Radius of curvature corresponding to the pitch angles γ_1 (item 36) and Γ_I (item 48)$=\mathbf{64/58}$

The radius of curvature should be within 1% of the cutter radius (item 7) – if not, proceed as follows:

(a) If item 65 is smaller than item 7, reduce $\tan \eta$ (item 20) and recalculate to item 65.
(b) If item 65 is larger than item 7, increase $\tan \eta$ (item 20) and recalculate to item 65.

If this second calculation is not within 1% of item 7, calculate $\tan \eta$ (item 20) using the following formula:

$$\tan \eta_3 = \frac{20_2 - 20_1}{66_2 - 66_1}[1 - 66_1] + 20_1$$

where subscript 1 refers to first calculation
2 refers to second calculation
3 refers to third calculation

66 $7/65$
67A $= 3 \times 50$
67B $= 1.0 - 3$
68A $= 5/34 - 17\ 35$
68B $= 35\ 37$
69 $37 + 40\ 67A$
70 Mean gear point to crossing point $= 49\ 51$
71 Distance from gear pitch apex to crossing point $= [12 \times 47] - 70$

+ indicates that pitch apex is beyond crossing point
− indicates that pitch apex is between gear and crossing point

72 Gear mean cone distance in the pitch plane $= \mathbf{12/49}$
73 Gear outer cone distance in the pitch plane

$$= \frac{0.5 \times 6}{49}$$

74 $73 - 72$
75 Gear mean working depth

$$= \frac{\text{Constant} \times 12 \times 45}{2}$$

where constant =

No. of teeth – pinion	Automotive constant	General
6	–	3.5
7	–	3.6
8	3.8	3.7
9	3.9	3.8
10	4.0	3.9
11	4.1	4.0
12 and over	4.2	4.0

76 $\dfrac{\mathbf{12 \times 46}}{\mathbf{7}}$

77 $\dfrac{\mathbf{49}}{\mathbf{45}} - \mathbf{76}$

78   Sum of pressure angles on the 2 sides of the teeth, ϕ_i

Note:
ϕ_i industrial drives:
      8 or more teeth (pinion) $= 42° 30'$
      less than 8 teeth (pinion) $= 45°$
ϕ_i trucks, tractors and buses $= 45°$
ϕ_i passenger cars $= 38°$

79   Sin ϕ_i
80 $\mathbf{78} \times 0.5$
81   Cos $\mathbf{78} \times 0.5$
82   Tan $\mathbf{78} \times 0.5$
83 $\mathbf{77/82}$
84   Sum of dedendum angles, in minutes, for duplex tooth taper

$$= \frac{10\,560 \times \mathbf{83}}{\mathbf{2}}$$

85   *Gear addendum factor.* For generated and formate ratios with pinions with 21 teeth or less (covers automotive field):

No. of teeth – pinion	Gear addendum factor
6	0.110
7	0.130
8	0.150
9 to 20	0.170

For generated hypoids with pinions with more than 20 teeth:

Gear ratio **1/2**	Gear addendum factor
1.0	0.500
0.9	0.450
0.8	0.425
0.7	0.400
0.6	0.375
0.5	0.350
0.4	0.325
0.3	0.300

86 1.150 − **85**

87 Gear addendum at mean cone distance = **75** × **85**

88 Gear dedendum at mean cone distance = [**75** × **86**] + 0.002 in

89 Gear addendum angle = **84** × **85**

See also item S89, page 107.

90 Sin **89**

91 Gear dedendum angle = **84** − **89**

See also item S91, page 107.

92 Sin **91**

93 Gear addendum at outside cone distance = **87** + [**74** × **90**]

94 Gear dedendum at outside cone distance = **88** + [**74** × **92**]

95 Clearance: [0.150 × **75**] + 0.002 in

96 Gear whole depth at outside cone distance = **93** + **94**

97 Gear working depth at outside cone distance = **96** − **95**

98 Gear face angle = **48** + **89**

99 Sin **98**

100 Cos **98**

101 Gear root angle = **48** − **91**

102 Sin **101**

103 Cos **101**

104 Cotan **101**

105 Gear outside diameter

$$= \frac{[\textbf{93} \times \textbf{50}]}{0.5} + \textbf{6}$$

106 70 + [**74** × **50**]

107 Gear crown to crossing point = **106** − [**93** × **49**]

108 $\dfrac{[\textbf{72} \times \textbf{90}] - \textbf{87}}{\textbf{99}}$

109 $\dfrac{[\textbf{72} \times \textbf{92}] - \textbf{88}}{\textbf{102}}$

110   Distance from gear face apex to crossing point $= \mathbf{71 - 108}$
111   Distance from gear root apex to crossing point $= \mathbf{71 + 109}$
112    $\mathbf{12 + [70 \times 104]}$
113   Sin $\varepsilon = \mathbf{5/112}$
114   Cos $\varepsilon = \sqrt{1 - \mathbf{113^2}}$
115   Tan $\varepsilon = \mathbf{113/114}$
116   Sin $\gamma_0 = \mathbf{103 \times 114}$
117   Pinion face angle $= \gamma_0$
118   Cos **117**
119   Tan **117**

120    $\dfrac{\mathbf{[102 \times 111] + 95}}{\mathbf{103}}$

121   Face apex beyond crossing point – pinion

$$= \frac{\mathbf{[5 \times 113] - 120}}{\mathbf{114}}$$

122   Tan $\lambda^1 = \dfrac{\mathbf{38 \times 67A}}{\mathbf{69}}$

123A λ^1
123B   Cos λ^1
124A $\Delta\lambda^1 = \mathbf{39 - 123A}$
124B   Cos $\Delta\lambda^1$
125A $\alpha_P = \mathbf{117 - 36}$
125B   Cos α_P
126A $\mathbf{[113. \, 67B - 68B]}$
126B $\mathbf{-[113. \, 67B - 68B]}$
127   **123B/124B**
128   **63A + 87. 68B**
129   **118/125B**
130   **74. 127**
131   Pinion crown to crossing point $= \mathbf{128 + 130. \, 129 + 75. \, 126A}$
132   **4. 127 − 130**
133   Pinion front to crossing point $= \mathbf{128 - 132. \, 129 + 75. \, 126B}$
134   **121 + 131**
135   Pinion outside diameter

$$= \frac{\mathbf{119 \times 134}}{0.5}$$

136    $\dfrac{\mathbf{[70 \times 100]}}{\mathbf{99}} \mathbf{+ 12}$

137   Sin $\varepsilon_0 = \mathbf{5/136}$
138   ε_0
139   Cos ε_0

140 $\dfrac{[99 \times 110] + 95}{100}$

141 Pinion root apex to crossing point

$$= \dfrac{[5 \times 137] - 140}{139}$$

+ indicates that pinion root apex lies beyond crossing point
− indicates that pinion root apex is before crossing point

142 Sin $\gamma_R = 100 \times 139$
143 Pinion root angle $= \gamma_R$
144 Cos γ_R
145 Tan γ_R
146 Minimum backlash
147 Maximum backlash − recommended backlash:

Backlash figures shown are for a gear pair and should be shared equally between pinion and wheel.

DP	Backlash (in)
1	0.020–0.030
2	0.012–0.016
3	0.008–0.011
4	0.006–0.008
6	0.004–0.006
10	0.002–0.004
20 and finer	0.001–0.003

148 $90 + 92$
149 $96 - [4 \times 148]$
150 Gear inside cone distance $= 73 - 4$

Note: In order to assure satisfactory tooth taper, the following procedure should be used to determine whether duplex tooth taper or tilted root line tooth taper is preferable:

Calculate items 89 and 91 for standard tooth taper as follows:

S89 Gear addendum angle

$$= \dfrac{3438 \; \mathbf{87}}{72}$$

S91 Gear dedendum angle

$$= \dfrac{3438 \; \mathbf{88}}{72}$$

A1 Sum of dedendum angles − standard taper $= \mathbf{S89} + \mathbf{S91}$

A2   Angle taper root

$$=\frac{84}{1}-18$$

A3   When angle taper root is positive:
Sum of dedendum angles – tilted root line tooth taper = **18 A1**
When angle taper root is negative:
Sum of dedendum angles – tilted root line tooth taper = **84**

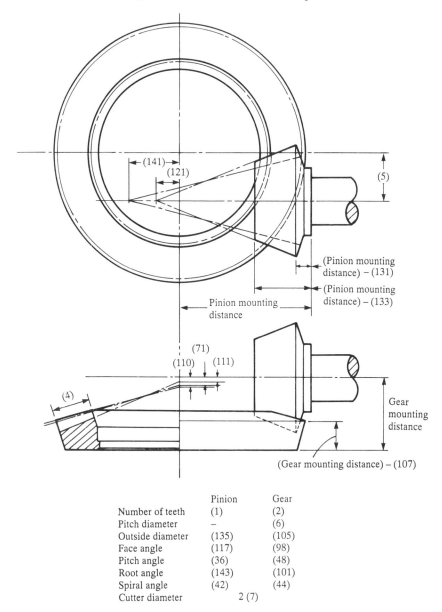

	Pinion	Gear
Number of teeth	(1)	(2)
Pitch diameter	–	(6)
Outside diameter	(135)	(105)
Face angle	(117)	(98)
Pitch angle	(36)	(48)
Root angle	(143)	(101)
Spiral angle	(42)	(44)
Cutter diameter	2 (7)	

Figure 8.4   Hypoid gear layout

Table 8.1 Hypoid gear data

		Pinion	Gear
1	Gear DP		
2	Pinion offset:		
	above centre		**5**
	below centre		
3	Gear facewidth		**4**
4	Hand of spiral – pinion		
5	Average pressure angle		**80**
6	Direction of rotation – pinion		
7	Cutter diameter		2×7
8	No. of teeth	**1**	**2**
9	Driver	–	–
10	Pitch circle diameter	–	**6**
11	Addendum	–	**93**
12	Dedendum	–	**94**
13	Working depth	–	**97**
14	Whole depth	–	**96**
15	Pitch apex before/beyond crossing point	–	**71**
16	Face apex before/beyond crossing point	**121**	**110**
17	Crown to crossing point	**131**	**107**
18	Front crown to crossing point	**133**	–
19	Outside diameter	**135**	**105**
20	Pitch angle	**36**	**48**
21	Face angle	**117**	**98**
22	Root angle	**143**	**101**
23	Root apex before/beyond crossing point	**141**	**111**
24	Spiral angle	**42**	**44**
25	Offset angle in plane of rotation	**23**	**33**
26	Means radius	**17**	**12**

A4 Gear addendum angle – tilted root line tooth taper = **85 A3**
A5 Gear dedendum angle – tilted root line tooth taper = **A3 − A4**

Notes:
(a) Items A4 and A5 should be used to replace the values calculated in the duplex tooth taper calculations for items 89 and 91, respectively. Tilted root line tooth taper gears represent a compromise between duplex tooth taper gears, as calculated on pages 100–107 inclusive, and standard tooth taper gears when the former would result in an excessive amount of depthwise taper and the latter an excessive amount of thickness taper.
(b) All common ratios operating at 90° shaft angles may be designed by the method given, provided that there are no fewer than 6 teeth on the pinion or less than 40 teeth on the gear pair.
(c) Table 8.1 gives the dimensions which should be given on the hypoid gear drawings with their relevant reference numbers.
(d) The hypoid gear layout in Figure 8.4 shows the reference numbers for the required dimensions.

Hypoid bevel gears – metric module

The calculation of metric module hypoid bevel gears is similar to the calculations for diametral pitch hypoid bevel gears, the exceptions being as follows:

(a) All dimensions will be in millimetres
(b) The calculations which follow will replace the same number calculation in the preceding diametral pitch gear calculations

4   *Gear facewidth*. Recommended facewidth is 0.3 × Cone distance or 10 × Module whichever is smaller.

6   Wheel pitch circle diameter = **2** × Module

7   Cutter radius – recommended values:

Gear or wheel PC dia. (mm)	Cutter rad. (mm)
75–135	44.450
100–170	57.150
110–190	63.500
130–230	76.200
135–240	79.375
165–285	95.250
195–345	114.300
260–455	152.400
350–610	203.200
455–800	266.700

88   Gear dedendum at mean cone distance = $[75 \times 86] + 0.05$ mm

95   Clearance:

$$[0.150 \times 75] + 0.05 \text{ mm}$$

146   Minimum backlash

147   Maximum backlash – recommended backlash

Module	Backlash (mm)
25.4	0.50–0.75
12.7	0.30–0.40
8.47	0.20–0.28
6.35	0.15–0.20
4.23	0.10–0.15
2.54	0.05–0.10

In the case of the basic working depth for hypoid bevel gears, the following calculations apply:

(a) Diametral pitch gears:

Basic working depth

$$= \frac{2.000}{\text{Gear mean normal diametral pitch}}$$

(b) Metric module gears:

Basic working depth $= 2.000 \times$ Gear mean normal module

9

Worm gears

Worms gears are used to transmit motion between shafts at right angles which do not lie in a common plane.

They can be and are occasionally used to connect shafts at other angles, but these unusual conditions are not considered in this chapter.

A pair of worm gears consists of a cylindrical worm having helical teeth or threads similar to a helical gear, meshing with a wheel having a concave or hollow face.

Although worm gears serve the same purpose as helical gears with shafts at 90° angle (crossed helicals), they differ from them in that line tooth contact is obtained, compared with point contact, and this enables them to carry much greater loads.

Worm gears can therefore be used for the transmission of power, and the reduction ratio is equal to the number of teeth on the wheel divided by the number of threads or starts on the worm, and since the worm may have a single thread a large reduction ratio can be obtained with a single pair of gears.

Other conditions being equal, however, efficiency falls with the increase in ratio, so that high ratios from a single pair of gears can only be obtained at the expense of efficiency. However, due to modern improvements in tooth design and surface finish, combined with the use of selected materials for ratios below 50:1, the efficiency rarely falls below 80%.

Where fairly large reduction ratios are required, worm gears offer a very compact form of gear drive and the tooth action which is mainly sliding leads to smooth and silent action.

The standard form of worm thread is involute in a section at right angles to the axis and is such as would be generated by a basic rack surface having a straight-sided normal section. An alternative form of thread is a trapezoidal worm which is straight-sided in the normal section, as in a screw thread.

The fillet radius for the worm threads and the wheel teeth shall not be less than the clearance.

Should any process not corresponding to this method of generation be employed, some latitude in the profile of the worm threads is permissible, provided that the correct conjugate action between the worm and wheel is maintained.

In the calculation of the worm, careful distinction must be made between the terms 'pitch' and 'lead'.

The term 'lead' is defined as the distance which any one thread advances in one revolution of the worm. The term 'pitch' – more correctly called the 'linear pitch' – is the distance between the centres of two adjacent threads.

The lead and pitch are equal for a single-threaded worm; for a double-threaded worm the lead is twice the linear pitch, and for a triple-threaded worm the lead is three times the linear pitch.

Trapezoidal worm gear calculations – diametral pitch

1 Lead = No. of starts – worm × Axial pitch – worm
2 Linear pitch

$$= \frac{\text{Lead}}{\text{No. of threads – worm}}$$

3 Addendum – worm = 0.3183 × Linear pitch
4 Pitch diameter – worm = (2 × Centres) – PC dia. – wheel
5 Pitch diameter – wheel

$$= \frac{\text{No. of teeth – wheel × Linear pitch}}{\pi}$$

6 Centres

$$= \frac{\text{PC dia. – worm + PC dia. – wheel}}{2}$$

7 Whole depth – worm = 0.6866 × Linear pitch
8 Outside diameter – worm = PC dia. – worm + (2 × Addendum – worm)
9 Bottom (root) diameter – worm = Outs. dia. – worm – (2 × Whole depth – worm)
10 Lead (helix) angle – worm

$$= \text{Cotan}^{-1} \frac{\text{PC dia. – worm} + \pi}{\text{Lead}}$$

$$= \tan^{-1} \frac{\text{Lead}}{\text{PC dia. – worm} \times \pi}$$

11 Width of thread tool at end = Linear pitch × 0.31
12 Throat diameter – wormwheel = PC dia. – wormwheel + (2 × Addendum)
13 Wormwheel throat radius

$$= \frac{\text{Outs. dia. – worm}}{2} - (2 \times \text{Addendum})$$

14 Diameter wormwheel to sharp corners

$$= 2(\text{Radius – wormwheel throat})$$

$$- \left[\text{radius – wormwheel throat} \times \cos \frac{\text{Face angle – wormwheel}}{2} \right] + \text{Throat dia. – wormwheel}$$

where face angle – wormwheel is the angle from the centre of the radius of curvature of throat, inclusive to the outer edge of the wormwheel.

15   Minimum length of worm for complete action

$$= \sqrt{8 \times PC \ dia. - wormwheel \times Addendum}$$

16   Dedendum – worm = Linear pitch × 0.3683

17   Minimum facewidth – worm

$$= \sqrt{Outs. \ dia. - wormwheel^2 - PC \ dia. - wormwheel^2}$$

18   Maximum facewidth – wormwheel

$$= \frac{\pi \times Outs. \ dia. - worm \times PC \ dia. - worm \times \tan \ Axial \ PA}{Lead}$$

19   Axial pressure angle

$$= \tan^{-1}\left(\frac{\tan \ Normal \ press. \ angle}{\cos \ Lead \ angle}\right)$$

where normal PA = 20°.

Involute helicoid worm gears

Involute helicoid worm gears can be proportioned in the same way as trapezoidal worm gears, but Dr H.E. Merritt evolved an alternative method of calculating them. This method, known as the $t/q/m$ system, was adopted in the British Standard Specification No. 721.

This system simplifies calculations and ensures good proportions and tooth forms over the whole range of designs. It is based on the following:

(a) The pitch is defined by the axial module of the worm threads: Axial module $(m) = 0.3183 \times$ Axial pitch
(b) A diameter quotient is introduced which is the ratio of the nominal pitch diameter of the worm to the module:

$$Diameter \ quotient \ (q) = \frac{Worm \ pitch \ dia.}{Module}$$

and

$$Worm \ pitch \ dia. = Diameter \ quotient \times Module$$

The diameter quotient is usually made a whole number and the worm pitch diameter is then the same as that of a spur gear of the same module pitch having 'q' number of teeth.

The designation '$t/q/m$', together with the handing, completely defines the worm. For example:

'3/9/0.2' indicates a worm as follows:

Starts $t = 3$
Pitch dia. $d = 9 \times 0.2 = 1.8$ in
Axial pitch $m = 0.2\pi = 0.6283$

A pair of worm gears can be briefly described by the addition of the number of teeth 'T' on the wheel, as follows: $t/T/q/m$.

Involute helicoid worm gear calculations

Diametral pitch

1 Axial module $= 0.3183 \times$ Axial pitch
2 Normal pressure angle $= 20°$
3 Diameter quotient – worm

$$= \frac{\text{Worm pitch dia.}}{\text{Module}}$$

4 Revolutions per minute:

Worm $=$
Wheel $=$

5 No. of starts – worm
6 No. of teeth – wheel
7 Ratio

$$= \frac{\text{No. of teeth} - \text{wheel}}{\text{No. of starts} - \text{worm}}$$
$$= \frac{\text{Rev/min} - \text{worm}}{\text{Rev/min} - \text{wheel}}$$

8 Axial pitch – worm and circular pitch – wheel $= \pi \times$ Axial module

Trapezoidal worm gears – see Figure 9.1.

Suffixes:

$d =$ Pitch diameter – worm
$D =$ Pitch diameter – wheel
$C =$ Centres
$p_a =$ Axial pitch – worm
$p =$ Circular pitch – wheel
$L =$ Lead
$\lambda =$ Lead angle
$a =$ Addendum – worm
$A =$ Addendum – wheel
$b =$ Dedendum – worm
$B =$ Dedendum – wheel
$D_t =$ Throat diameter – wheel

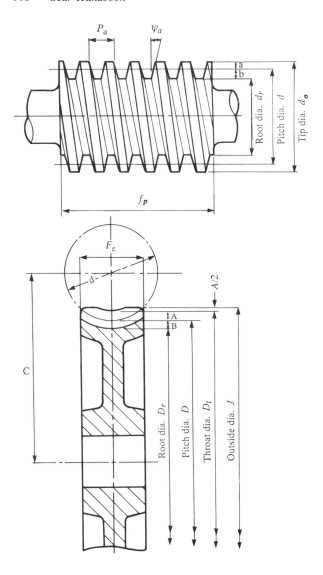

Figure 9.1   Detail dimensions – trapezoidal worm gears

d_o = Outside diameter – worm
J = Outside diameter – wheel
d_r = Root diameter – worm
D_r = Root diameter – wheel
ψ_a = Axial pressure angle
f_p = Minimum facewidth –worm
F_e = Maximum facewidth – wheel

9   PC diameter – worm = Axial module × Diameter quotient

10 PC diameter – wheel = No. of teeth – wheel × Axial module

11 Centres = 0.500 × Axial module (No. of teeth – wheel + Dia. quotient – worm)

12 Lead = π × Axial module × No. of starts – worm

13 Lead angle

$$= \tan^{-1}\left(\frac{\text{No. of starts} - \text{worm}}{\text{Diameter quotient} - \text{worm}}\right)$$

14 Normal module

$$= \frac{\text{Axial module} \times \text{Dia. quotient} - \text{worm}}{\sqrt{\text{No. of starts} - \text{worm}^2 + \text{Dia. quotient} - \text{worm}^2}}$$

15 Axial pressure angle

$$= \tan^{-1}\left(\frac{\tan\ \text{Normal PA}\sqrt{\text{No. of starts} - \text{worm}^2 + \text{Dia. quotient} - \text{worm}^2}}{\text{Diameter quotient} - \text{worm}}\right)$$

Involute helicoid worm gears – see Figures 9.2 and 9.3.

Suffixes:

m = Module
ψ_n = Normal pressure angle
q = Diameter quotient – worm
d = Pitch diameter – worm
D = Pitch diameter – wheel
C = Centres
L = Lead
λ = Lead angle
p_a = Axial pitch – worm
p = Circular pitch – wheel
m_n = Normal module
ψ_a = Axial pressure angle
ψ_t = Transverse pressure angle
d_o = Base diameter
λ_o = Base lead angle
a = Addendum – worm
A = Addendum – wheel
b = Dedendum – worm
B = Dedendum – wheel
c = Clearance
d_a = Tip diameter – worm
J = Outside diameter – wheel
D_t = Throat diameter – wheel
d_r = Root diameter – worm
D_r = Root diameter – wheel
f_p = Minimum facewidth – worm
F_e = Maximum facewidth – wheel

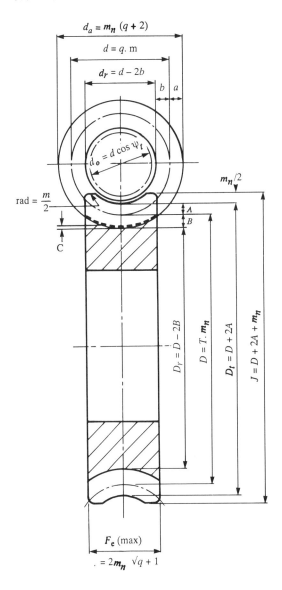

Figure 9.2   Dimensions of involute helicoid worm gears 't/q/m' system

$$m = \text{Axial module} = \frac{\text{Axial pitch}}{\pi}$$

16   Transverse pressure angle

$$= \tan^{-1}\left(\frac{\tan \text{ Normal PA}\sqrt{\text{No. of starts} - \text{worm}^2 + \text{Dia. quotient} - \text{worm}^2}}{\text{No. of starts} - \text{worm}}\right)$$

17   Base diameter = PC diameter – worm × cos Transverse PA

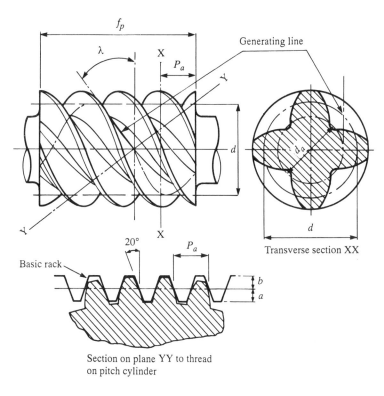

Figure 9.3 Involute helicoid worm 4 start, showing basic dimensions

18 Base lead angle

$$= \cos^{-1}\left(\frac{\text{Dia. quotient } - \text{ worm} \times \cos \text{ Normal PA}}{\sqrt{\text{No. of starts } - \text{ worm}^2 + \text{Dia. quotient } - \text{ worm}^2}}\right)$$

19 Addendum – worm = Module
20 Dedendum – worm = Module (2.20 × cos Lead angle – 1)
21 Addendum – wheel = Module (2.00 × cos Lead angle – 1)
22 Dedendum – wheel = Module(1 + 0.20 cos Lead angle)
23 Clearance = 0.2 Module × cos Lead angle
24 Outside (tip) diameter – worm

$$= \text{Module } (2.00 + \text{Dia. quotient } - \text{ worm})$$

or

$$= \text{PC dia. } - \text{ worm} + (2 \times \text{Addendum } - \text{ worm})$$

25 Outside diameter – wheel = PC dia. – wheel + (2 × Addendum – wheel) + Module
26 Throat diameter – wheel = PC dia. – wheel + (2 × Addendum – wheel)
27 Root diameter – worm = PC dia. – worm – (2 × Dedendum – worm)
28 Root diameter – wheel = PC dia. – wheel – (2 × Dedendum – wheel)

29   Minimum facewidth – worm

$$=\sqrt{\text{Outs. dia. – wheel}^2 - \text{PC dia. – wheel}^2}$$

30   Maximum facewidth – wheel

$$=2 \times \text{Module}\sqrt{1 + \text{Diameter quotient – worm}}$$

31   Rubbing velocity

$$=0.262 \text{ Module} \times \text{Rev/min – worm}\sqrt{\text{No. of starts – worm}^2 + \text{Dia. quotient – worm}^2}$$

Notes – Diameter quotient:

The efficiency of a worm and wheel increases with the increase in lead angle up to a maximum when the angle is approximately 45°, because since:

$$\tan \text{Lead angle} = \frac{\text{No. of starts – worm}}{\text{Diameter quotient – worm}}$$

then the lead angle is 45° when:

$$\text{Dia. quotient – worm} = \text{No. of starts – worm}$$

The value of the diameter quotient limits the diameter of the worm shaft, and the minimum value of the diameter quotient depends upon the permissible deflection. In order to obtain the necessary stiffness, a value for the diameter quotient greater than the number of starts – worm is usually necessary.

It is preferable for the diameter quotient to be an integer, and the preferred values selected to cover a wide range of designs are 7, 8, 9 and 10. Should it be necessary to depart from the above, a choice may be made from the following values which should cover all cases: 5.5, 6, 6.5, 7, 7.5, 8, 9, 10, 12, 14, etc.

A guide to the choice of the diameter quotient was devised by Dr H. Walker, whereby the values for the 'ratio factor' and 'centre distance factor' are taken from tables produced by Dr Walker and multiplied together, the result being an approximate value for the diameter quotient, i.e.

$$\text{Diameter quotient – approx.} = \text{Ratio factor} \times \text{Centre distance factor}$$

The value obtained is used to select a preferred value which should be checked for suitability by the calculation of torsional stress, bending stress and deflection.

Dr Walker's figures for 'ratio factor' and 'centre distance factor' are given in Tables 9.1 and 9.2.

To restrict the number of possible designs and enable standard tools to be used to full advantage, it is desirable that some limitation should be placed on the choice of module to be used. Therefore, the following first and second choices should be adhered to if possible.

First choices – preferred axial modules:

0.052   0.06   0.068   0.076   0.084   0.092   0.10   0.12   0.14   0.16   0.18   0.20
0.22   0.24   0.26   0.28   0.34   0.38   0.42   0.46   0.50   0.54   0.58   0.62   0.68
0.76   0.84   0.92   1.00

Table 9.1   Ratio factor

No. of teeth (wheel)	No. of starts (worm)						
	1	2	3	4	5	6	7
20	4.8	4.7	4.6	4.4	4.2	4.0	3.6
25	5.4	5.4	5.3	5.2	4.9	4.6	4.3
30	5.9	6.0	6.0	5.9	5.7	5.4	5.0
35	6.4	6.5	6.6	6.6	6.5	6.2	5.9
40	6.9	7.0	7.1	7.2	7.2	7.0	6.8
45	7.4	7.5	7.7	7.7	7.7	7.7	7.6
50	7.9	8.1	8.2	8.2	8.3	8.3	8.3
55	8.4	8.6	8.7	8.8	8.8	8.8	8.8
60	8.9	9.2	9.3	9.3	9.4	9.4	9.5
65	9.4	9.7	9.8	9.8	9.9	10.0	10.1
70	9.9	10.2	10.3	10.4	10.5	10.7	10.8

Table 9.2   Centre distance factor

Worm speed (rev/min)	Centre distance (in)								
	3	4	5	6	8	10	12	14	17
0	1.52	1.40	1.31	1.24	1.17	1.13	1.11	1.08	1.07
100	1.45	1.32	1.23	1.18	1.12	1.08	1.06	1.04	1.01
200	1.37	1.25	1.18	1.13	1.07	1.04	1.01	0.99	0.97
300	1.33	1.22	1.14	1.09	1.04	1.00	0.97	0.96	0.94
400	1.30	1.19	1.12	1.07	1.02	0.98	0.95	0.94	0.92
600	1.27	1.17	1.09	1.05	0.99	0.95	0.93	0.91	0.89
800	1.26	1.15	1.07	1.03	0.97	0.93	0.91	0.89	0.87
1000	1.24	1.13	1.06	1.01	0.95	0.91	0.89	0.87	0.86
1200	1.21	1.11	1.04	0.99	0.93	0.90	0.88	0.86	0.85
1500	1.18	1.08	1.02	0.97	0.92	0.88	0.86	0.85	0.83

Second choices – axial modules:

0.056   0.064   0.072   0.08   0.088   0.096   0.11   0.13   0.15   0.17   0.19   0.21
0.23   0.25   0.27   0.29   0.32   0.36   0.40   0.44   0.48   0.52   0.56   0.60   0.65
0.72   0.80   0.88   0.96

The need to use intermediary figures between the above lists of first and second choices can usually be avoided by varying the actual centre distance from the standard dimensions.

Notes:

(a) The ratio for a single pair of gears should not be less than 5:1 and not exceed 50:1.

Worm gear ratios below 5:1 do not give any advantage.

Above 50:1 ratios, multi-stage arrangements are generally more compact, efficient and less expensive.
(b) The number of teeth in the wheel should not be less than about 40 for trapezoidal worms of $14\frac{1}{2}$–15° pressure angle and not less than 20 for involute helicoid worms of 20° pressure angle.

Unless an exact ratio is an absolute necessity, ratios with no common factor between the number of teeth on the wheel and the number of threads on the worm should be selected.
(c) The nearest whole number to the following equation:

$$\frac{50}{\text{Gear ratio} + 2}$$

provides a guide for the choice of the number of threads on the worm.
(d) Rubbing speeds in excess of 4000 ft/min should be avoided.
(e) Maximum efficiency is obtained when the lead angle

$$= 45° - \left(\frac{\tan^{-1}\ \text{Coefficient of friction}}{2}\right)$$

The actual lead angle is generally much less than this value.

A good approximation for the overall efficiency can be obtained from the following formula:

$$\left(100 - \frac{\text{Gear ratio}}{2}\right)\%$$

Having completed the general calculations for the worm gear pair, it only remains to decide the manufacturing and inspection tolerances.

The British Standard methods of arriving at these dimensions are given in the following pages and cover the dimensional tolerances as shown:

(a) Pitch tolerance – worm
(b) Profile tolerance – worm
(c) Worm thread thickness tolerance
(d) Pitch tolerance – wheel

32 *Pitch tolerance – worm.* The departure from pitch should not exceed the values obtained from the table below,

where d_t = no. of inches in the reference diameter of the worm
L_{ap} = no. of inches in the axial distance between any of two points at the same radial distance from the axis
θ = no. of degrees in the smaller angle between the plane containing the axis and one point, and the plane containing the axis and the other point

Class of gear	Pitch tolerances – worm Permissible error (in)
A	$0.000\,32\sqrt{L_{ap}} + 0.000\,016\sqrt{(\theta d_t)} + 0.000\,2$
B	$0.000\,5\sqrt{L_{ap}} + 0.000\,025\sqrt{(\theta d_t)} + 0.000\,32$
C	$0.000\,8\sqrt{L_{ap}} + 0.000\,04\sqrt{(\theta d_t)} + 0.000\,5$
D	$0.001\,2\sqrt{L_{ap}} + 0.000\,063\sqrt{(\theta d_t)} + 0.000\,8$

The tolerances in the table above cover all types of deviation in helix and spacing of worm threads, e.g. those usually known as 'transverse pitch tolerance', 'axial pitch tolerance' and 'undulations'.

For transverse pitch deviation, the first term becomes zero.

For axial pitch deviation, the second term is zero.

For checking undulation height or normal pitch deviations, all three terms are required.

33   Profile tolerances – worm:

Class of gear	Tolerance (in)
A	$0.00025 \times$ Module $-$ axial $+ 0.00012$
B	$0.0004 \times$ Module $-$ axial $+ 0.00016$
C	$0.0010 \times$ Module $-$ axial $+ 0.00025$
D	$0.0025 \times$ Module $-$ axial $+ 0.0006$

Note: The deviation shall be measured as a departure from the straight-line generator tangential to the base cylinder coincident with the actual profile at mid-working depth.

The profile deviation should not exceed the values obtained from the formulae given and should be measured normal to the thread surface.

34   *Worm thread thickness tolerance.* The departure of worm thread normal thickness from the design thickness should not exceed the values obtained from the formulae in the following table:

Class of gear	Tolerance (in)
A	$+ 0.0000$
	$- (0.0025 \times$ Axial module $+ 0.0008)$
B	$+ 0.0000$
	$- (0.0035 \times$ Axial module $+ 0.0013)$
C	$+ 0.0000$
	$- (0.0063 \times$ Axial module $+ 0.002)$
D	$+ 0.0000$
	$- (0.010 \times$ Axial module $+ 0.0032)$

35   *Pitch tolerance – wheel.* The adjacent and the cumulative pitch deviation measured in a plane normal to the gear axis and on each set of flanks independently should not exceed the values obtained from the formulae in the table below,

where $L =$ any selected length of arc, in inches, including an arc of one pitch but not greater than $\pi D_f 2$

$D_f =$ wheel pitch (reference) circle diameter

Class of gear	Tolerance (in)
A	$0.000\,2\sqrt{L}+0.000\,1$
B	$0.000\,5\sqrt{L}+0.000\,25$
C	$0.001\,3\sqrt{L}+0.000\,63$
D	$0.003\,2\sqrt{L}+0.001\,60$

36 *Backlash allowance.* In order to allow for expansion of the wormwheel at working temperature, backlash must be present at workshop temperature.

Allowable backlash values (based on a temperature of 68°F), which may be achieved by adjusting the wormwheel tooth thickness, are given below,

where m = axial module
        T = no. of teeth – wormwheel

Grade	Minimum	Maximum
1	$0.000\,25m(T+7)+0.000\,5$	$0.000\,25m(T+20)+0.002$
2	$0.000\,25m(T+7)+0.000\,5$	$0.000\,25m(T+40)+0.002$
3	$0.000\,25m(T+15)+0.001\,0$	$0.000\,25m(T+50)+0.002\,5$
4	$0.000\,25m(T+15)+0.001\,5$	$0.000\,25m(T+65)+0.004$
5	$0.000\,25m(T+15)+0.001\,5$	$0.000\,25m(T+80)+0.006$

Any of the grades may be associated with any class of gear at the discretion of the designer.

The following suggestions are given by way of example:

Grade 1: Suitable where backlash tolerances relate to critical requirements, such as timing gears and some control mechanisms

Grade 2: Applicable to precision drives of machine tools

Grades 3–5: Suitable for industrial applications, grade 5 providing adequate backlash for working temperatures of the order of 250°F

Grades 4 and 5: Normally used in axle transmission gear designs

37   Handing of worm gears:

Worm. If, when viewed in the direction of the worm axis, the thread recedes in a clockwise direction, the worm is right hand; if the thread recedes in an anti-clockwise direction, the worm is left hand (Figure 9.4).

Wheel. If, when viewed in the direction of the wheel axis, the teeth recede in a clockwise direction, the wheel is right hand; when they recede in an anti-clockwise direction, the wheel is left hand (Figure 9.4).

A worm and wheel meshing together, with axis at 90° angle, must both be the same hand.

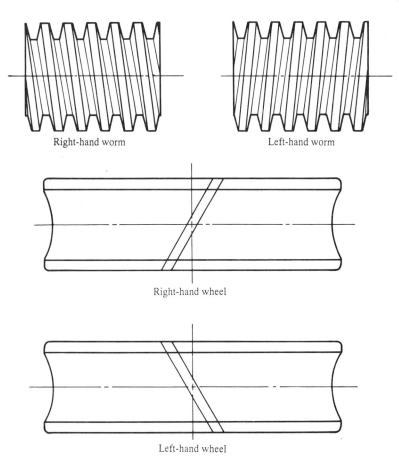

Right-hand worm   Left-hand worm

Right-hand wheel

Left-hand wheel

Figure 9.4   Handing of worms and wheels

38   *Direction of rotation.* The relative directions of rotation of worm and wheel for right- and left-hand gears are illustrated in Figure 9.5.

As can be seen in the illustrations, for a given direction of rotation of the worm, the handing of the gears must be varied to suit the direction of rotation of the wheel.

Metric module – worm gears

Trapezoidal gear calculations

The calculations for metric module worm gears are similar to those for diametral pitch worm gears, as can be seen on page 129 onwards, but this does not apply to the inspection and manufacturing tolerances. Obviously, all dimensions are in millimetres.

The British Standard methods for calculating the manufacturing and inspection tolerances for metric module worm gears are given in the following pages.

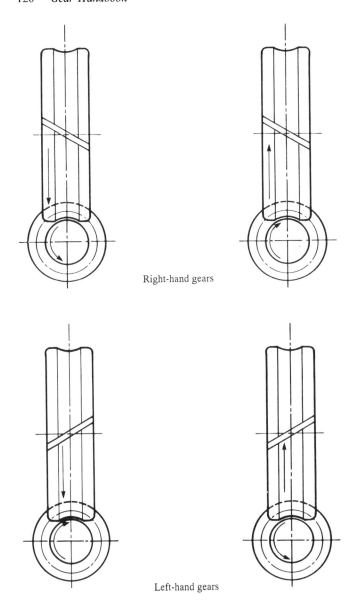

Right-hand gears

Left-hand gears

Figure 9.5   Directions of rotation of worm and wheel

1   *Pitch tolerance – worm*. The tolerances for pitch accuracy shall not exceed the values given by the formulae in the following table,

where L_x = the axial distance between any two points at the same radial distance from the worm axis, in millimetres

θ = the smaller of the two angles formed by radii through two points on a worm thread surface projected onto a transverse plane of the worm

d_1 = the pitch (reference) circle diameter of the worm, in millimetres

Class of gear	Pitch tolerance (mm)
A	$0.001\,6\sqrt{L_x}+0.000\,08\sqrt{(\theta d_1)}+0.005$
B	$0.002\,5\sqrt{L_x}+0.000\,126\sqrt{(\theta d_1)}+0.008$
C	$0.004\sqrt{L_x}+0.000\,2\sqrt{(\theta d_1)}+0.013$
D	$0.006\sqrt{L_x}+0.000\,32\sqrt{(\theta d_1)}+0.020$

Note: The tolerances cover all types of deviation in helix and spacing of worm threads, e.g. those usually known as 'transverse pitch tolerance', 'axial pitch tolerance' and 'undulations'.

For transverse pitch tolerance, the first term becomes zero.

For axial pitch deviation, the second term is zero.

For checking undulation height or normal pitch deviations, all three terms are required.

2 *Profile tolerance – worm*. The profile deviation when measured normal to the surface should not exceed the values given by the formulae in the table below, where $m=$ axial pitch.

Class of gear	Profile tolerance (mm)
A	$0.000\,25m+0.003$
B	$0.000\,4m+0.004$
C	$0.001\,0m+0.006$
D	$0.002\,5m+0.015$

Note: The deviation should be measured as a departure from the straight-line generator tangential to the base cylinder coincident with the actual profile at mid-working depth.

3 *Worm thread thickness tolerance*. The tolerances on worm thread thickness should be as given by the formulae in the table below, where $m=$ axial pitch.

Class of gear	Worm thread thickness tolerance (mm)
A	$+0.000$ $-0.002\,5m+0.020$
B	$+0.000$ $-0.003\,5m+0.033$
C	$+0.000$ $-0.006\,3m+0.051$
D	$+0.000$ $-0.010m+0.081$

4 *Wormwheel pitch tolerance.* The adjacent and cumulative pitch deviation measured in a plane normal to gear axis and on each set of flanks independently should not exceed the values shown in the table below.

Class of gear	Wormwheel pitch tolerance (mm)
A	$0.001\,0\sqrt{L}+0.002\,5$
B	$0.002\,5\sqrt{L}+0.006\,4$
C	$0.006\,6\sqrt{L}+0.016\,0$
D	$0.016\,1\sqrt{L}+0.040\,6$

Note: L is any selected length of arc, in millimetres, including an arc of one pitch but is not greater than:

$$\frac{\pi \times \text{Wheel reference dia.}}{2}$$

5 *Normal backlash.* To allow for expansion of the wormwheel at working temperature, backlash has to be present at workshop temperature.

Backlash values based on a temperature of 20°C should be within the limits of the values given by the formulae in the following table below,

where m = axial module

z_2 = no. of teeth – wormwheel

These values should be achieved by adjusting the wormwheel tooth thickness.

Grade	Minimum (mm)	Maximum (mm)
1	$0.000\,25m(z_2+7)+0.013$	$0.000\,25m(z_2+20)+0.05$
2	$0.000\,25m(z_2+7)+0.013$	$0.000\,25m(z_2+40)+0.05$
3	$0.000\,25m(z_2+15)+0.025$	$0.000\,25m(z_2+50)+0.06$
4	$0.000\,25m(z_2+15)+0.038$	$0.000\,25m(z_2+65)+0.10$
5	$0.000\,25m(z_2+15)+0.038$	$0.000\,25m(z_2+80)+0.15$

Note: Any of the grades of backlash may be associated with any class of gear at the discretion of the designer.

Grade 1: Suitable where backlash tolerances relate to critical requirements, such as timing gears and some control mechanisms.

Grade 2: Applicable to precision drives of machine tools.

Grades 3–5: Suitable for industrial applications, grade 5 providing adequate backlash for working temperatures of the order of 120°C.

Grades 4 and 5: Normally used for axle transmission gears.

The calculations for metric module worm gears are carried out as follows:

1 No. of teeth or threads – worm:

Industrial gears:

$$\text{No. of threads} = \frac{7 + 2.4\sqrt{\text{Centre distance}}}{\text{Gear ratio}}$$

Use nearest whole number to answer.

Axle transmission gears:

$$\text{No. of threads} = \frac{7 + 1.6\sqrt{\text{Centre distance}}}{\text{Gear ratio}}$$

No. of threads taken to nearest whole number below the answer above.

2 No. of teeth – wormwheel = Gear ratio × No. of threads – worm

Note: For single thread worms, No. of teeth – wormwheel = Gear ratio

The No. of teeth – wormwheel for vehicle transmission gears should not be less than 17.

3 *Diameter factor*. The diameter factor should be selected from one of the following values: 6, 6.5, 7, 7.5, 8, 8.5, 9, 9.5, 10, 11, 12, 13, 14, 17, 20. These values ensure geometric similarity between all worms having the same values for the number of threads – worm and the diameter factor.

For any given combination of number of threads – worm and the diameter factor, all angular dimensions of a worm can be calculated and all linear dimensions will be proportional to the selected modules.

The diameter factor should be selected from Figure 9.6.

4 Lead angle – worm thread:

$$= \tan^{-1}\frac{\text{No. of threads – worm}}{\text{Diameter factor}}$$

5 Worm reference circle diameter = Diameter factor × Axial module

6 Worm thread addendum = Module

7 Clearance:

$$\text{Minimum} = 0.2 \text{ Module} \times \cos \text{Lead angle – worm}$$
$$\text{Maximum} = 0.25 \text{ Module} \times \cos \text{Lead angle – worm}$$

8 Worm thread dedendum:

$$\text{Minimum} = \text{Module (cos Lead angle – worm} \times 2.2 - 1)$$
$$\text{Maximum} = \text{Module (cos Lead angle – worm} \times 2.25 - 1)$$

9 Worm tip diameter

$$= \text{Worm ref. circle dia.} + 2 \times \text{Module}$$
$$= \text{Module (Diameter factor} + 2)$$

10 Worm root diameter = Worm ref. circle dia. − (2 × Worm thread dedendum)

11 Axial pitch = π × No. of threads – worm × Axial module

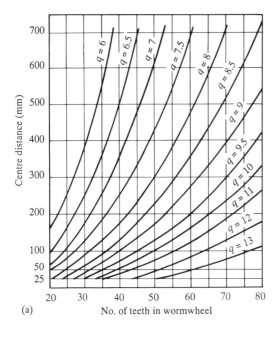

(a)

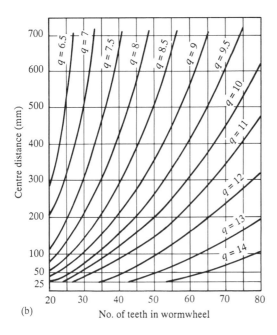

(b)

Figure 9.6   Diameter factor – values: (a) any worm speed; (b) worm speeds up to 300 rev/min

12 Normal pressure angle $= 20°$

13 Base lead angle – worm thread:

$$= \cos^{-1} \cos \text{Lead angle} - \text{worm thread} \times \cos \text{Normal PA}$$

14 Base diameter – involute helicoid

$$= \frac{\text{Axial pitch}}{\pi \times \text{Base lead angle} - \text{worm thread}}$$

15 Length of worm $= 14 \times \text{Axial module} \times \cos \text{Lead angle} - \text{worm thread}$

16 Constant chord thickness – worm $= \text{Axial module} (0.7444 \times \cos \text{Lead angle} - \text{worm thread} + 0.6428)$

17 Constant chord height – worm

$$= \text{Axial module} - \left(\frac{\text{Constant chord thick.} - \text{worm}}{2} \times \tan 20° \right)$$

18 Reference circle diameter – wormwheel $= 2 \times \text{Centre distance} - \text{Ref. circle dia.}$ – worm

19 Wormwheel throat diameter $= 2 \times \text{Centre distance} - (\text{Worm root dia.} + 2 \times \text{Clearance})$

20 Wormwheel root diameter $= 2 \times \text{Centre distance} - (\text{Worm tip dia.} + 2 \times \text{Clearance})$

21 Wormwheel tip diameter:

Minimum $= \text{Wormwheel throat dia.} + 0.4 \text{ Axial module}$
Maximum $= \text{Wormwheel throat dia.} + \text{Axial module}$

22 Wormwheel gorge radius $= 0.5 (\text{Worm root dia.} + 2 \times \text{Clearance})$

23 Clearance:

Minimum $= 0.2 \text{ Axial module} \times \cos \text{Worm lead angle}$
Maximum $= 0.25 \text{ Axial module} \times \cos \text{Worm lead angle}$

24 Wormwheel effective facewidth

$$= 2 \times \text{Axial module} \times \sqrt{(\text{Diameter factor} + 1)}$$

25 Axial module

$$= \frac{\text{Axial pitch}}{\pi}$$

26 Normal module $= \text{Axial module} \times \cos \text{Worm lead angle}$

27 Axial pitch $= \pi \times \text{Axial module}$

28 Normal pitch $= \text{Axial pitch} \times \cos \text{Worm lead angle}$

29 Length of root – wormwheel teeth $= (\text{Worm tip dia.} + 2 \times \text{Clearance}) \sin^{-1} x$, where

$$x = \frac{\text{Wormwheel effective facewidth}}{\text{Worm tip dia.} + 2 \times \text{Clearance}}$$

Note: Angle $\sin^{-1}$ is in radians.

10

Spur and helical gear tooth stress calculations

This chapter deals with various formulae available to the designer for the calculation of the stress and expected life of spur and helical gears.

If a sample pair of gears is used in these formulae, a fairly wide scatter of results will arise, especially with the formulae that do not take into account the accuracy of the gear teeth and the running centres along with the mounting or casing stiffness and the gear tooth hardness, both in depth of hardness and surface hardness.

The formulae are given in separate sections within this chapter.

Lewis stress formula

Spur and helical gears

1 Tangential load on teeth (lb)

$$= \frac{\text{Torque transmitted (lb/in)}}{\text{Pitch circle radius (in)}}$$

$$= \frac{63\,000 \times \text{Horsepower transmitted}}{\text{Pitch circle rad. (in)} \times \text{rev/min}}$$

$$= \frac{33\,000 \times \text{Horsepower}}{\text{Pitch line velocity (ft/min)}}$$

2 Safe working stress (lb/in²)

$$= \frac{\text{Tangential load on teeth (lb)}}{\text{Tooth width (in)} \times \text{Circular pitch} \times \text{Lewis form factor}}$$

where

(a) Tooth width is measured across the pitch line for spur gears and along the helix angle for helical gears.

(b) The Lewis form factor is calculated as follows:

Full depth teeth – $14\frac{1}{2}°$ pressure angle:

$$\text{Lewis form factor}=0.124-\frac{0.684}{\text{No. of teeth on gear}}$$

Full depth teeth – 20° pressure angle:

$$\text{Lewis form factor}=0.154-\frac{0.912}{\text{No. of teeth on gear}}$$

Stub teeth – 20° pressure angle:

$$\text{Lewis form factor}=0.175-\frac{0.900}{\text{No. of teeth on gear}}$$

Buckingham stress formula

Spur and helical gears

1 Dynamic load – spur gears

$$=\frac{0.05\times\text{Pitch line velocity (ft/min)}\times(\text{Tooth width}\times\text{Deform. factor}+\text{Load}}{0.05\times\text{Pitch line velocity (ft/min)}+\sqrt{\text{Tooth width}\times\text{deform. factor}+\text{Load}}}+\text{Load}$$

where

(a) Load is the tangential load on teeth – see page 132.
(b) Deformation factor is taken from the following table:

| Material | Tooth form | Error in action | | | | | |
		0.0005 in	0.001 in	0.002 in	0.003 in	0.004 in	0.005 in
Cast iron and cast iron	$14\frac{1}{2}°$ full	400	800	1600	2400	3200	4000
Cast iron and steel	$14\frac{1}{2}°$ full	550	1100	2200	3300	4400	5500
Steel and steel	$14\frac{1}{2}°$ full	800	1600	3200	4800	6400	8000
Cast iron and cast iron	20° full	415	830	1660	2490	3320	4150
Cast iron and steel	20° full	570	1140	2280	3420	4560	5700
Steel and steel	20° full	830	1660	3320	4980	6640	8300
Cast iron and cast iron	20° stub	430	860	1720	2580	3440	4300
Cast iron and steel	20° stub	590	1180	2360	3540	4720	5900
Steel and steel	20° stub	860	1720	3440	5160	6880	8600

From test results, the errors in action fall into the following categories:

1   *Well-cut commercial gears*:

from 0.002 in for gears from 6 DP and finer
from 0.004 in for gears of 2 DP

If gears are cut with care and accuracy, the error in action is reduced to even smaller amounts, as shown in the table below.

DP	Class 1 gear	Class 2 gear	Class 3 gear
1	0.004 8	0.002 4	0.001 2
2	0.004 0	0.002 0	0.001 0
3	0.003 2	0.001 6	0.000 8
4	0.002 6	0.001 3	0.000 7
5	0.002 2	0.001 1	0.000 6
6 and finer	0.002 0	0.001 0	0.000 5

Classes 1, 2 and 3 depict the improvement in error in action as the gear-cutting accuracy improves.

The noise of operation is usually a very good check for the accuracy of the gears, and the table below gives a guide as to the accuracy required for various pitch line velocities and will assist with the selection of the correct class of gear to meet specified speed conditions. Where extreme quietness of operation is required, a higher order of accuracy than that shown is necessary. The values shown in the table should keep the noise of operation and the intensity of the dynamic load within reasonable limits.

Maximum error in action between gears					
Pitch line velocity (ft/min)	Error in action	Pitch line velocity (ft/min)	Error in action	Pitch line velocity (ft/min)	Error in action
250	0.003 7	1750	0.001 7	3250	0.000 8
500	0.003 2	2000	0.001 5	3500	0.000 7
750	0.002 8	2250	0.001 3	4000	0.000 6
1000	0.002 4	2500	0.001 2	4500	0.000 6
1250	0.002 1	2750	0.001 0	5000	0.000 5
1500	0.001 9	3000	0.000 9	and above	

Beam strength of teeth. The beam strength of the gear teeth is calculated using the Lewis formula to determine the safe static strength.

Safe static beam load on teeth (lb) = Safe static bending stress for material × CP × FW × Y, where safe static bending stress is in pounds per square inch (see table below)

> CP = circular pitch of gear
> FW = facewidth, in inches
> Y = tooth form factor (see below and page 136).

The flexural endurance limit of the material gives a satisfactory value for the safe static stress. Fatigue tests on steel indicate that this endurance limit follows the Brinell hardness number closely. The table below gives the flexural endurance limits for a range of materials at varying Brinell hardnesses.

Material	Brinell hardness no.	Safe static bending stress (lb/in^2)
Grey iron	160	12 000
Semi-steel	190	18 000
Phosphor bronze	100	24 000
Steel	150	36 000
Steel	200	50 000
Steel	240	60 000
Steel	280	70 000
Steel	320	80 000
Steel	360	90 000
Steel	400	100 000

Tooth form factors. The tooth form factor is obtained by considering the gear tooth as a beam, fixed at one end and loaded at the other end.

Table 10.1 gives the tooth form factor values for various tooth forms with varying numbers of teeth.

Margin of safety. The static beam strength of the tooth should always be greater than the dynamic load.

The following safety factors are given as guidelines:

(a) Steady loads:
   Safe static beam load = 1.25 × Dynamic load
(b) Pulsating loads:
   Safe static beam load = 1.35 × Dynamic load
(c) Shock loads:
   Safe static beam load = 1.50 × Dynamic load

These values should be modified to suit as experience is gained.

Table 10.1   Tooth form factor values

No. of teeth	$14\frac{1}{2}°$ Composite and involute form	$14\frac{1}{2}°$ Variable centre distance	20° Involute (full depth)	Small pinions (20° full depth)	20° Involute stub tooth	Internal drives (20° full depth) Spur pinion	Internal drives (20° full depth) Internal gear
5				0.102		0.102	
6				0.096		0.102	
7				0.090		0.102	
8				0.084		0.103	
9				0.084		0.103	
10				0.084		0.103	
11				0.084		0.104	
12	0.067	0.125	0.078	0.084	0.099	0.104	
13	0.071	0.123	0.083	0.086	0.103	0.104	
14	0.075	0.121	0.088	0.088	0.108	0.105	
15	0.078	0.120	0.092		0.111	0.105	
16	0.081	0.120	0.094		0.115	0.106	
17	0.084	0.120	0.096		0.117	0.109	
18	0.086	0.120	0.098		0.120	0.111	
19	0.088	0.119	0.100		0.123	0.114	
20	0.090	0.119	0.102		0.125	0.116	
21	0.092	0.119	0.104		0.127	0.118	
22	0.093	0.119	0.105		0.129	0.119	
24	0.095	0.118	0.107		0.132	0.122	
26	0.098	0.117	0.110		0.135	0.125	
28	0.100	0.115	0.112		0.137	0.127	0.220
30	0.101	0.114	0.114		0.139	0.129	0.216
34	0.104	0.112	0.118		0.142	0.132	0.210
38	0.106	0.110	0.122		0.145	0.135	0.205
43	0.108	0.108	0.126		0.147	0.137	0.200
50	0.110	0.110	0.130		0.151	0.139	0.195
60	0.113	0.113	0.134		0.154	0.142	0.190
75	0.115	0.115	0.138		0.158	0.144	0.185
100	0.117	0.117	0.142		0.161	0.147	0.180
150	0.119	0.119	0.146		0.165	0.149	0.175
Rack	0.124	0.124	0.154		0.175		

Limit load for wear. The limit load for wear depends upon the surface endurance limits of the gear materials, the radii of curvature of the mating profiles, as well as upon the relative hardness of the mating surfaces. A harder material in the pinion will cold-work the surface of the softer and more malleable material of the mating gear and thus increase its surface endurance limit materially.

Limiting static load for wear (lb) = PC dia. (pinion) (in) × Facewidth (in) × Load stress – factor × Ratio factor, where:

(a) Load stress – factor (see pages 138 and 139)

$$= \frac{S_c^2 \times \sin \phi}{1400} \left(\frac{1}{E_1} + \frac{1}{E_2} \right)$$

(b) Ratio factor:

(i) For spur gears

$$= \frac{2 \times \text{No. of teeth} - \text{gear}}{\text{Total no. of teeth} - \text{pinion and gear}}$$

(ii) For internal gears

$$= \frac{2 \times \text{No. of teeth} - \text{gear}}{\text{No. of teeth} - \text{gear} - \text{No. of teeth} - \text{pinion}}$$

(c) S_c = surface endurance limit – material (lb/in^2)
   ϕ = pressure angle
   E_1 = modulus of elasticity pinion material
   E_2 = modulus of elasticity gear material (see page 139)

Note: The value of the limiting static load for wear should always be equal to or greater than the value of the dynamic load.

Surface endurance limit. Values of the surface endurance limit for steel appear to vary quite consistently with its Brinell hardness number. For values up to approximately 400 Brinell hardness, the values for the surface endurance limits are given in the table below.

Brinell hardness no.	Surface endurance limit (lb/in^2)
150	50 000
200	70 000
250	90 000
300	110 000
350	130 000
400	150 000

When the Brinell hardness number is above 400, the steel does not appear to have a definite endurance limit. The length of life appears to vary inversely as the 10/3 power of the load. Thus, if the load is doubled the life will be approximately one-tenth as long.

The table below gives values for the surface endurance limit to be used with these harder steels.

Brinell hardness no.	Surface endurance limit (lb/in²)			
	10 000 000 repetitions	20 000 000 repetitions	50 000 000 repetitions	100 000 000 repetitions
450	188 000	170 000	147 000	132 000
500	210 000	190 000	165 000	148 000
550	233 000	210 000	182 000	163 000
600	255 000	230 000	200 000	179 000

Load stress – factor. The values of the load stress – factor for various combinations of materials, taking into consideration the cold-working received in operation, are given in Table 10.2.

The classification 'cast iron' also includes the ordinary semi-steels. Some of the high-test semi-steels and other special alloys of cast iron have a greater modulus of elasticity than cast iron, and the value for the load stress – factor as well as the value of the dynamic load for such materials must be calculated directly from their own specific properties.

Table 10.2 Load stress factor values

Pinion material	Brinell no.	Gear material	Brinell no.	Endurance limit	Stress factor $14\frac{1}{2}°$	Stress factor 20°
Steel	150	Steel	150	50 000	30	41
Steel	200	Steel	150	60 000	43	58
Steel	250	Steel	150	70 000	58	79
Steel	200	Steel	200	70 000	58	79
Steel	250	Steel	200	80 000	76	103
Steel	300	Steel	200	90 000	96	131
Steel	250	Steel	250	90 000	96	131
Steel	300	Steel	250	100 000	119	162
Steel	350	Steel	250	110 000	144	196
Steel	300	Steel	300	110 000	144	196
Steel	350	Steel	300	120 000	171	233
Steel	400	Steel	300	125 000	186	254
Steel	350	Steel	350	130 000	201	275
Steel	400	Steel	350	140 000	233	318
Steel	400	Steel	400	150 000	268	366
Steel	150	Cast iron		50 000	44	60
Steel	200	Cast iron		70 000	87	119
Steel	250	Cast iron		90 000	144	196
Steel	150	Ph. bronze		50 000	46	62
Steel	200	Ph. bronze		70 000	91	124
Steel	250	Ph. bronze		85 000	135	204
Cast iron		Cast iron		90 000	193	284

Note: In Table 10.2 the load stress factor values are given for both $14\frac{1}{2}°$ and $20°$ pressure angle gears.

The values of the load stress factor for hardened steel are given in Table 10.3.

Table 10.3 Load stress factor values – hardened steel

Brinell no.	Endurance limit	Stress factor $14\frac{1}{2}°$	Stress factor $20°$
	10 000 000 repetitions of stress		
450	188 000	421	575
500	210 000	525	718
550	233 000	647	884
600	255 000	775	1058
	20 000 000 repetitions of stress		
450	170 000	344	470
500	190 000	430	588
550	210 000	525	718
600	230 000	630	861
	50 000 000 repetitions of stress		
450	147 000	257	351
500	165 000	324	443
550	182 000	394	544
600	200 000	476	651
	1000 000 000 repetitions of stress		
450	132 000	208	284
500	148 000	261	356
550	163 000	316	432
600	179 000	382	522

Note; In Table 10.3 the load stress factor values are given for both $14\frac{1}{2}°$ and $20°$ pressure angle gears.

Physical constants of metals:

Material	Modulus of elasticity (lb/in^2)	Modulus of rigidity (lb/in^2)	Coeff. of linear thermal expansion (per °F)	Thermal conductivity (BTU/in/min per °F)	Weight (lb/in^3)
Steel	30×10^6	12×10^6	6.5×10^{-6}	0.06	0.28
Cast iron	17×10^6	6.7×10^6	5.5×10^{-6}	0.06	0.26
Phosphor bronze	17×10^6	7×10^6	10×10^{-6}	0.16	0.32
Gun-metal	13×10^6	5×10^6	10×10^{-6}	0.08	0.30

Dynamic load – alternative method. The equation given on page 133 for the dynamic load is an approximation and E. Buckingham gave an alternative solution to produce a more accurate result.

This figure is calculated as follows:

$$\text{Dynamic load} = W + \sqrt{f_a(2f_2 - f_a)}$$

where

$$f_a = \frac{f_1 \times f_2}{f_1 + f_2}$$

$$f_1 = 0.002\,5 \left(\frac{R_1 + R_2}{R_1 \times R_2}\right)^2 mV^2$$

$f_2 = (F \times C) + W$
W = total applied load (lb)
R_1 = pitch circle radius – pinion (in)
R_2 = pitch circle radius – gear (in)
m = effective mass at pitch line of gears
V = pitch line velocity (ft/min)
F = facewidth of gears (in)
C = deformation factor (see table on page 133)

The effective mass at pitch line of gears (m) is calculated as follows:

$$m = \frac{m_1 \times m_2}{m_1 + m_2}$$

where

$m_1 = m_p + m_b$
$m_2 = m_g + m_d$

$$m_p = \frac{P^2 N_1 F}{64}\left[\frac{0.002R_1^2 + 1}{0.001R_1^2 + 1}\right]$$

$$m_b = \frac{\sqrt{B_1^2 + 4 \times A_1 \times C_1} - B_1}{2 \times A_1}$$

$$m_g = \frac{P^2 N_2 F}{64}\left[\frac{0.002R_2^2 + 1}{0.001R_2^2 + 1}\right]$$

$$m_d = \frac{\sqrt{B_2^2 + 4 \times A_2 \times C_2} - B_2}{2 \times A_2}$$

P = circular pitch (in)
N_1 = no. of teeth – pinion
F = facewidth of gears (in)
R_1 = pitch circle radius – pinion (in)
$B_1 = (m_p + m_g)A_1 + em_g Z_1$
$C_1 = em_a m_g Z_1$

$$A_1 = 0.002\,5\left(\frac{R_1 + R_2}{R_1 \times R_2}\right)^2 m_a V^2$$

e = error in action (see table on page 133).

$$Z_1 = \frac{\text{Load (lb) at } R_1 \text{ to twist connection}}{\text{Torsional deflection at } R_1 \text{ (in)}}$$

m_a = effective mass of masses connected to pinion at radius R_1
R_2 = pitch circle radius – gear (in)
V = pitch line velocity (ft/min)
N_2 = no. of teeth – gear
$B_2 = (m_p + m_g)A_2 + em_p Z_2$
$C_2 = em_c m_p Z_2$

$$A_2 = 0.002\,5\left(\frac{R_1 + R_2}{R_1 \times R_2}\right)^2 m_c V^2$$

$$Z_2 = \frac{\text{Load (lb) at } R_2 \text{ to twist connection}}{\text{Torsional deflection at } R_2 \text{ (in)}}$$

m_c = effective mass of parts connected to gear at radius R_2

In many cases it is desirable to have a general formula covering average conditions rather than specific ones, particularly where the values of the many factors are unknown or indeterminate. The following equations give the value of the 'effective mass at the pitch line of gears' for such average conditions:

Effective mass at pitch line of gears, m

$$= C_m\left[\frac{m_p m_g}{m_p + m_g}\right]$$

with connected mass equal to approx. 10 times mass of gear blanks,

where:

C_m = mass factor – see following table, page 142

$$m_p = \frac{P^2 N_1 F}{64}\left[\frac{0.002 R_1^2 + 1}{0.001 R_1^2 + 1}\right]$$

$$m_g = \frac{P^2 N_2 F}{64}\left[\frac{0.002 R_2^2 + 1}{0.001 R_2^2 + 1}\right]$$

P = circular pitch (in)
N_1 = no. of teeth – pinion
N_2 = no. of teeth – wheel
F = facewidth – gears (in)
R_1 = pitch circle radius – pinion (in)
R_2 = pitch circle radius – gear (in)

Where the connected masses are negligible, the value of $C_m = 1.00$.

For pinions of solid disc form:

$$m_p = \frac{\text{Weight (lb)}}{64}$$

Mass factors (values of C_m):

Velocity (ft/min)	C_m	Velocity (ft/min)	C_m	Velocity (ft/min)	C_m
0	10.000	700	2.932	1800	1.621
100	8.203	800	2.681	2000	1.533
200	6.332	900	2.480	2500	1.382
300	5.081	1000	2.314	3000	1.285
400	4.253	1200	2.058	3500	1.220
500	3.677	1400	1.872	4000	1.175
600	3.254	1600	1.731	5000	1.120

2   *Dynamic load – helical gears.* The load-carrying ability of any gears may be limited by either the beam strength of the gear tooth, the surface endurance limit of the materials or the heat of operation. The lower of these values should be used to establish the load-carrying ability of any given drive.

Considerable uncertainty still exists as to the nature and extent of the dynamic loads on helical gear teeth. Several different formulae are more or less widely used for this purpose, but sufficient data is not yet available to determine which one gives the most accurate figure for the dynamic load. In order to bring several of these together for comparative use, in the absence of more exact information, the following are presented.

In most cases the dynamic load is assumed to be directly proportional to the applied load. This is not true in the case of spur gears, but the smoother running characteristics of helical gears may make it nearer the truth than in the case of spur gears. The dynamic load is the maximum momentary load in operation.

For slow speed helical gears (with pitch line velocities below 2000 ft/min), the following formula is often used:

$$\text{Dynamic load (lb)} = \left(\frac{1200 + V}{1200}\right) W$$

For intermediate speed helical gears (with pitch line velocities between 2000 and 4000 ft/min), the following formula is used:

$$\text{Dynamic load (lb)} = \left(\frac{3000 + V}{3000}\right) W$$

For high-speed helical gears (with pitch line velocities over 4000 ft/min), the following formula is used:

$$\text{Dynamic load (lb)} + \left(\frac{78 + \sqrt{V}}{78}\right) W$$

where

V = pitch line velocity (ft/min)
W = tangential load (lb)

The load-carrying ability of a pair of helical gears may be limited by either the beam strength of the gear tooth or the surface endurance limit of the material.

The lower of these two values should be used to establish the load-carrying ability of any given pair of helical gears.

The following equations, which take into consideration the helix angle, have been developed from the spur gear equations, and appear to check with reasonable consistency service data on helical gears operating under a wide variety of speeds and loads.

Dynamic load (lb). The dynamic load is the maximum momentary load set up by the operating or dynamic conditions.

Dynamic load (lb)

$$= \frac{0.05V(W + F_a C \cos^2 \psi) \cos \psi}{0.05V + \sqrt{W + F_a C \cos^2 \psi}}$$

where

V = pitch line velocity (ft/min)

$$W = \frac{33\,000 \times \text{hp}}{V}$$

F_a = active facewidth (in)
C = deformation factor – see table on page 133
ψ = helix angle
hp = horsepower transmitted

Note: For planetary gear trains, the velocity of the actual tooth engagement must be used to determine the dynamic load. For materials not shown in the table on page 133, the deformation factor should be determined from the following formulae:

20° stub tooth form:

$$\text{Deformation factor} = \frac{0.115e}{\left(\dfrac{1}{E_1} + \dfrac{1}{E_2}\right)}$$

$14\frac{1}{2}°$ full-depth tooth form:

$$\text{Deformation factor} = \frac{0.107e}{\left(\dfrac{1}{E_1} + \dfrac{1}{E_2}\right)}$$

20° full-depth tooth form:

$$\text{Deformation factor} = \frac{0.111e}{\left(\dfrac{1}{E_1} + \dfrac{1}{E_2}\right)}$$

A guide to the amount of error in action for the various classes of gear finish is given on pages 133 and 134.

Beam strength of teeth. The load on helical gear teeth is not uniform across the face of the gear because the elastic deformation (on perfect gears) must be uniform. While it takes a greater load at the middle of the tooth height than at the tips to obtain this uniform deformation when the face is wide enough to have the contact extend over the entire height of the active profiles of the teeth, the intensity of the load near the middle will be approximately $1\frac{1}{3}$ times the average intensity of the tooth load.

In some cases the beam strength of helical gear teeth is calculated by the spur gear formulae, using the normal circular pitch and normal pressure angle. The values calculated by using this method will be safe, as they will be less than the actual figures obtained using the helical gear formula.

A closer approximation to the beam strength of a helical gear tooth is obtained using a modification of the Lewis formula and assuming the load to be applied near the middle of the tooth height, as shown below:

Limiting beam load on teeth (lb) (plane of rotation)

$$= 0.75 \, S_t P_N F_a Y \cos \psi$$

where

$S_t =$ bending endurance limit of material (see table on page 135)
$P_N =$ normal circular pitch (in)
$F_a =$ active facewidth (in)
$Y =$ tooth form factor
$\psi =$ helix angle – gear tooth

Note: The value of Y should be determined using the virtual number of teeth, which can be calculated as follows:

Virtual number of teeth on gear

$$= \frac{\text{Actual no. of teeth on gear}}{\cos \text{ Helix angle}^3}$$

Tooth form factor. The tooth form factor is obtained by considering the gear tooth as a beam fixed at one end and loaded through the middle of the tooth.

Table 10.4 gives the tooth form factor values for various tooth forms with varying numbers of teeth.

Margin of safety. The static beam strength of the tooth should always be greater than the dynamic load.

The following safety factors are given as guidelines:

(a) Steady loads: Safe static beam load $= 1.25 \times$ Dynamic load
(b) Pulsating loads: Safe static beam load $= 1.35 \times$ Dynamic load
(c) Shock loads: Safe static beam load $= 1.50 \times$ Dynamic load

These values should be modified when found desirable by experience.

Table 10.4   Tooth form factor values

Virtual no. of teeth	$14\frac{1}{2}°$ Composite and involute system	20° Involute (full-depth system)	Small pinions (20° full depth)	20° Involute stub (tooth system)	Internal drives (20° full-depth system)	
					Spur pinion	Internal gear
5			0.173		0.200	
6			0.163		0.201	
7			0.153		0.202	
8			0.142		0.203	
9			0.142		0.204	
10			0.142		0.205	
11			0.142		0.206	
12	0.113	0.132	0.142	0.158	0.207	
13	0.120	0.141	0.146	0.164	0.208	
14	0.127	0.149	0.149	0.172	0.209	
15	0.132	0.156		0.177	0.210	
16	0.137	0.160		0.184	0.211	
17	0.142	0.163		0.187	0.215	
18	0.146	0.166		0.192	0.218	
19	0.150	0.170		0.196	0.222	
20	0.153	0.173		0.200	0.225	
21	0.156	0.176		0.203	0.228	
22	0.158	0.178		0.206	0.230	
24	0.162	0.182		0.211	0.233	
26	0.166	0.187		0.216	0.236	
28	0.170	0.190		0.219	0.239	0.400
30	0.172	0.193		0.222	0.242	0.393
34	0.176	0.200		0.227	0.246	0.387
38	0.180	0.207		0.232	0.250	0.380
43	0.183	0.214		0.235	0.253	0.372
50	0.187	0.221		0.241	0.256	0.364
60	0.192	0.227		0.246	0.260	0.356
75	0.195	0.234		0.252	0.264	0.348
100	0.198	0.241		0.257	0.268	0.340
150	0.202	0.248		0.264	0.273	0.332
Rack	0.210	0.262		0.280		

Limit load for wear. The limit load for wear depends upon the surface endurance limits of the materials, the radii of curvature of the mating profiles, as well as upon the relative hardness of the mating surfaces. A harder material for the pinion will cold-work the surface of the softer and more malleable materials of the mating gear and thus increase its surface endurance limit materially.

Limiting static load for wear (lb)

$$= \frac{\text{PC dia. (pinion) (in)} \times \text{Facewidth (in)} \times \text{Load stress factor} \times \text{Ratio factor}}{\cos \text{ Helix angle}^2}$$

Note: This value for the limiting static load for wear should be equal to or greater than the value of the dynamic load, where

(a) Load stress factor

$$= \frac{S_c^2 \sin \phi_n}{1400} \left(\frac{1}{E_1} + \frac{1}{E_2} \right)$$

(b) Ratio factor:

For external helical gears

$$= \frac{2 \times \text{No. of teeth} - \text{gear}}{\text{Total no. of teeth} - \text{pinion and gear}}$$

For internal helical gears

$$= \frac{2 \times \text{No. of teeth} - \text{gear}}{\text{No. of teeth} - \text{gear} - \text{No. of teeth} - \text{pinion}}$$

(c) S_c = surface endurance limit – material (lb/in^2)
ϕ_n = normal pressure angle
E_1 = modulus of elasticity – pinion material
E_2 = modulus of elasticity – gear material (see page 139)

(d) Load stress factor – See note on page 138 and Table 10.2 (page 138) for values of various combinations of materials, and Table 10.3 (page 139) for values for hardened steels which are given for a range of both Brinell hardness numbers and gear life.

(e) Surface endurance limit. The values for the surface endurance limit and explanatory notes are given on pages 137 and 138.

Tuplin stress formula

Professor W.A. Tuplin produced two methods of calculating gear tooth stresses. The first method gives the allowable surface and bending stresses, then after later research he produced a formula for calculating the load capacity of a pair of gears. Both of these methods are given in the following pages.

Allowable surface stress = Speed factor (surface stress) × Basic allowable surface stress for material

For values of:

speed factor (surface stress), see Figure 10.1, page 147
basic allowable surface stress, see Figure 10.2, page 148

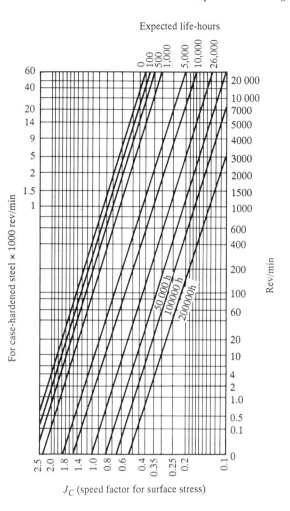

Figure 10.1

or

Allowable surface stress

$$= \frac{2.5 \times 10^6}{V_s + 100}$$

Allowable bending stress = Speed factor (bending stress) × Basic allowable bending stress for material

For values of:

speed factor (bending stress), see Figure 10.3, page 150
basic allowable bending stress, see Figure 10.2, pages 148 and 149

Figure 10.2   Basic allowable stresses for material for gears (excluding worm and crossed helical)

Surface stress S_{CO}	Bending stress S_{BO}	Material	Condition	Approx. BS	Equiv. En	Tensile strength (ton/in²)	Brinell hardness (core)	Maximum thickness (in)
700	7 000	Phosphor-bronze	Sand-cast	421		12	69	
850	8 500	Phosphor-bronze	Chill-cast	421		15	82	
1 000	10 000	Phosphor-bronze	Centrifugally cast	421		17	90	
850	11 000	Malleable iron		309⎰310⎱		20	140	
1 000	5 800	Cast iron	Ordinary grade	821		12	165	
1 350	7 600	Cast iron	Medium grade	821		16	210	
1 450	10 000	Cast iron	High grade	821		22	220	
1 450	16 000	0.4% Carbon cast steel	As cast	592		35	145	
			Forged steels					
1 450F	18 000f	0.4% carbon (w)	Normalized		8	35	145	6
1 800	20 000	1½%Mn (w)	Normalized		14B	38	180	6
2 100F	24 000f	55% carbon	Normalized		9	45	210	6
2 400	24 000	3% Nickel	Heat-treated		21	45	200	6
2 700[F	27 000f	1½% Ni 1% Cr	Heat-treated		24	50	220	6
3 000F	30 000f	3½% Ni 1% Cr	Heat-treated		27	55	250	6
*3 000F	30 000F	0.6% carbon* 5% Cr	Heat-treated		11	55	250	2¼
*3 500	36 000	0.6% carbon* 5% Cr	Heat-treated		11	65	250	2½
3 500F	36 000f	3½% Ni 1% Cr	Heat-treated		27	65	290	6
4 000	38 000	3½% Ni 1% Cr	Heat-treated		27	70	320	6
4 400	41 000	3½% Ni 1% Cr	Heat-treated		27	80	360	4
5 500	45 000	3½% Ni 1% Cr	Heat-treated		27	100	440	2

10 000	34 000g	2% Ni Mo	Case-hardened	34	40	200	3
11 000	43 000g	3% Ni Cr	Case-hardened	36	55	250	3
12 600	50 000g	4% Ni Cr	Case-hardened	39	80	360	3
7 500	20 000	3% Cr Nitrided	R	40A	45	201	6
8 500	27 000	3% Cr Nitrided	U		60	269	
10 000	38 000	3% Cr V, Nitrided	85 ton	40C	85	375	$2\frac{1}{2}$

For fabric impregnated with synthetic resin take $S_{BO} = 0.6 \times$ tensile strength (lb/in²) and ignore surface stress.

F = Flame-hardening multiplies this value by 2.0.

f = Flame-hardening multiplies this value by 0.8.

g = This value may be multiplied by 1.8 if special care is taken to give the tooth flanks and root surfaces a very smooth finish, entirely free from scratches, sharp corners and other blemishes, and to leave the root fillets unground.

[= Induction hardening multiplies this value by 2.0.

w = Can be welded without unreasonable difficulty.

* = As this steel is difficult to cut accurately it should be used only for helical gears with helix angles less than 10° and for which Class 3 tolerances are adequate.

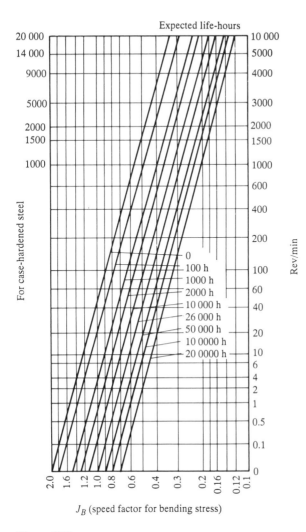

Figure 10.3

where

$$V_S = \text{Maximum sliding speed of teeth}$$

$$= 0.75 V dn \left(\frac{1}{t_1} + \frac{1}{t_2} \right) \cos \psi \ (\text{ft/min})$$

or

$$= 0.24 V p_n (n_1 + n_2) \ (\text{ft/min})$$

$$V = 4 - \frac{10}{\text{No. of teeth} - \text{max.}}$$

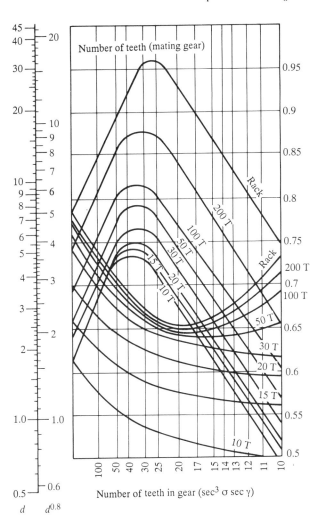

Figure 10.4 (*left*) Values of $d^{0.8}$ for d; (*above*) Strength factor Y

or

$$1 + \frac{20}{\text{No. of teeth} - \text{min.}}$$

Note: V is the maximum value for both gears of the pair.

$d =$ pitch circle diameter of gear
$n =$ rev/min of gear
$t_1 =$ no. of teeth – pinion
$t_2 =$ no. of teeth – wheel
$\psi =$ helix angle

p_n = circular (normal) pitch
n_1 = rev/min – pinion
n_2 = rev/min – wheel

Allowable load per 1 inch facewidth:

For surface stress

$$= \left(\frac{2.5 \times 10^6}{V_S + 100}\right) \times \frac{R_g}{R_g + 1} \times \frac{d^{0.8}}{4}$$

or

$$= J_{C1} \times S_{CO1} \times \frac{R_g}{R_g + 1} \times \frac{d^{0.8}}{4}$$

or

$$= J_{C2} \times S_{CO2} \times \frac{R_g}{R_g + 1} \times \frac{d^{0.8}}{4}$$

using whichever is the lower value.

For bending stress

$$= J_{B1} \times S_{BO1} \times Y_1 \times \frac{p_n}{\pi}$$

or

$$= J_{B2} \times S_{BO2} \times Y_2 \times \frac{p_n}{\pi}$$

using whichever is the lower value, where

V_S = maximum sliding speed of teeth (see page 150)
R_g = Gear ratio
$d^{0.8}$ = pitch (mean) diameter to the power 0.8 (see Figure 10.4)
J_{C1} = speed factor (surface stress) – pinion (see Figure 10.1)
S_{CO1} = basic allowable surface stress – pinion (see Figure 10.2)
J_{C2} = speed factor (surface stress) – wheel (see Figure 10.1)
S_{CO2} = basic allowable surface stress – wheel (see Figure 10.2)
J_{B1} = speed factor (bending stress) – pinion (see Figure 10.3)
S_{BO1} = basic allowable bending stress – pinion (see Figure 10.2)
J_{B2} = speed factor (bending stress) – wheel (see Figure 10.3)
S_{BO2} = basic allowable bending stress – wheel (see Figure 10.2)
Y_1 = strength factor – pinion (see Figure 10.4)
Y_2 = strength factor – wheel (see Figure 10.4)
p_n = normal circular pitch

Where gears are running at higher speeds with higher loads, a more accurate stress assessment is required, and Professor W.A. Tuplin added to the previous formulae as shown below. These formulae cover spur gears, helical gears, straight and spiral bevel gears, worm gears and crossed helical gears.

Allowable tooth load (lb) per 1 inch facewidth as determined by materials and geometry of the gear pair for surface stress:

Type of gear	Allowable tooth load (lb) per 1 in facewidth
Spur or helical	$(J_{RC1} \times S_{CO1}) \dfrac{Я d_1 R_g}{R_g + 1}$ *or* $(J_{RC2} \times S_{CO2}) \dfrac{Я d_1 R_g}{R_g + 1}$ *or* $\left[\dfrac{10^{10} \times \beta}{(V_S + 100)(n_1 + 10\,000)}\right] \dfrac{Я d_1 R_g}{R_g + 1}$ whichever gives the lower value
Straight or spiral bevel	$(J_{RC1} \times S_{CO1}) \dfrac{Я d_1 (K - F)}{1.1K\left(\cos \gamma_1 + \dfrac{\cos \gamma_2}{R_g}\right)}$ *or* $(J_{RC2} \times S_{CO2}) \dfrac{Я d_1 (K - F)}{1.1K\left(\cos \gamma_1 + \dfrac{\cos \gamma_2}{R_g}\right)}$ *or* $\left[\dfrac{10^{10} \times \beta}{(V_S + 100)(n_1 + 10\,000)}\right] \dfrac{Я d_1 (K - F)}{1.1K\left(\cos \gamma_1 + \dfrac{\cos \gamma_2}{R_g}\right)}$ whichever gives the lower value
Wormwheel	$(J_{RC2} \times S_{SO2}) \dfrac{D}{4}$ *or* $\left[\dfrac{10^{10} \times \beta}{(V_S + 100)(n_1 + 10\,000)}\right] \dfrac{D}{4}$ whichever gives the lower value
Crossed helical wheel	$(J_{RC2} \times S_{SO2}) \dfrac{D^2}{75F}$ *or* $\left[\dfrac{10^{10} \times \beta}{(V_S + 100)(n_1 + 10\,000)}\right] \dfrac{D^2}{75F}$ whichever gives the lower value

Allowable tooth load (lb) per 1 inch facewidth as determined by materials and geometry of the gear pair for bending stress:

Type of gear	Allowable tooth load (lb) per 1 in facewidth
Spur or helical	$(J_{RB1} \times S_{BO1} \times Y_1)\dfrac{p_n}{\pi}$ *or* $(J_{RB2} \times S_{BO2} \times Y_2)\dfrac{p_n}{\pi}$ whichever gives the lower value
Straight or spiral bevel	$(J_{RB1} \times S_{BO1} \times Y_1)\dfrac{p_n}{\pi} \times \dfrac{(K-F)}{1.1K}$ *or* $(J_{RB2} \times S_{BO2} \times Y_2)\dfrac{p_n}{\pi} \times \dfrac{(K-F)}{1.1K}$ whichever gives the lower value
wormwheel	$J_{RB2} \times S_{BO2} \left(\dfrac{Y_2 + 3F_2}{d_{B1}}\right)\dfrac{p_n}{\pi}$
Crossed helical	$\dfrac{J_{RB2} \times S_{BO2} \times Y_2 \times p_n^2(\cos \phi)}{5F}$

where

J_{RC1} = surface stress repetition factor – pinion (see Figure 10.5)
J_{RC2} = surface stress repetition factor – wheel (see Figure 10.5)
S_{CO1} = basic allowable surface stress – pinion (see Figure 10.2)
S_{CO2} = basic allowable surface stress – wheel (see Figure 10.2)
$Ɏ$ = zone factor (see page 156)
d_1 = root diameter – pinion
R_g = gear ratio
β = lubrication factor (see page 155)
V_S = maximum sliding speed of teeth (see page 150)
K = cone distance
F = facewidth – tooth
γ_1 = meshing cone angle – pinion
γ_2 = meshing cone angle – wheel
n_1 = revolutions per minute – pinion
D = pitch (mean) diameter – wheel
Y_1 = strength factor – pinion (see Figure 10.4)
Y_2 = strength factor – wheel (see Figure 10.4)
p_n = normal circular pitch
J_{RB1} = bending stress repetition factor – pinion (see Figure 10.5)
J_{RB2} = bending stress repetition factor – wheel (see Figure 10.5)

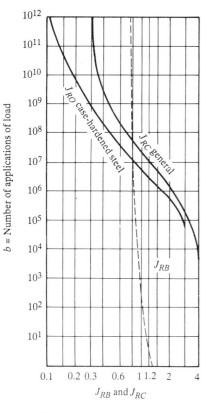

Figure 10.5   Surface stress repetition factor J_{RC}; bending stress repetition factor J_{RB}

S_{BO1} = basic allowable bending stress – pinion (see Figure 10.2)
S_{BO2} = basic allowable bending stress – wheel (see Figure 10.2)
F_R = actual facewidth of wormwheel or $p_n + 0.33d_{B1}$ (whichever is less)
d_{B1} = blank diameter – wormwheel
ϕ = helix or spiral angle
S_{SO2} = basic allowable surface stress for gears of crossed axis (see page 157)

Lubrication factor, β:

		Factor, β	
Gear materials	Lubricant	Parallel axis or intersecting	Crossed axis
Case-hardening steel/ case-hardening steel	Mineral oil	2.5	1.0
Other steel/other steel	Mineral oil	1.5	0
Steel/bronze	Mineral oil	4.0	2.5
Case-hardening steel/ case-hardening steel (smooth finish)	Anti-scuffing oil	5.0	2.0
Other steel/other steel	Anti-scuffing oil	3.0	0

Class of tolerance 'Z'	e_b	Transmission error $\times 10^{-6}$		Zone factor, Ʌ	
		e_s			
		Helical teeth	Straight teeth	Helical teeth	Straight teeth
1	$200(1+p_t)$	$200p_n$	$400p_n$	0.24*	
2	$400(1+p_t)$	$400p_n$	0.22		
3	$600(1+p_t)$	$600p_n$	$800p_n$	0.20	$\dfrac{13+V_1+V_2+Z}{100}$
6	$1200(1+p_t)$	$1200p_n$	$2400p_n$	0.15	

*If no. of teeth – pinion exceeds 32, multiply by $\left(1.25 - \dfrac{8}{t_1}\right)$

where

$Z=1$, high-precision gears
$Z=2$, high-class gears – tooth speeds up to 2500 ft/min
$Z=3$, good commercial quality gears – speeds up to 1000 ft/min
$Z=6$, for tooth speeds up to 500 ft/min in rough operating conditions
$e_b=$ random transmission error over one pitch
$p_t=$ transverse pitch (normal pitch $\times$ sec helix angle)
$e_s=$ amplitude of period transmission error at tooth engagement frequency
$p_n=$ normal circular pitch
$V_1=$ blank diameter factor – pinion (see pages 150 and 151)
$V_2=$ blank diameter factor – wheel (see pages 150 and 151)
'Z' $=$ class of tolerance

Professor Tuplin, following further research, arrived at a more accurate method of calculating the load capacity of a pair of gears as follows:

Load capacity of a pair of gears:

1 Tangential load

$$= \frac{\text{Torque} \times 2}{\text{PC dia. (gear)}}$$

2 Gear maximum speed

$$= \text{rpm (driving gear)} \times \frac{\text{No. of teeth (pinion)}}{\text{No. of teeth (gear)}}$$

3 Tooth speed

$$= \frac{\text{PC dia. (gear)} \times \pi \times \text{Rev/min (gear)}}{12}$$

Basic allowable surface stress for materials of crossed axis gears:

Material ref. no.	Material of wheel	Material of pinion (worm)				
		1	2	3	4	5
1	Case-hardened and ground steel, En 34, etc.	700*				500†
2	Nickel chrome steel, En 27 (55 ton)					450†
3	0.5% Carbon steel, En 9 (50 ton)					400†
4	0.4% Carbon steel, En 8 (45 ton)					400†
5	Grey cast iron	500†	450†	400†	400†	700†
6	Sand-cast phosphor-bronze	700	700	700	700	700†
7	Chill-cast phosphor-bronze	900	900	900	800	800†
8	Centrifugally cast phosphor-bronze	1200	1100	1100	1100	1000†

*Indicates only for high-precision crossed helical gears smoothly finished and run in with anti-weld oil.
†Indicates sliding speed not to exceed 500 ft/min.

4 Fix expected life of gears, in hours
5 Calculate revolutions of gear for expected life = No. of hours – life × 60 × Rev/min (gear)
6 Obtain values of J_{RC} and J_{RB} from Figure 10.5, page 155
7 Obtain values of S_{CO} and S_{BO} from Figure 10.2, page 148
8 Calculate values of:

$$R_B = \frac{\text{Internal diameter of rim}}{\text{Dia. of gear at mid-depth of teeth}}$$

9 Calculate values of 'A' for both gears:

$$A = \frac{\text{Density of material}}{\text{Density of steel}} \times \sqrt{1 + R_B^2}$$

For density of materials, see page 139.

10 Calculate value of 'B':

$$B = \frac{1}{(1 - R_B^4)(1 + i)}$$

where

$$i = \frac{I_a}{I_g \left(\dfrac{1 + 4I_a[nt/60]^2}{K}\right)}$$

I_a = moment of inertia of rotor about its axis
I_g = moment of inertia of gear about its axis
I_a and I_g can be calculated using the following formula:

$$\frac{\text{Width} \times \dfrac{\text{Density of material}}{\text{Density of steel}}(\text{Outside dia.}^4 - \text{Inside dia.}^4)}{14\,000}$$

K = torsional stiffness of connection

$$K = \frac{1.16 \times 10^6 \times \dfrac{\text{Mod. of elast. } - \text{ material}}{\text{Mod. of elast. } - \text{ steel}}(\text{Outs. dia.}^4 - \text{ Inside dia.}^4)}{\text{Length}}$$

n = rev/min – pinion
t = no. of teeth – pinion

For density of materials, see page 139.
For modulus of elasticity, see page 139.

11 Calculate compliance of teeth and rims (lb/in^2) of spur or helical gears made of steel:

$$H = \left[0.7 \sec \phi + 0.011(A_1 + \text{GR} \times A_2)^2 \times \left(B_1 + \frac{B_2}{\text{GR}^2}\right)\right] \times 10^{-6}$$

where

ϕ = helix or spiral angle
A_1 = calculation 9, page 157 – pinion
GR = gear ratio
A_2 = calculation 9, page 157 – wheel
B_1 = calculation 10, page 157 – pinion
B_2 = calculation 10, page 157 – wheel

12 Calculate critical rotational speed (rev/min) of pinion:

$$n_c = \frac{5600}{t_1 d_1} \sqrt{\frac{B_1 + \dfrac{B_2}{\text{Gear ratio}}}{H}}$$

where

t_1 = no. of teeth – pinion
d_1 = pitch (mean) diameter – pinion
B_1 = see calculation 10, page 157 – pinion
B_2 = see calculation 10, page 157 – wheel
H = see calculation 11, above

13 Calculate

$$n/n_c = \frac{2t_1 d_1 n_1 (R_g + 4)\sqrt{1+i}}{10^7}$$

where

n_1 = rev/min – pinion
t_1 = no. of teeth – pinion
d_1 = pitch (mean) diameter – pinion
R_g = gear ratio, T/t
d_o = base circle diameter – pinion

and

$$i\left(\frac{d_1}{d_o}\right) = \frac{\text{PC dia.} - \text{Base dia.}}{\text{Base dia.}} \sqrt{\frac{\text{PC dia.} - \text{Base dia.}}{\text{PC dia.} + \dfrac{\text{Base dia.}}{8}}}$$

Note: *i* applies only to the pinion.

14 Obtain values of A_b, A_s and A_L from Figures 10.6 and 10.7.

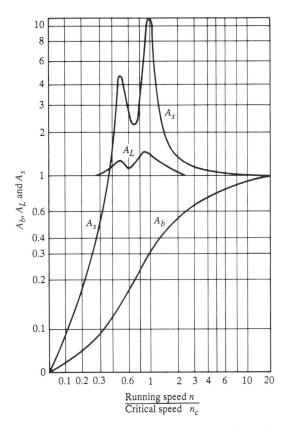

Figure 10.6 Dynamic load factors – straight teeth

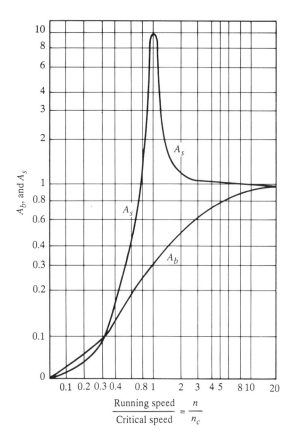

Figure 10.7   Dynamic load factors – helical teeth

15   Calculate values of:

V_1 for pinion
V_2 for gear

where

$$V_{min.} = 1 + \left(\frac{20}{\text{No. of teeth}} \right)$$

$$V_{max.} = 4 - \left(\frac{10}{\text{No. of teeth}} \right)$$

The values for V_1 and V_2 should be midway between $V_{min.}$ and $V_{max.}$

16   Calculate maximum sliding velocity:

$$V_S = 0.75 V d_n \left(\frac{1}{t_1} + \frac{1}{t_2} \right) \cos \phi \, (\text{ft/min})$$

or

$$= 0.24 V p_n (n_1 + n_2) \, (\text{ft/min})$$

where

> $V =$ maximum value of V_1 or V_2 for both pinion and gear
> $d =$ ref. (mean) diameter of gear
> $n =$ revolutions per minute of gear
> $t_1 =$ no. of teeth – pinion
> $t_2 =$ no. of teeth – wheel
> $\phi =$ spiral or helix angle
> $p_n =$ circular (normal) pitch
> $n_1 =$ revolutions per minute – pinion
> $n_2 =$ revolutions per minute – wheel

17 Obtain value of zone factor, λ (see table on page 156)

18 Calculate allowable tooth load (lb) per 1 in facewidth, as determined by materials and geometry of the gear pair for surface stress (G_{JMC}) (see pages 153 and 154).

19 Calculate allowable tooth load (lb) per 1 in facewidth, as determined by materials and geometry of the gear pair by bending stress (G_{JMB}) (see pages 154 and 155).

20 Calculate random transmission error over 1 pitch, e_b (see table on page 156).

21 Calculate amplitude of periodic transmission error at tooth-engagement frequency, e_s, (see table on page 156).

22 Calculate the value of:

$$\frac{A_b \times e_b}{H}$$

where

> A_b is obtained from calculation 14, page 159
> e_b is obtained from calculation 20, above
> H is obtained from calculation 11, page 158

23 Calculate the value of:

$$\frac{A_s \times e_s}{H}$$

where

> A_s is obtained from calculation 14, page 159
> e_s is obtained from calculation 20, above
> H is obtained from calculation 11, page 158

24 Calculate the values of tooth load (lb/in width) corresponding to the external torque on the gear with surface stress as the limitation (G_{JAC}).

Straight teeth:

$$G_{\text{JAC}} = \frac{G_{\text{JMC}} - (A_b \times e_b)/H}{1 + A_L}$$

or

$$G_{JAC} = G_{JMC} - \frac{A_b \times e_b}{H} - \frac{A_s \times e_s}{H}$$

whichever is the greater.

Helical teeth:

$$G_{JAC} = 0.75 G_{JMC} - 10^6 A_b e_b$$

where

G_{JMC} is obtained from calculation 18, page 161

$\dfrac{A_b \times e_b}{H}$ is obtained from calculation 22, page 161

$\dfrac{A_s \times e_s}{H}$ is obtained from calculation 23, page 161

A_L is obtained from calculation 14, page 159
A_b is obtained from calculation 14, page 159
e_b is obtained from calculation 20, page 161

25 Calculate the values of tooth load (lb/in width) corresponding to the external torque on the gear teeth with bending stress as the limitation (G_{JAB}).

Straight teeth:

$$G_{JAB} = \frac{G_{JMB} - (A_b \times e_b)/H}{1 + A_L}$$

or

$$G_{JAB} = G_{JMB} - \frac{A_b \times e_b}{H} - \frac{A_s \times e_s}{H}$$

whichever is the greater.

Helical teeth:

$$G_{JAB} = 0.75 G_{JMB} - 10^6 A_b e_b$$

where

G_{JMB} is obtained from calculation 19, page 161

$\dfrac{A_b \times e_b}{H}$ is obtained from calculation 22, page 161

$\dfrac{A_s \times e_s}{H}$ is obtained from calculation 23, page 161

A_L is obtained from calculation 14, page 159
A_b is obtained from calculation 14, page 159
e_b is obtained from calculation 20, page 161

The foregoing formulae were devised to provide a safeguard against the possibility of scuffing of the tooth surface; this, however, is far too restrictive in some circumstances, particularly where case-hardened steel is concerned. Research work which shows scatter in the results and in records of the performance of gears in service is so wide that there is no justification for any load-capacity formula that purports to go into a lot of fine detail. My current thoughts on this subject have produced a fairly simple formula for estimating life of gear; this is especially useful where loads and speeds are high and the life required of the gears is only short.

Among the factors that influence scuffing, the quality of the oil is obviously the most important one, and I am not sure that anyone is very confident about it. Certainly laboratory tests devised to induce scuffing invariably produce widely scattered results; and where loads and speeds are high, it is not possible to say beforehand whether there will be any scuffing or not. A small amount of scuffing is unimportant and, of course, this is especially the case where the life required of the gears is only short.

The above quote is from a letter written by Professor W.A. Tuplin to me, while we were both working on the problem of designing a train of transmission gears, used to connect the two crankshafts in the B.R.M. H.16 – 3-litre Formula One racing engine. The letter also contained the following formulae:

Tuplin formulae for life expectation of gears

No. of contacts permitted by contact stress

$$= 10^9 \left[\frac{S_{CO} C^2 f A R_g}{7.5 M_1 (1 + R_g)^3} \right]^6 \pm 50\%$$

No. of contacts permitted by bending stress

$$= 10^9 \left[\frac{S_{BO} C f p_n A H}{7.5 M_1 (1 + R_g)} \right]^{12} \pm 50\%$$

where

S_{CO} = basic contact stress factor (lb/in^2), see table on page 164
S_{BO} = basic bending stress factor (lb/in^2), see table on page 164
C = gear centres (in); this is negative for pinion and internal gears
f = facewidth (in)

A = unity or $0.7 + \dfrac{0.3f}{p_n}$, whichever is less

R_g = gear ratio = $\dfrac{\text{No. of teeth } - \text{ wheel}}{\text{No. of teeth } - \text{ pinion}}$

p_n = normal circular pitch
M_1 = external torque – pinion (lb/in)

$$H = 1.2 - 2.4 \left(\frac{1}{t} + \frac{1}{T} \right) \left[1 - 1.5 \left(\frac{p_n}{p_a} \right)^2 \right]^{3/2}$$

In most applications:

$$H = 1 \text{ is normally adequate}$$

$$\text{(if the wheel is an internal gear, add} \left(\frac{2t}{T}\right)^2 \text{)}$$

t = no. of teeth – pinion
T = no. of teeth – wheel
p_a = axial circular pitch

For rack and pinion:

No. of contacts permitted by contact stress

$$= \frac{C^2 R_g}{(1+R_g)^3} = \frac{d^2}{4}$$

No. of contacts permitted by bending stress

$$= \frac{C}{1+R_g} = \frac{d}{2}$$

where

d = diameter of pinion at mid-working depth (in)

Ref. no.	Steel	UTS (ton/in^2) core	Brinell (core)	Treatment	S_{BO}	S_{CO}
1	En 8	35–40	145	Normalized	18 000	1 450
2	En 8	35–40	145	Flame-hardened	14 500	2 900
3	En 9	45–50	210	Normalized	21 000	2 100
4	En 19	40–45	200	Flame-hardened	17 000	4 100
5	En 24	50–55	210	Induction-hardened	27 000	6 000
6	En 27	55–60	250	Heat-treated	31 000	3 100
7	En 34	35–45	360	Case-hardened	35 000 (g)	10 000
8	En 39	75–85	375	Case-hardened	50 000 (g)	12 000
9	En 40	55–65	270	Nitrided (U. condition)	20 000	7 500

g = multiply by 1.8 for bending stress factor if root fillets are machined smoothly and not ground after hardening

Satisfactory material combinations for gears are as follows – reference numbers:

1 and 2	2 and 3	2 and 4	3 and 5	5 and 6
6 and 7	7 and 7	8 and 8	8 and 9	9 and 9
1 and 3	3 and 6	4 and 5	5 and 9	7 and 8

Notes:

(a) Formula assumes that after some running under load, every tooth shows evidence of contact on 7 out of 10 equal divisions of the facewidth, and that the gears produce no excessive noise at full speed and full load.

(b) The minimum viscosity of the oil picked up by the gear teeth can be calculated using the following formula:

$$40 + \frac{3000\sqrt{S_{co}}}{V + 15} \text{ sec Redwood No. 1}$$

where

S_{co} = that of the softer material of the gear pair, see page 164

$$V = \frac{0.5 \times C \times n}{1 + R_g}$$

C = gear centres
n = revolutions per minute – pinion

$$R_g = \text{gear ratio} = \frac{\text{No. of teeth} - \text{wheel}}{\text{No. of teeth} - \text{pinion}}$$

(c) Life expectation is reduced if the gears run continuously at any of the three critical pinion speeds in the vicinities of:

$$n_1 = \frac{300\,000(1 + R_g)}{C \times t}$$

$$n_2 = \frac{1.9 \times 10^6(1 + R_g)}{C \times T}$$

$$n_3 = \frac{1.9 \times 10^6(1 + R_g)}{C \times t}$$

where

n_1, n_2 and n_3 = three critical pinion speeds

$$R_g = \text{gear ratio} = \frac{\text{No. of teeth} - \text{wheel}}{\text{No. of teeth} - \text{pinion}}$$

C = gear centres
t = no. of teeth – pinion
T = no. of teeth – wheel

Hertz stress formula

The Hertz stress formula can be used for calculating the gear tooth loading and is used as a basis for most of the other gear stress formulae.

Hertzian stresses

Compressive stress (q) max.

$$= \frac{4 \times \omega}{\pi \times Z}$$

Max. shear stress $= 0.295 \times q$

where

> $\omega =$ normal load per unit length of contact
> $Z =$ width of contact band

The maximum shear stress occurs at a maximum depth of $0.393Z$

where

$$Z = 4 \sqrt{\frac{\omega r}{\pi} \left(\frac{1 - \Upsilon_1^2}{E_1} \right) + \left(\frac{1 - \Upsilon_2^2}{E_2} \right)}$$

> $r =$ relative radius of curvature
> $1/r = 1/r_1 = 1/r_2$, where r_1 and r_2 are meshing diameters of gears
> $\Upsilon_1, \Upsilon_2 =$ Poisson's ratio for materials of gears – see below
> $E_1, E_2 =$ Young's modulus for materials of gears – see page 139

Poisson's ratio values for gear materials:

> steel: 0.30–0.31
> brass: 0.33
> cast iron: 0.27

Note: For gears made of steel, Poisson's ratio may be neglected.

Assuming a value of 0.3 for Υ_1 and Υ_2:

$$Z = 3.82 \sqrt{\frac{\omega r}{\pi} \left(\frac{1}{E_1} + \frac{1}{E_2} \right)}$$

or

$$Z = 3.05 \sqrt{\frac{\omega r}{E_1}}$$

$\therefore$ Compressive stress $q_{max.}$

$$= 0.418 \sqrt{\frac{\omega E^1}{r}}$$

where

$$\frac{1}{E^1} = \frac{1}{2} \left(\frac{1}{E_1} + \frac{1}{E_2} \right)$$

Surface stress

$$(S_c) = \omega/r$$

where

ω = normal load per unit length of contact
r = relative radius of curvature
$\therefore q_{max.} = 0.418\sqrt{S_c E^1}$

For steel/steel gears:

$$E^1 = 30\,000\,000\,\text{lb/in}^2$$
$$\therefore q_{max.} = 2290\sqrt{S_c}$$

Hertz K factor

$$= \frac{F_1}{d} \times \frac{p+1}{p}$$

where

F_1 = tangential load/inch facewidth (lb)
d = pitch circle dia. (pinion) (in)
p = reduction ratio

For spur gears:

$$\Upsilon = \frac{d \, \sin \, \phi}{2}\left(\frac{p}{p+1}\right)$$

where

ϕ = pressure angle

Assuming whole of load on one pair of teeth:

$$F_1 = \omega \, \cos \, \phi$$

From

$$q_{max.} = 2290\sqrt{\frac{\omega}{r}}$$

we arrive at

$$q_{max.} = 3240\sqrt{\frac{K}{\sin \, \phi \, \cos \, \phi}}$$

With 20° pressure angle:

$$q_{max.} = 5710\sqrt{K}$$
$\therefore$ For spur gears with 20° pressure angle

$$S_c = 6.3K$$

For helical gears:

$$r = \frac{d}{2}\left(\frac{p}{p+1}\right)\frac{\sin \phi_n}{\cos^2 \sigma}$$

$$W = \frac{F_t \times L}{\cos \sigma \times \cos \phi_n}$$

where

F_t = tangential load/inch facewidth (lb)
L = facewidth
σ = helix angle
ϕ_n = normal pressure angle

Helical gears with 20° pressure angle and 30° helix angle:

$$q_{max.} = 4050\sqrt{K}$$

$$S_c = 3.15K$$

where

K = Hertz factor, see page 167

BS 436: 1940 – Strength and Horse-power

Capacity of gears

The gear stress formulae given in BS 436: 1940 were originally issued in 1932, but recently this Standard has come under heavy criticism because of its shortcomings, mainly in not dealing with the differentials between gears produced to very high standards in material, gear cutting and finish, and heat treatment, as against the average commercially cut and finished gear.

The horse-power rating of helical and spur gears is calculated from the following formulae:

Horse-power for wear

$$= \frac{X_c S_c Z F N T}{12600 \; KP}$$

Horse-power for strength

$$= \frac{X_b S_b Y F N T}{12\,600 P^2}$$

The allowable tangential load per 1 inch facewidth for suitably lubricated gears should not exceed the value obtained from the following formulae:

Allowable tangential load – wear

$$=\frac{X_c Z S_c}{K}$$

Allowable tangential load – strength

$$=\frac{X_b Y S_b}{P}$$

Note: Both the horse-power capacity and allowable tangential load for any pair of gears is the lowest of the four figures, when calculated for both the pinion and wheel,

where the factors are calculated as follows:

1 *Speed factors, X_b and X_c.* The speed factors X_b and X_c for strength and wear, respectively, for the appropriate running times should be taken from Figures 10.8 and 10.9, respectively.

2 *Surface stress factor, S_c.* The surface stress factor S_c should be taken from Table 10.5.

3 *Zone factor, Z*

Helical gears: The zone factor Z for helical gears with 30° helix angle should be taken from Figure 10.10. For gears with other helix angles, the zone factor obtained from Figure 10.10 should be multiplied by $0.75 \times \sec^2$ Helix angle.

Spur gears: The zone factor Z for spur gears with 20° pressure angle should be taken from Figure 10.11.

Internal gears: The zone factor Z for internal gears is equal to the one for the same combination of teeth on an external gear pair multiplied by

$$\left(\frac{\text{Gear ratio} + 1}{\text{Gear ratio} - 1} \right)$$

4 Facewidth, F
5 Revs per min – wheel, N
6 No. of teeth – wheel, T
7 *Pitch factor, K.* The pitch factor K is equal to the diametral pitch$^{0.8}$ and can be taken from Figure 10.12. This chart in all instances refers to the diametral pitch on a section at right angles to the axis.

8 Diametral pitch, P
9 *Bending stress factor, S_b.* The bending stress factor S_b should be taken from Table 10.5.

10 *Strength factor, Y*

Helical gears: The strength factor Y for helical gears with 30° helix angle and 20° pressure angle should be taken from Figure 10.13, provided that the facewidth is sufficient to give overlap.

For other helix angles, the strength factor taken from Figure 10.13 should be multiplied by $1.33 \cos^2$ Helix angle.

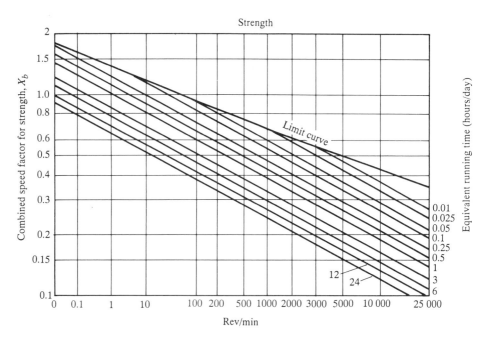

Figure 10.8   Combined speed and running time factors for spur and helical gears – for strength

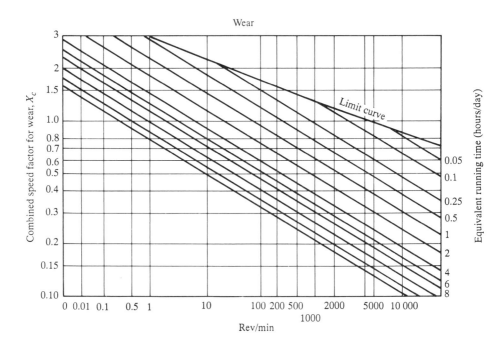

Figure 10.9   Combined speed and running time factors for spur and helical gears – for wear

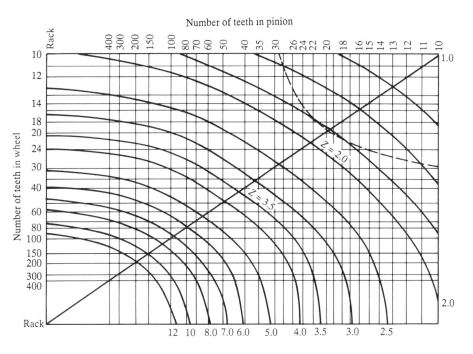

Figure 10.10   Zone factor – helical gears: 30° helix angle, 20° normal pressure angle

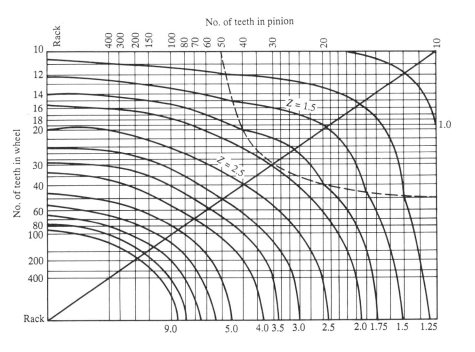

Figure 10.11   Zone factor – full depth. Spur gears: 20° pressure angle

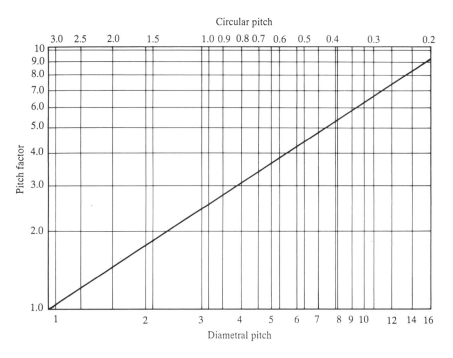

Figure 10.12   Pitch factor K for spur, helical and bevel gears

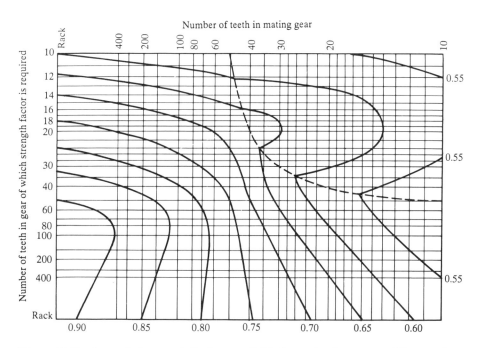

Figure 10.13   Strength factor – helical gears: 30° helix angle. Spur gears: 20° normal pressure angle

Table 10.5 Basic surface stress and bending stress factors

Material *Note:* The matter within square brackets refers to the condition of the finished gear and is not part of the title of the material specification	BS No.	Condition (letters refer to tensile range symbols for hardened and tempered material as given in BS 970)	Limiting ruling section (in)	Min. tensile strength of standard test piece (ton/in^2)	Min. Brinell No. (BS 240)	Basic surface stress factor S_c	Basic bending stress factor S_b
FABRIC	—	—	—	—	—	—	4 500
MALLEABLE CAST IRON							
Whiteheart malleable iron castings, Grade W/22/4	309	—	—	20	140	850	12 000
Blackheart malleable iron castings, Grade B20/10	310	—	—	20	140	850	12 000
CAST IRON							
Iron castings for gears and gear blanks:							
ordinary grade	821	As cast		12	165	1 025	5 800
ditto Medium grade	821	As cast		16	210	1 350	7 600
ditto High grade	821	As cast		22	220	1 450	10 500
ditto	821	Heat treated		22	300	2 100	10 500

Table 10.5 (*Cont.*)

Material *Note*: The matter within square brackets refers to the condition of the finished gear and is not part of the title of the material specification	BS No.	Condition (letters refer to tensile range symbols for hardened and tempered material as given in **BS** 970)	Limiting ruling section (in)	Min. tensile strength of standard test piece (ton/in²)	Min. Brinell No. (BS 240)	Basic surface stress factor S_c	Basic bending stress factor S_b
PHOSPHOR-BRONZE							
Phosphor bronze castings for gear blanks	1400–PB2-C	Sand-cast	–	12	69	710	7 200
Ditto	1400–PB2-C	Chill-cast	–	15	82	880	9 100
Ditto	1400–PB2-C	Centrifugally cast	–	17	90	1 000	10 000
CAST STEEL 0.35–0.45%	–	–	–	35	152	1 400	19 000
FORGED STEELS (*a*) *Carbon steels* '30' carbon steel [normalized]	970 En 5	–	$2\frac{1}{2}$	32	143	1 400	17 000

Material	Spec	Grade					
'30' carbon steel [hardened and tempered]	970 / En 5	P / —	$2\frac{1}{2}$ / 6	35 / 35	152 / 152	1 600 / 1 400	21 000 / 19 000
'40' carbon steel [normalized]	970 / En 8	Q / —	2 / 4	40 / 45	179 / 201	2 000 / 2 300	24 500 / 24 000
ditto [hardened and tempered]	970 / En 9	S	$1\frac{1}{8}$	50	223	2 650	30 500
'55' carbon steel [normalized] ditto [hardened and tempered] ditto, ditto	970 / En 9	T	$1\frac{1}{8}$	55	248	3 000	33 500
(b) Carbon–chromium steels							
'60' carbon–chromium steel [hardened and tempered]	970 / En 11	T	$2\frac{1}{2}$	55	248	3 000	33 500
ditto, ditto	970 / En 11	V	$2\frac{1}{2}$	65	293	3 600	39 500
1% chromium steel [hardened and tempered]	970 / En 18	T	$1\frac{1}{8}$	55	248	3 000	33 500
(c) Carbon–manganese steels							
carbon–manganese steel [normalized]	970 / En 14B	—	6	38	179	1 800	22 500
ditto [hardened and tempered]	970 / En 14B	Q	4	40	179	2 000	24 500
ditto, ditto	970 / En 14B	R	$2\frac{1}{2}$	45	201	2 300	27 000
carbon–manganese steel [higher tensile]	970 / En 15	R	$2\frac{1}{2}$	45	201	2 300	27 000
ditto	970 / En 15	S	$\frac{7}{8}$	50	223	2 650	30 500

Table 10.5 (*Cont.*)

Material *Note*: The matter within square brackets refers to the condition of the finished gear and is not part of the title of the material specification	BS No.	Condition (letters refer to tensile range symbols for hardened and tempered material as given in BS 970)	Limiting ruling section (in)	Min. tensile strength of standard test piece (ton/in²)	Min. Brinell No. (BS 240)	Basic surface stress factor S_c	Basic bending stress factor S_b
(d) Manganese–molybdenum steels							
manganese–molybdenum steel [hardened and tempered]	970 En 16	R	6	45	201	2 300	27 000
ditto	970 En 16	T	$2\frac{1}{2}$	55	248	3 000	33 500
manganese–molybdenum steel (higher molybdenum) [hardened and tempered]	970 En 17	R	6	45	201	2 300	27 000
ditto	970 En 17	T	4	55	248	3 000	33 500
(e) Manganese–nickel–molybdenum steels							
manganese–nickel–molybdenum steel [hardened and tempered]	970 En 13	—	6	40	179	2 000	24 500

(f) Chromium–molybdenum steels

Material	Spec						
1% chromium–molybdenum steel [hardened and tempered]	970 En 19	S	4	50	223	2 650	30 500
ditto	970 En 19	U	$2\frac{1}{8}$	60	269	3 300	36 500
ditto	970 En 19	W	$1\frac{1}{8}$	70	311	4 000	41 000
1% chromium–molybdenum steel (high molybdenum) [hardened and tempered]	970 En 20	T	$2\frac{1}{2}$	55	248	3 000	33 500
ditto	970 En 20	V	$1\frac{1}{8}$	65	293	3 600	39 500
3% chromium–molybdenum steel [hardened and tempered]	970 En 29	T	6	55	248	3 000	33 500
ditto	970 En 29	Z	$2\frac{1}{2}$	100	444	6 000	49 500

(g) Nickel steels

Material	Spec						
3% nickel steel [hardened and tempered]	970 En 21	R	4	45	201	2 300	27 000
3½% nickel steel [hardened and tempered]	970 En 22	T	$2\frac{1}{2}$	55	248	3 000	33 500

(j) Nickel–chromium steels

Material	Spec						
3% nickel–chromium steel [hardened and tempered]	970 En 23	T	6	55	248	3 000	33 500
ditto	970 En 23	V	$2\frac{1}{2}$	65	293	3 600	39 500
4¼% nickel–chromium steel [hardened and tempered]	970 En 30A	–	6 when hardened in oil $2\frac{1}{2}$ when hardened in air	100	444	6 000	49 500

Table 10.5   (*Cont.*)

Material. *Note*: The matter within square brackets refers to the condition of the finished gear and is not part of the title of the material specification	BS No.	Condition (letters refer to tensile range symbols for hardened and tempered material as given in BS 970)	Limiting ruling section (in)	Min. tensile strength of standard test piece (ton/in²)	Min. Brinell No. (BS 240)	Basic surface stress factor S_c	Basic bending stress factor S_b
(k) *Nickel–chromium–molybdenum steels*							
1½% nickel – chromium– molybdenum steel [hardened and tempered]	970 En 24	T	6	55	248	3 000	33 500
ditto	970 En 24	Z	$1\frac{1}{8}$	100	444	6 000	49 500
2½% nickel–chromium– molybdenum steel (medium carbon) [hardened and tempered]	970 En 25	T	6	55	248	3 000	33 500
ditto	970 En 25	Z	$2\frac{1}{2}$	100	444	6 000	49 500

2½% nickel–chromium–molybdenum steel (high carbon) [hardened and tempered]	970 En 26	U	6	60	269	—	—	3 300	36 500
ditto	En 26	Z	4	100	444	—	—	6000	49 500
3% nickel–chromium–molybdenum steel [hardened and tempered]	970 En 27	T	6	55	248	—	—	3000	33 500
ditto	970 En 27	W	4	70	311	—	—	4000	41 000
3½% nickel–chromium–molybdenum steel [hardened and tempered]	970 En 28	U	6	60	269	—	—	3 300	36 500
ditto	970 En 28	Y	2½	80	363	—	—	4650	44 000
4¼% nickel–chromium–molybdenum steel [hardened and tempered]	970 En 30B	—	6 when hardened in oil 2½ when hardened in air	100	444	—	—	6000	49 500

SURFACE-HARDENED STEELS

FORGED STEELS

(a) *Carbon steels*

'40' carbon steel [normalized, surface hardened in water]	970 En 8	—	6	35	152	498	550	2 800	17 000
'55' carbon steel [normalized, surface hardened in air]	970 En 9	—	4	45	201	520	580	4 000	21 500

Table 10.5 (*Cont.*)

Material Note: The matter within square brackets refers to the condition of the finished gear and is not part of the title of the material specification	BS No.	Condition (letters refer to tensile range symbols for hardened and tempered material as given in BS 970)	Limiting ruling section (in)	Min. tensile strength of standard test piece (ton/in²)	Core hardness Min. Brinell No. (BS 240)	Case hardness		Basic surface stress factor S_c	Basic bending stress factor S_b
						Min. Brinell No. (BS 240)	Min. HV (BS427)		
(b) *Carbon–chromium steel* '60' carbon–chromium steel [hardened, tempered and surface hardened in air]	970 En 11	T	$2\frac{1}{2}$	55	248	534	600	5 100	26 500
(g) *Nickel steel* $3\frac{1}{2}$% nickel steel [hardened, tempered and surface hardened in air] En 22	970	T	$2\frac{1}{2}$	55	248	500	550	5 100	26 500
(j) *Nickel–chromium steel* 3% nickel–chromium steel [hardened, tempered and surface hardened in air] En 23	970	T	6	55	248	500	550	5 100	26 500

(k) Nickel–chromium–molybdenum steels

$1\frac{1}{2}$% nickel–chromium–molybdenum steel [hardened, tempered and surface hardened in air]	970 En 24	T	6	55	248	490	540	5 100	26 500
$2\frac{1}{4}$% nickel–chromium–molybdenum steel (medium carbon) [hardened, tempered and surface hardened in air]	970 En 25	T	6	55	248	445	480	5 100	26 500
$2\frac{1}{4}$% nickel–chromium–molybdenum steel (high carbon) [hardened, tempered and surface hardened in air]	970 En 26	U	6	60	269	500	550	5 600	29 000
3% nickel–chromium–molybdenum steel [hardened, tempered and surface hardened in air]	970 En 27	T	6	55	248	445	480	5 100	26 500
$3\frac{1}{2}$% nickel–chromium–molybdenum steel [hardened, tempered and surface hardened in air]	970 En 28	U	6	60	269	500	550	5 600	29 000

CASE-HARDENED STEELS

FORGED STEELS

(a) Carbon steel

Carbon case-hardening steel	970 En 32B	—	$1\frac{1}{8}$	32	140	—	750	9 200	40 000

(g) Nickel steels

3% nickel case-hardening steel	970 En 33	—	$1\frac{1}{2}$	45	201	—	750	10 500	47 000

Table 10.5 (*Cont.*)

Material Note: The matter within square brackets refers to the condition of the finished gear and is not part of the title of the material specification	BS No.	Condition (letters refer to tensile range symbols for hardened and tempered material as given in BS 970)	Limiting ruling section (in)	Min. tensile strength of standard test piece (ton/in²)	Min. Brinell No. (BS 240)	Basic surface stress factor S_c	Basic bending stress factor S_b
(h) Nickel–molybdenum steels							
2% nickel–molybdenum case-hardening steel (lower carbon)	970 En 34	–	1⅛	45	201	750	10 500
2% nickel–molybdenum case-hardening steel (higher carbon)	970 En 35	–	1⅛	55	248	750	11 000
(j) Nickel–chromium steels							
3% nickel–chromium case-hardening steel	970 En 36	T	1⅛	55	248	710	11 000
4¼% nickel–chromium case-hardening steel	970 En 39A	–	–	85	388	710	13 000
4¼% nickel–chromium–molybdenum case-hardening steel	970 En 39B	–	–	85	388	710	13 000

The effectiveness of any fraction x of an axial pitch is $\frac{1}{3}(2+x^2)$; if the facewidth F is less than the axial pitch p_n and is therefore insufficient to give overlap, the strength factor should be multiplied by

$$\frac{1}{3}\left[2+\left(\frac{\text{Facewidth}}{\text{Axial pitch}}\right)^2\right]$$

Spur gears: The strength factor Y for spur gears with 20° pressure angle is the same as that for helical gears with 30° helix angle and should be taken from Figure 10.13, page 172.

Internal gears: The strength factor Y for the pinion gears used with internal gearing shall be the same as that for a pinion of the same number of teeth running with a rack.

The strength factor Y for the internal gear shall be the same as that of a rack running with a pinion having the same number of teeth as the actual pinion, multiplied by

$$\left(1+\frac{3}{T}\right)$$

where

$T=$ no. of teeth in the internal gear

Factor of safety. When it is desirable to give a factor of safety for gears as regards strength, in the same manner that is usually adopted for the strength of materials in other engineering material calculations, then the following formula should be used:

$$\text{Factor of safety} = \frac{S_t \times Y \times F \times N \times T}{\text{hp transmitted} \times P^2 \times 126\,000}$$

where

$S_t=$ ultimate tensile stress – material (lb/in^2)
$Y=$ strength factor – see page 169
$F=$ facewidth of gear
$N=$ revolutions per minute – wheel
$T=$ no. of teeth – wheel
$P=$ diametral pitch

Automobile gears

The formulae given on page 168 for the calculation of horse-power are intended for gears used for industrial purposes which are running more or less continuously, and, in the case of change speed gearboxes, when each individual gear is, generally speaking, only subjected to occasional use, it is possible to allow higher stresses.

The formulae may be adapted to the design of automobile change speed gears by substituting for the speed factor X_b or X_c (see page 169) the following values:

$$\text{for forward gears} = \frac{15 + G_t}{30}$$

$$\text{for reverse gears} = \frac{15 + G_t}{25}$$

where

G_t = gradient factor, and is calculated using the following formula:

$$G_t = \frac{100 \times M \times R_o}{W_G \times r}$$

where

M = maximum engine torque (lb/in)
R_o = overall reduction in gear under review

$$= \frac{\text{Engine rpm}}{\text{Road wheel rpm}}$$

W_G = gross laden weight of vehicle plus any trailer if used (lb)
r = tyre rolling radius (in)

Note: The load capacity of constant mesh gears is calculated for the condition which is most frequently used, i.e. in a conventional gearbox, the gear next to top gear.

As a result of the shortcomings of BS 436: 1940, a new Standard (BS 436: 1986) has been issued. This Standard is principally based on ISO 6336.
A brief history of the movement in gear stressing shows that:

(a) 1932 – BS 436 was first issued
(b) 1940 – BS 436 was revised
(c) 1957 – International Standards Organization (ISO) agreed on the basis of a procedure for rating involute gears
(d) 1973 – British Gear Manufacturers' Association half-yearly technical meeting; a paper was presented proposing a new gear rating procedure
(e) 1980 – ISO issued Draft Standard DP 6336, parts 1 to 4, for comment
(f) 1986 – British Standards Institution issued the new version of BS 436; this Standard draws heavily on ISO DIS 6336

The new BS 436: 1986 takes the following points into account:

(a) gear accuracy
(b) is applicable over a wide range of applications, dimensions and proportions
(c) deals with some of the aspects of surface-hardened gears
(d) vibrations arising from both internal and external sources
(e) the effect of the lubricant film and gear flank roughness
(f) stress concentration effects in the tooth root
(g) the effect of residual stress in the tooth root
(h) the effect of bending stress on the tooth flank stress cycle.

BS 436: 1986 – Strength and Horse-power

Capacity of Gears

The calculation procedure in BS 436: 1986 is used to calculate gear load-carrying capacity both in terms of stresses and power.

The calculations are carried out for both the pinion and wheel and the lowest of the four figures arrived at, taken as the stress allowable on the gear pair.

Contact stress calculations:

Permissible contact stress, σ_{HP}

$$= \sigma_{Hlim.} \frac{Z_L Z_V Z_R Z_M Z_W Z_X Z_N}{S_{Hmin}} \, (\mathrm{MN/m^2})$$

Actual calculated contact stress, σ_H

$$= Z_H Z_E Z_\varepsilon \sqrt{\frac{F_{HC}}{bd_1} \times \frac{(u+1)}{u}} \times K_A K_v K_{H\alpha} K_{H\beta} \, (\mathrm{MN/m^2})$$

Permissible power capacity and torque based on contact stress:

Permissible power capacity, P_{HP}

$$= \frac{bd_1^2 \pi n_1}{60 \times 10^6} \times \frac{u}{u+1} \times \frac{1}{Z_H^2 Z_\varepsilon^2} \times \frac{1}{K_A} \times \frac{1}{K_v} \times \frac{1}{K_{H\alpha} K_{H\beta}} \times \left(\frac{\sigma_{HP}}{Z_E}\right)^2 \, (\mathrm{kW})$$

Permissible torque capacity, T_{HP}

$$= \frac{60 \times 10^3}{2\pi} \times \frac{P_{HP}}{n_1} - \mathrm{N.m}$$

Peak torque capacity for contact stress, $T_{H,\,max.}$

$$= T_{HP} K_\Delta K_v \left(\frac{\sigma_{HY} Z_M}{\sigma_{HP} S_{Hmin.}}\right)^2 - \mathrm{N.m}$$

where

1     $\sigma_{Hlim} = \sigma_{HD} Z_G Z_C$
σ_{HD} can be taken from Figure 10.14
Z_G for wheel can be taken from Figure 10.15
Z_G for pinion is the larger of:
(a) $= (1.02 - 0.02 \times \text{Gear ratio}) Z_{Gwheel}$
(b) $= 0.9 Z_{Gwheel}$
Z_C for surface-hardened steels can be taken from Figure 10.16
$\sigma_{Hlim} =$ endurance limit for contact stress for gears $(\mathrm{MN/m^2})$
$\sigma_{HD} =$ endurance limit for contact stress for discs $(\mathrm{MN/m^2})$
$Z_G =$ disc/gear correlation factor for contact stress
$Z_C =$ case depth factor for contact stress
$\sigma_B =$ ultimate tensile strength $(\mathrm{MN/m^2})$
$\rho_{rel.} =$ radius of relative curvature
$c_{eff.} =$ effective case depth (mm)
$c_{lim.} =$ limiting case depth (see Table 10.6)

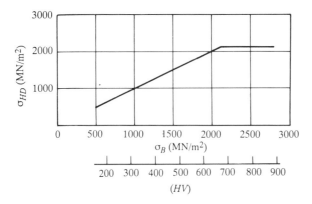

Figure 10.14   Values of σ_{HD} (Note: Values of σ_{HD} in this figure are derived from disc tests performed under the auspices of the Admiralty Vickers Gear Research Association and the Navy and Vickers Gear Research Association)

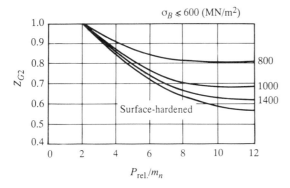

Figure 10.15   Values of Z_G [Note: For internal gears the value of $\rho_{\text{rel.}}$ for an equivalent external gear should be used, i.e. the value of $\rho_{\text{rel.}}$ obtained from B.10 should be multiplied by $(|u| - 1)/(|u| + 1)$]

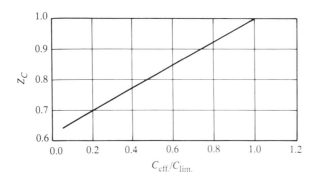

Figure 10.16   Case depth factor, Z_C

Table 10.6 Limiting case depth

Hardening process	Limiting case depth ($c_{\text{lim.}}$)†
Carburizing and hardening	$0.16m_n$
Nitriding	$0.16m_n$
Induction hardening	$0.32m_n$

†m_n = normal module

$\rho_{\text{rel.}}$ is calculated from one of the following two formulae:

(a) $= \dfrac{d_1}{2} \times \dfrac{u}{(n+1)} \times \dfrac{\cos \alpha_t \, \tan \alpha_{tw}}{\cos \beta_b}$

(b) $= \dfrac{d_{w1}}{2} \times \dfrac{u}{(u+1)} \times \dfrac{\sin \alpha_{tw}}{\cos \beta_b}$

d_1 = PC dia. (pinion) (mm)
d_{w1} = PC dia. (pinion) − Pitch cylinder (mm)
u = gear ratio
α_t = transverse pressure angle at PC dia. (rad.)
α_{tw} = transverse pressure angle at pitch cylinder (rad.)
β_b = base helix angle (rad.)

2   Z_L – lubricant factor for contact stress
Z_R – roughness factor for contact stress
Z_V – speed factor for contact stress
The value of the product $Z_L Z_V$ should be taken from Figure 10.17, where
V = pitch line velocity (m/sec).

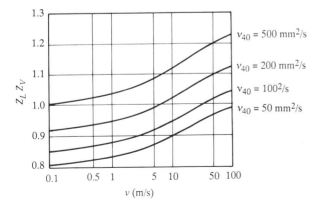

Figure 10.17 Combined speed and lubricant factors, $Z_L Z_V$ (v_{40} is the kinematic viscosity of lubricant at 40°C, in mm²/s or cSt)

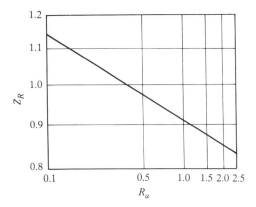

Figure 10.18   Roughness factor, Z_R

The value of Z_R should be taken from Figure 10.18, where

$$R_a = \frac{R_{a1} + R_{a2}}{2}$$

if the pinion and wheel roughnesses are different,
or

$$R_a = \frac{R_z}{6}$$

if the roughness is measured in terms of R_z.

   R_o = arithmetic average roughness (CLA value)
   R_{a1} = arithmetic average roughness – pinion (CLA value)
   R_{a2} = arithmetic average roughness – wheel (CLA value)
   R_z = mean roughness (μm)
   μm = 0.001 mm

3 Z_M – *Material quality for contact stress.* The values of Z_M should be taken from the table below, where

Material	Value of Z_M		
	Quality A	Quality B	Quality C
Surface-hardened steels	1.0	0.9	0.8
Through-hardened or normalized steels	1.0	0.9	0.8
Through-hardened or normalized cast steels	0.9	0.8	0.7
Nodular cast iron	0.9	0.8	0.7
Other cast irons	0.7	0.5	0.5

Quality A defines the maximum requirement for materials and their heat treatments for special applications, e.g. high power or high reliability requirements

Quality B defines the requirements for materials and their heat treatments for the majority of industrial gears at reasonable cost

Quality C defines the minimum requirements for materials and their heat treatments for lightly loaded gears in non-critical applications

4 Z_W – *Work-hardening factor for contact stress.* The work-hardening factor accounts for the increase in surface durability due to meshing a through-hardened steel gearwheel with a surface-hardened pinion. In all other cases $Z_W = 1.0$.

For gearwheels with hardness less than 400 HV, the value of Z_W should be taken from Figure 10.19.

For gearwheels with hardness equal to or greater than 400 HV, $Z_W = 1.0$.

Where roughness is measured in terms of R_z, then R_a should be calculated as follows:

$$R_a = \frac{R_z}{6}$$

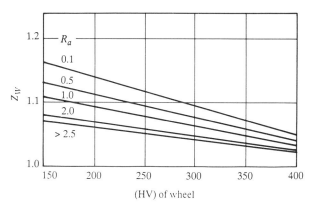

Figure 10.19   Values of Z_W

5 Z_X – *Size factor for contact stress.* The size factor is included to take into account possible influences of size on material quality and its response to heat treatment, and any other manufacturing processes involved in the production of the gear. The value is taken as $Z_X = 1.0$.

6 Z_N – *Life factor for contact stress.* The life factor for contact stress takes into account the increase in permissible stress if the number of stress cycles is less than the endurance life.

If the gear pair is subject to variable duty and the design torque has therefore been calculated using the variable duty procedure (see page 193), then $Z_N = 1.0$.

Otherwise the value of Z_N should be taken from the S/N curve of the material if it is available. Failing this, it should be taken from Figure 10.20.

The number of cycles of tooth loading, N, are those appropriate to both pinion and wheel, respectively, taking into account the gear ratio and the number of pinions and wheels in mesh. The curves in Figure 10.20 are defined as follows:

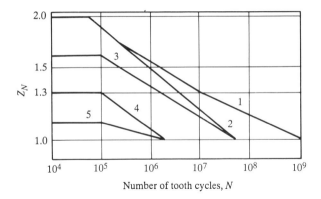

Figure 10.20   Life factor for contact stress, Z_N (see text for definition of curves)

Curve 1 is for through-hardened steels, surface-hardened steels with case depth greater than or equal to the limiting case depth, and cast irons other than grey cast iron when some pitting is permissible.

Curve 2 is for through-hardened steels and cast irons other than grey cast iron when pitting is not permissible.

Curve 3 is for surface-hardened steels with case depth greater than or equal to the limiting case depth when pitting is not permissible.

Curve 4 is for surface-hardened steels with case depth less than the limiting case depth, bronze and grey cast iron.

Curve 5 is for bath nitrided steels.

7 $S_{Hmin.}$ – *Minimum demanded safety factor on contact stress.* The choice of the minimum demanded safety factor is to be agreed between the gear manufacturer and the purchaser.

Note: The value of $S_{Hmin.}$ should reflect the confidence in the actual operating conditions and material properties being truly reflected in this standard. When the load histogram is not surely known or where high tooth loads are likely to occur due to circumstances outside the scope of this standard, an appropriately high value of the minimum demanded safety factor should be used.

The recommended ranges of $S_{Hmin.}$ are as follows:

(a) For normal industrial applications, $S_{Hmin.} = 1.0–1.2$
(b) For high reliability and critical applications (high consequential damage, loss of life, etc.),
    $S_{Hmin.} = 1.3–1.6$

8 Z_H – *Zone factor for contact stress.* The zone factor for contact stress, Z_H, accounts for the influence of tooth flank curvature at the pitch point on Hertzian stress and converts the tangential force at the reference cylinder to a normal force at the pitch cylinder.

The zone factor is calculated using the following formulae:

(a) For gears at standard centres:

$$Z_H = 2\sqrt{\frac{\cos\ \text{Base helix angle}}{\sin\ (2\times\text{Transverse press angle})}}$$

(b) For gears at non-standard centres:

$$Z_H = \sqrt{\frac{2\times\cos\ \text{Base helix angle}\times\cot\ \text{Trans. press. angle (pitch cyl.)}}{\cos^2\ \text{Trans. press. angle}\times\sin\ \text{Trans. press. angle (pitch cyl.)}}}$$

9 Z_E – *Elasticity factor for contact stress.* The elasticity factor accounts for the influence of the specific material properties, E (modulus of elasticity) and v (Poisson's ratio) on the Hertzian stress.

The elasticity factor is calculated from the following formula:

$$Z_E = \sqrt{\frac{1}{\pi\left(\dfrac{1-v_1^2}{E_1}+\dfrac{1-v_2^2}{E_2}\right)}}$$

The table below gives the values of Z_E for some combinations of materials.

Gear materials	Z_E
Steel/steel	189
Steel/SG cast iron	181
SG cast iron/SG cast iron	174
Grey iron/grey iron	146

The properties of bronzes can be obtained from BS 1400.

10 Z_ε – *Contact ratio factor for contact stress.* The contact ratio factor accounts for the load-sharing influence of the transverse contact ratio and the overlap ratio on the specific loading, and is calculated using the following formulae:

(a) Spur gears:

$$Z_\varepsilon = \sqrt{\frac{4-\varepsilon_\alpha}{3}}$$

(b) Helical gears, where $\varepsilon_\beta < 1$:

$$Z_\varepsilon = \sqrt{\left[\frac{4-\varepsilon_\alpha)}{3}\times(1-\varepsilon_\beta)\right]+\frac{\varepsilon_\beta}{\varepsilon_\alpha}}$$

(c) Helical gears, where $\varepsilon_\beta > 1$:

$$Z_\varepsilon = \sqrt{\frac{1}{\varepsilon_\alpha}}$$

where

$$\varepsilon_\alpha = \frac{\text{Length of path of contact}}{\text{Transverse base pitch}}$$

$$\varepsilon_\beta = \frac{\text{Facewidth} \times \sin \text{ Helix angle}}{\pi \times \text{Normal module}}$$

(d) Length of path of contact:

for external gears

$$= 0.5\left(\sqrt{d_{a1}^2 - d_{b1}^2} + \sqrt{d_{a2}^2 - d_{b2}^2}\right) - a \sin \alpha_{tw}$$

for internal gears

$$= 0.5\left(\sqrt{d_{a1}^2 - d_{b1}^2} - \sqrt{d_{a2}^2 - d_{b2}^2}\right) - a \sin \alpha_{tw}$$

where

d_{a1} = tip diameter – pinion (mm)
d_{b1} = base diameter – pinion (mm)
d_{a2} = tip diameter – wheel (mm)
d_{b2} = base diameter – wheel (mm)
a = centre distance (mm)
α_{tw} = transverse pressure angle at pitch cylinder (rad)

$$\alpha_{tw} = \tan^{-1}\left(\frac{\tan \text{ Nominal press. angle}}{\cos \text{ Helix angle}}\right)$$

(e) Transverse base pitch

$$= \frac{m_n \pi \cos \alpha_t}{\cos \beta}$$

where

m_n = normal module (mm)
α_1 = transverse pressure angle at pitch cylinder (rad)
β = helix angle (rad)

11 F_{Ht} – *Nominal tangential force for contact stress.* The nominal tangential force for contact stress is calculated using one of the following formulae:

(a)
$$= \frac{2000 T_{H1}}{d_1}$$

(b)
$$= \frac{1000 P_H}{v}$$

where

T_{H1} = actual torque based on contact stress (nm)
d_1 = reference diameter – pinion (mm)

P_H = actual power capacity based on contact stress (kW)
v = pitch line velocity (m/sec)

$$d_1 = \frac{Z_1 M_N}{\cos \beta}$$

Z_1 = number of teeth – pinion
M_N = normal module (mm)
β = helix angle (rad.)

If the gear pair is subject to variable duty or to intermittent high loads, the pinion torque should be calculated as follows:

$$T_{\infty i} = \left[\frac{1}{N_\infty} \Sigma (N_i T_i Q) \right]^{1/Q}$$

To arrive at the values for the preceding calculation, the following procedure should be followed:

(a) Arrange the applied pinion torques in descending order of magnitude.
(b) For each level of torque, calculate the number of cycles of tooth engagement experienced by both the pinion and wheel. The number of pinions and wheels in engagement and the gear ratio have to be taken into account.
(c) The value of Q_H is calculated as follows:

$$= \frac{\log(N_{H\infty}/N_{\sigma H\,max.})}{2 \, \log(\sigma_{H\,max.}/\sigma_{H\,lim.})}$$

where

$N_{H\infty}$ = no. of cycles at upper knee of S/N curve
$N_{\sigma H}$ = no. of cycles at lower knee of S/N curve
$\sigma_{H\,max.}$ = stress at upper knee of S/N curve (MN/m²)
$\sigma_{H\,lim.}$ = stress at lower knee of S/N curve (MN/m²)

See Figure 10.21 for the above values. Charts of this type should be used for the relevant materials, unless they are given in the table on page 194.

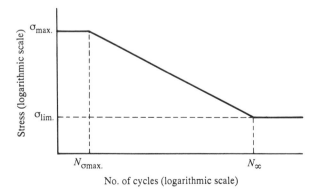

Figure 10.21 Typical S/N curve

The calculations should start with $i=1$, i.e. including the largest torque only, and continue with further values of T_i in descending order. The successive values of $T_{\infty i}$ should be calculated for the varying range of values of T_i (see calculation on page 193), where

T_i = applied pinion torques
N_∞ = no. of cycles at lower knee of S/N curve
N_i = no. of tooth cycles endured at specific torque
Q = exponent – see calculation (c) above and page 193.

Default values for contact stress S/N curve parameters:

	Material type 1*	Materials type 2	Material type 3	Material type 4	Material type 5
$N_{H\infty}$	10^9	5×10^7	5×10^7	2×10^6	2×10^6
$N_{\sigma H \text{ max.}}$	10^4	5×10^4	10^5	10^5	10^5
$\dfrac{\sigma_{H \text{ max.}}}{\sigma_{H \text{ lim.}}}$	2.0	2.0	1.6	1.3	1.1
Q_H	8.305	4.983	6.611	5.709	15.72

*For material types see curve numbers on page 190.

Note: In order to facilitate the calculations for surface stress when pitting is allowed, the three sections of the life curve (see Figure 10.20) have been approximated to one straight line. This will result in a slightly overestimated value of $T_{H\infty}$ for low numbers of cycles.

Notes:

(a) If any value of $T_{\infty i}$ is greater than the next level of torque $T_{(i+1)}$, then that value of $T_{\infty i}$ is used as T_∞ in the calculation of actual stress or power.
(b) If $T_{\infty i}$ is less than $T_{(i+1)}$, i.e. if condition (a) above does not apply but $T_{\infty(i+1)}$ is greater than $T_{(i+1)}$, then $T_{(i+1)}$ is used as T_∞ in the calculation of actual stresses or power.
(c) If, when all torques have been included, the final value of $T_{\infty i}$ is less than the final T_i, then $T_{\infty i}$ is used as T_∞ in the calculation of actual stress or power. If the final value of $T_{i\infty}$ is greater than the final value of T_i, then the final value of T_i is used. This is equivalent to using (a) and (b) above, plus an imaginary infinitesimal torque T_i.

12 u – Gear ratio
13 b – Facewidth (mm)
14 d_1 – Reference diameter – pinion (mm)
15 K_A – *Application factor*. The application factor accounts for load fluctuations from the mean load or loads in the load histogram caused by sources external to the gearing. The fluctuations depend on the characteristics of the prime mover, the driven machinery and the system vibration response to the working conditions.

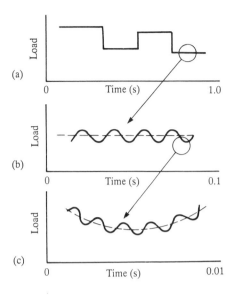

Figure 10.22 Constituent parts of typical gear load: (a) load histogram; (b) application factor; (c) dynamic factor

A typical total gear load is shown broken down into individual components, including the application factor (Figure 10.22).

The application factor, K_A, is assessed from measurements on similar existing systems or, if such information is not available, from the information given in Tables 10.7–10.9.

Table 10.7 Values of application factor

Load characteristic of prime mover	Load on driven machine			
	Uniform	Moderate shock	Medium shock	Heavy shock
Uniform	1.0	1.25	1.50	1.75
Light shock	1.10	1.35	1.60	1.85
Moderate shock	1.25	1.50	1.75	2.0
Heavy shock	1.50	1.75	2.0	2.25

Table 10.8 Examples of prime mover with different working characteristics

Character of operation	Prime mover
Uniform	Electric motor
Light shock	Steam turbine, gas turbine
Moderate shock	Multi-cylinder combustion engine
Heavy shock	Single cylinder combustion engine

Table 10.9   Examples of driven machines with different working characteristics

Character	Driven machine
Uniform	Generator, uniformly loaded belt or platform conveyors, worm conveyors, light elevators, packaging machines, feed gears for machine tools, ventilators, light centrifuges, centrifugal pumps, mixer for light fluids or constant density material, shearing, pressing, punching, turning gears, moving gears
Moderate shock	Non-uniformly loaded belt (e.g. mixed cargo) or platform conveyor, main drives of machine tools, heavy elevators, turning gears of cranes, industrial and mine ventilators, heavy centrifuges, centrifugal pumps, mixer for high-viscosity or variable-density materials, multi-cylinder piston pumps, feed pumps, extruders (general) calenders, rotary furnaces, rolling mills (continuous zinc strip, aluminium strip as well as wire and bar rolling mills)
Medium shock	Extruders for rubber, mixers with interrupted operations for rubber and plastics, ball mills (light), wood-working – mills, saws and lathes, billet rolling mills, lifting gear, single cylinder piston pump
Heavy shock	Excavators (bucket wheel gears, multi-bucket gears, sieve gears, power shovels), ball mills (heavy), rubber dough mills, breaker (stone, ore) metallurgical machines, heavy feed pumps, rotary drilling apparatus, brick moulding press, braking drums, peeling machines, cold-strip rolling mills, briquette press, pug mills

16 K_v – *Dynamic factor*. The dynamic factor accounts for load fluctuations arising from contact conditions at the gear teeth. The main influences are:

(a) Gear tooth accuracy
(b) The tooth contact frequency divided by the natural frequency of torsional oscillations due to pinion and wheel inertias acting against the mesh stiffness

The portion of a typical gear load accounted for by the dynamic factor is shown in Figure 10.22.

The values included in British Standard 436 Part 3, 1986, are appropriate.

Note: At low load the value of K_v may be higher than given by the Standard, but the stress will not exceed the stress at the maximum rating of the gear on which the values of K_v are based. If a gear pair is operating at or near resonance speed or at multiples or submultiples of resonance speed (particularly the second and third harmonics and subharmonics, respectively), then a thorough dynamic analysis is recommended. This is beyond the scope of this Standard.

The value of K_v is calculated from the following equation: $K_v = 1 + (K_{v350} - 1)B$.

For helical gears of overlap ratio greater than or equal to unity, K_{v350} should be taken from Figure 10.23.

For spur gears, the value of K_{v350} should be taken from Figure 10.24.

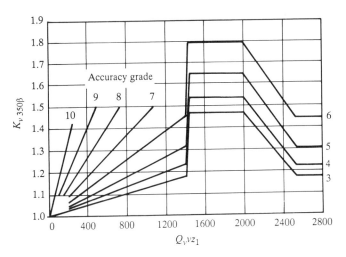

Figures 10.23 K_{v350} for helical gears, $\varepsilon\beta \geqslant 1$

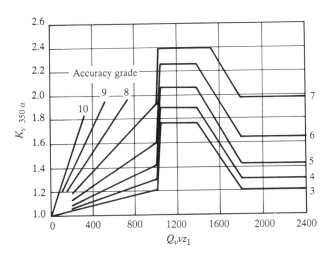

Figure 10.24 K_{v350} for spur gears

For helical gears with overlap ratio less than unity:

$$K_{v350} = K_{v350\beta} - \varepsilon_\beta(K_{v350\beta} - K_{v350\alpha})$$

where $K_{v350\beta}$ is the value of K_{v350} from Figure 10.23, and $K_{v350\alpha}$ is the value of K_{v350} from Figure 10.24.

The value of B is calculated using the following equation:

$$B = \left(\frac{350}{F_t K_A/b}\right)^x$$

The value of x is taken from the following table:

	Value of x	
Grade	$F_t K_A/b < 350$	$F_t K_A/b > 350$
3	0.473 6	0.293 1
4	0.611 0	0.421 1
5	0.715 3	0.540 2
6	0.801 7	0.636 1
7	0.863 5	0.730 3
8	0.900 5	0.795 4
9	0.933 4	0.868 7
10	0.953 0	0.895 4

If the value of $F_t K_A/b$ is less than 100, use $F_t K_A/b = 100$.

If the procedure is being used to calculate a maximum rating, estimate the value of $F_t K_A/b$ as follows:

$$\left(\frac{F_t K_A}{b}\right)_{est.} = d_1 \times \frac{u}{(u+1)} \times \frac{1}{K_{v350}} \times \left(\frac{\sigma_{HP}}{Z_H Z_E Z_\varepsilon}\right)^2$$

where

F_t = nominal tangential force at reference circle, F_{Ht} (see page 192)
K_A = application factor (see page 194)
b = gear facewidth (mm)
d_1 = reference diameter of pinion (mm)
u = gear ratio
K_{v350} = dynamic factor for $F_t K_A/b = 350$ (see above)
σ_{HP} = permissible contact stress (permissible Hertzian pressure) (MN/m^2)
Z_H = zone factor for Hertzian pressure at pitch point for contact stress (see page 190)
Z_E = elasticity factors for contact stress (see page 191)
Z_ε = contact ratio factor for contact stress (see page 191)

where σ_{HP} is the lower of the values for pinion and wheel.

Note: It is advisable to check the accuracy of this estimate when the rating has been calculated and, if necessary, recalculate K_v using the new value of F_t.

17 $K_{H\alpha}$ and $K_{H\beta}$ – *load distribution factors*. The face load factor for contact stress, $K_{H\beta}$, is the maximum specific load divided by the mean specific load. It accounts for the increase in local load due to maldistribution of load across the face of the gear caused by deflections, alignment and helix modifications including:

pinionshaft bending deflections
pinionshaft torsional deflections

misalignment due to manufacturing tolerances
end-relief
helix correction
crowning

The calculation of the face load factor involves:

(a) determination of the mean load intensity, W_m
(b) determination of the mesh misalignment due to deflections and manufacturing tolerance modified by the effect of running-in and helix modifications, $F_{\beta y}$
(c) determination of mesh stiffness, c_γ
(d) calculation of the face load factor, $K_{H\beta}$

where

$$W_m = F_t K_A K_v / b_{\text{eff.}}$$

when the tangential load on the gears is known and the procedure is being used to calculate a safety factor.

If the calculated value of W_m is less than $100\,\text{N/mm}$, use $W_m = 100\,\text{N/mm}$.

If the procedure is being used to determine the maximum rating of the gear pair, an estimated value of F_m should be calculated as follows:

$$F_{m\,\text{est.}} = bd_1 \frac{u}{(u+1)} \times \left(\frac{\sigma_{HP}}{Z_H Z_E Z_\varepsilon}\right)^2$$

where σ_{HP} is the minimum of σ_{HP1} and σ_{HP2} and

$$W_{m\,\text{est.}} = \frac{F_{m\,\text{est.}}}{b_{\text{eff.}}}$$

$$b_{\text{eff.}} = \frac{b - I_c}{2}$$

If higher accuracy is required, the procedure can be used iteratively by calculating a value of $K_{H\beta}$ using $W_{m\,\text{est.}}$, then recalculating using $W_{m\,\text{est.}}/K_{H\beta}$. Three such iterations normally converge to give a constant value of $K_{H\beta}$.

F_T = tangential load (N) (see page 192)
K_A = application factor (see page 194)
K_v = dynamic factor (see page 196)
b = facewidth (mm)
d_1 = reference diameter of pinion (mm)
u = gear ratio
σ_{HP} = permissible contact stress (permissible Hertzian pressure) (MN/m^2)
Z_H = zone factor for Hertzian pressure at pitch point for contact stress (see page 190)
Z_E = elasticity factor for contact stress (see page 191)
Z_ε = contact ratio factor for contact stress (see page 191)

The effective mesh alignment, $F_{\beta y}$, should be calculated, if:

(a) the gears are helix corrected

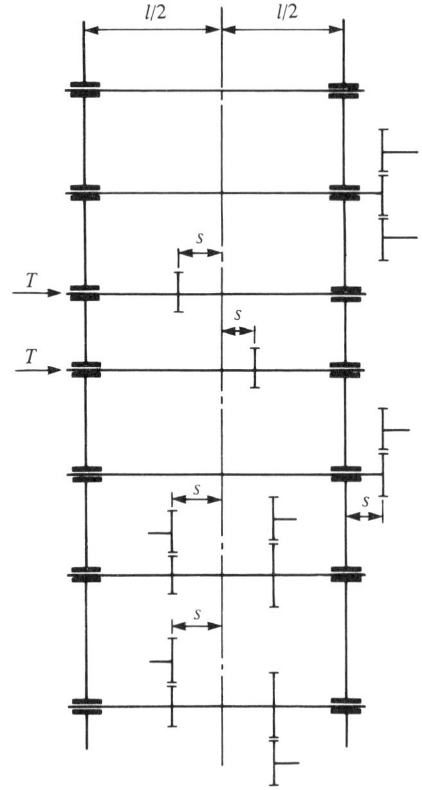

		Factor K	
		Shrink fit	Key fit
(a)		0.0 $(s = 0)$	0.0 $(s = 0)$
(b)		0.0 $(s = 0)$	0.0 $(s = 0)$
(c)		0.48	0.8
(d)		−0.48	−0.8
(e)		1.33	1.33
(f)		−0.36	−0.6
(g)		−0.6	−1.0

Figure 10.25   Constant K for calculation of f_{SH}

(b) the gear layout does not conform to Figure 10.25.
(c) substantial forces other than pure shaft torque are to be applied, i.e. pulley loads, etc.
(d) wheel shaft deflections are significant.

Then $F_{\beta y}$ is calculated by a thorough analysis of all contributions to the mesh misalignment, i.e. bearing clearances, case and shaft deflections, manufacturing tolerance, etc.:

$$F_{\beta y} = q_y \times F_{\beta x} : -0.001 \text{ mm}$$

where

q_y – misalignment due to running-in – Reduction factor

$$= \frac{q_{y1} + q_{y2}}{2}$$

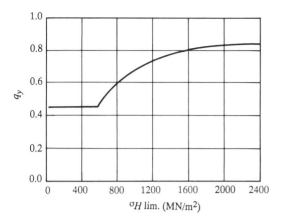

Figure 10.26 Values of q_y

q_y for pinion and gear should be obtained from Figure 10.26 (for $\sigma_{H\,lim.}$ see page 185)

$F_{\beta x}$ – mesh misalignment prior to running-in – 0.001 mm

$$= |\,1.33f_{SH} \pm f_{ma}\,|$$

The negative sign should only be used if the gears are adjusted on assembly and if the contact pattern is inspected to justify the assumption.

f_{SH} – mesh alignment due to shaft deflections – 0.001 mm:

For spur and single helical gears:

$$f_{SH} = W_m A \left[\left| 1 + K \frac{ls}{d_1^2} \left(\frac{d_1}{d_{SH1}} \right)^4 - 0.3 \right| + 0.3 \right] \times \left(\frac{b}{d_1} \right)^2$$

For double helical gears:

$$f_{SH} = W_m 2A \left[\left| 1.5 + K \frac{ls}{d_1^2} \left(\frac{d_1}{d_{SH1}} \right)^4 - 0.3 \right| + 0.3 \right] \times \left(\frac{b}{2d_1} \right)^2$$

where

W_m = mean load intensity (N/mm) (see page 199)
A = auxiliary value (see table on page 202)
K = constant (see Figure 10.25)
l = bearing span (mm)
s = 0.3l; if s is greater than 0.3l (see Figure 10.25)
d_1 = reference diameter – pinion (mm)
d_{SH1} = diameter – pinion shaft (mm)
b = facewidth

	Auxiliary value, A	
Gear pairs without crowning or end-relief (mm . μm/N)	Gears with suitably chosen crowning (mm . μm/N)	Gear pairs with suitably chosen end-relief (mm . μm/N)
0.023	0.012	0.016

f_{ma} – mesh misalignment due to manufacturing tolerance:

(a) For gears without helix modification and without any adjustment on assembly:
$f_{ma} = f_{H\beta}$.

where $f_{H\beta}$ = the larger of the tooth alignment tolerances of both the pinion and wheel.

(b) For gears with crowning or gears where contact is adjusted on assembly:
$f_{ma} = 0.5 f_{H\beta}$.

provided that this assumption is verified by inspection of the contact marking under light load.

(c) For gears with suitable end-relief: $f_{ma} = 0.7 f_{H\beta}$.

Notes: The value of $F_{\beta x}$ should be the maximum of:

(i) the value from $f_{ma} = 0.5 f_{H\beta}$
(ii) $0.005 W_m$
(iii) half the actual manufacturing tolerance (the higher value of pinion and wheel)

c_y – mean value of total tooth stiffness (or mesh stiffness) per unit facewidth (N.μm/mm)

For gears conforming to the basic rack profile specified in BS 436, parts 1 and 2, and with $1.2 \leqslant \varepsilon_\alpha \leqslant 1.9$, average values of c_y are:

(a) For steel/steel gear pair, $c_y = 20$ N·μm/mm
(b) Steel/SG cast iron gear pair, $c_y = 18.2$ N·μm/mm
(c) SG cast iron/SG cast iron gear pair, $c_y = 16.8$ N·μm/mm
(d) Steel/grey cast iron gear pair, $c_y = 14.8$ N·μm/mm
(e) Grey cast iron/grey cast iron gear pair, $c_y = 11$ Nμm/mm

$K_{H\beta}$ – face load factor:

1   For $K_{H\beta} > 2$

$$K_{H\beta} = \sqrt{\frac{2c_y F_{\beta y}}{W_m}}$$

2   For $K_{H\beta} \leqslant 2$

$$K_{H\beta} = 1 + \frac{c_y F_{\beta y}}{2 W_m}$$

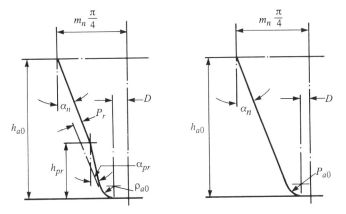

Note: For the purposes of calculation $h_{fp}=h_{ao}$ and $\rho_{fp}=\rho_{ao}$ See pages 215 and 216.

Figure 10.27　Dimensions of the basic rack of the gearing

for　　c_y, see page 202
　　　　$F_{\beta y}$, see page 200
　　　　W_m, see page 199

$K_{H\alpha}$ – transverse load factor for contact stress:

The transverse load factor for contact stress accounts for the maldistribution of load down the tooth flank due to profile and pitch deviations and tooth modifications:

(a) For gears with total contact ratio, $\varepsilon_\gamma < 2$:

$$K_{H\alpha}=\frac{\varepsilon_\gamma}{2}\left[0.9+0.4\frac{c_y(f_{pe}-y_\alpha)}{W_mK_{H\beta}}\right]$$

(b) For gears with total contact ratio, $\varepsilon_\gamma \geqslant 2$:

$$K_{H\alpha}=0.9+0.4\sqrt{\frac{2(\varepsilon_\gamma-1)}{\varepsilon_\gamma}}\times\frac{c_y(f_{pe}-y_\alpha)}{W_mK_{H\beta}}$$

where

　　　　ε_γ = total content ratio (see page 204)
　　　　c_y = mean value of total tooth stiffness (see page 202)
　　　　f_{pe} = pitch tolerance for gear (BS 436: part 2: 1970, Table 3)
　　　　Y_α = running-in allowance (see page 205)
　　　　W_m = mean load intensity (see page 199)
　　　　$K_{H\beta}$ = face load factor (see page 202)

	Minimum and maximum values of $K_{H\alpha}$	
Gear type	Minimum value of $K_{H\alpha}$	Maximum value of $K_{H\alpha}$
Spur gears	1.00	$1/Z_\varepsilon^2$
Helical gears	1.15	$\varepsilon_\alpha/\cos^2 \beta_b$

Z_ε = contact factor for contact stress (see page 191)
ε_α = transverse contact ratio (see below)
β_d = base helix angle (rad.)
ε_α – transverse contact ratio

$$= \frac{g_\alpha}{p_{bt}}$$

ε_β – overlap ratio

$$= \frac{b \sin \beta}{\pi m_n}$$

ε_y – total contact ratio
$$= \varepsilon_\beta + \varepsilon_\alpha$$
g_α – length of path of contact:

(a) for external gears

$$= 0.5\left(\sqrt{d_{a1}^2 - d_{b1}^2} + \sqrt{d_{a2}^2 - d_{b2}^2} \right) - a \sin \alpha_{tw}$$

(b) for internal gears

$$= 0.5\left(\sqrt{d_{a1}^2 - d_{b1}^2} - \sqrt{d_{a2}^2 - d_{b2}^2} \right) - a \sin \alpha_{tw}$$

Note: For internal gears the centre distance is a negative quantity

p_{bt} – transverse base pitch

$$= \frac{m_n \pi \cos \alpha_t}{\cos \beta}$$

b = facewidth (mm)
β = helix angle (rad.)
m_n = normal module (mm)
d_{a1} = tip diameter – pinion (mm)
d_{b1} = base diameter – pinion (mm)
d_{a2} = tip diameter – wheel (mm)
d_{b2} = base diameter – wheel (mm)
a = centre distance (mm)
α_{tw} = transverse pressure angle – wheel (rad.)
α_t = transverse pressure angle (rad.)

Y_α – running-in allowance:

$$Y_\alpha = \frac{160}{\sigma_{H \text{ lim.}}} \times f_{pe} \, (\mu m)$$

for through-hardened steel and cast steels.

$$Y_\alpha = 0.275 f_{pe} \, (\mu m)$$

for cast iron and bronze.

$$Y_\alpha = 0.075 f_{pe} \, (\mu m)$$

for surface-hardened steels.

Notes:

1 For through-hardened and cast steels

$v \leqslant 5$ ⠀⠀⠀⠀⠀no limit
$5 < v \leqslant 10$ ⠀⠀⠀$Y_\alpha \leqslant 12\,800/\sigma_{H \text{ lim.}}$
$v > 10$ ⠀⠀⠀⠀$Y_\alpha \leqslant 6400/\sigma_{H \text{ lim.}}$

2 For cast iron and bronze

$v < 5$ ⠀⠀⠀⠀⠀no limit
$5 < v \leqslant 10$ ⠀⠀⠀$Y_\alpha \leqslant 22$
$v > 10$ ⠀⠀⠀⠀$Y_\alpha \leqslant 11$

3 For surface-hardened steels subject to $Y_\alpha \leqslant 3$ at any speed:

If the pinion and wheel are of different materials, then:

$$Y_\alpha = \frac{Y_{\alpha 1} + Y_{\alpha 2}}{2} \, (\mu m)$$

where

f_{pe} = tolerance on pitch (μm)
$\sigma_{H \text{ lim.}}$ = endurance limit for contact stress for gears (MN/m^2)
$Y_{\alpha 1}$ = running-in allowance – pinion (μm)
$Y_{\alpha 2}$ = running-in allowance – wheel (μm)

18 $S_{H \text{ min.}}$ and S_H – minimum demanded and actual safety factors on contact stress:

(A) Minimum demanded safety factor, $S_{H \text{ min.}}$:

The choice of the minimum demanded safety factor should be agreed between the gear manufacturer and the purchaser.

The recommended ranges of $S_{H \text{ min.}}$ are as follows:

(a) For normal industrial applications

$$S_{H \text{ min.}} = 1.0\text{–}1.2$$

(b) For high reliability and critical applications (high consequential damage, loss of life, etc.)

$$S_{h \text{ min.}} = 1.3 - 1/6$$

(B)   Actual safety factor, S_H:

$$S_H = \frac{S_{H\,min.} \times \sigma_{HP}}{\sigma_H}$$

where

σ_{HP} = permissible contact stress (MN/m^2) (see page 185)
σ_h = actual contact stress (MN/m^2) (see page 185)

Bending stress calculations

Permissible bending stress, σ_{FP}

$$= \frac{2\sigma_{FO}(\sigma_B - \sigma_R)Y_N Y_R Y_X Y_M Y_\delta}{(\sigma_B + \sigma_{FO} Y_N Y_R Y_X)S_{F\,min.}} \text{(MN/m}^2)$$

Actual calculated bending stress, σ_F

$$= \frac{F_t}{bm_n} \times Y_F Y_S Y_\beta K_A K_V K_{f\alpha} K_{F\beta} \text{(MN/m}^2)$$

Permissible power capacity and torque based on bending stress:

(A)   Permissible power capacity, P_{FP}

$$= \frac{bd_1 n_1 m_n}{60 \times 10^6/\pi} \times \frac{1}{Y_F} \times \frac{1}{Y_S} \times \frac{1}{Y_\beta} \times \frac{1}{K_A} \times \frac{1}{K_V} \times \frac{1}{K_{F\alpha}K_{F\beta}} \times \sigma_{FP} \text{(kW)}$$

(B)   Permissible torque capacity, T_{FP}

$$= \frac{60 \times 10^3}{2\pi} \times \frac{P_{FP}}{n_1} \text{(nm)}$$

Subsurface bending in surface-hardened gears:

$$\sigma_{FP\,core} = \frac{(\sigma_{B\,core} - \sigma_{R\,core})Y_M Y_N Y_X}{(1 + 0.5Y_N Y_X)S_{F\,min.}}$$

Because of the possibility of a subsurface bending failure, especially when the hardened case is thin, a check should be made at the case/core junction. In these calculations, the permissible stresses are calculated as above in which the properties relate to the core material.

To allow for the reduced bending stress below the surface, the actual bending stress is calculated as shown below using the value of the actual calculated bending stress, σ_F (above):

$$\sigma_{F\,core} = \sigma_F \times \left(\frac{1-2c}{m_n}\right) \times \frac{Y_{S\,red.}}{Y_S}$$

where

$$Y_{S\,red.} = Y_S - \left[\frac{C}{0.16m_n} \times (Y_S - 1)\right]$$

or

$$Y_{S \text{ red.}} = 1$$

whichever is the greater.

The power capacity based on core bending stress is calculated as follows:

$$P_{FP \text{ core}} = P_{FP} \times \frac{\sigma_F}{\sigma_{F \text{ core}}} \times \frac{\sigma_{FP \text{ core}}}{\sigma_{FP}}$$

Idler duty. For frequently reversing duties or any drive where the direction of loading on the teeth is reversed each cycle (e.g. idler gears or planets in epicyclic gearing), the permissible tooth root stress is calculated using the following formula:

$$\sigma_{FP} = \frac{\sigma_{FO}(\sigma_B - \sigma_R) Y_M Y_N Y_R Y_X Y_\delta}{\sigma_B S_{F \text{ min.}}}$$

$$\sigma_{FP} \geqslant \sigma_F$$

The permissible core root stress can be calculated as follows:

$$\sigma_{FP \text{ core}} = \frac{0.5(\sigma_{B \text{ core}} - \sigma_{R \text{ core}}) Y_M Y_N Y_X}{S_{F \text{ min.}}}$$

Peak torque capacity for bending stress:

$$T_{F \text{ max.}} = T_{FP} K_A K_Y \left(\frac{\sigma_{FY} Y_M Y_S Y_{\delta \text{ stat.}}}{\sigma_{FP} S_{F \text{ min.}}} \right) (\text{Nm})$$

For surface-hardened gears, a further requirement is a calculation of the peak torque capacity of the core material in this calculation. The value of σ_{FY} above should be replaced by the value of $\sigma_{FY \text{ core}}$ calculated as follows:

$$\sigma_{FY \text{ core}} = \frac{\sigma_{B \text{ core}} Y_X}{1.0 - \left(\dfrac{2C}{m_n} \right)}$$

where

1 σ_{FO} – *basic endurance limit for bending stress*. The basic endurance limit for bending stress used in the above British Standard is based on the fully reversed bending endurance limit of a 7.62 mm (0.3 in) diameter polished specimen, at a 99% confidence level.

This stress has to be modified for the effects of loading condition, size, surface finish, quality and life before it can be used as a permissible stress for gear tooth root bending calculations.

These factors are included in the equation for the permissible bending stress, σ_{FP} (see page 206).

The basic endurance limit should be taken from Figure 10.28.

2 σ_B – ultimate tensile strength (MN/m^2)

3 σ_R – *Residual stress* (MN/m^2). The values of the residual stress, σ_R, are given in the table below.

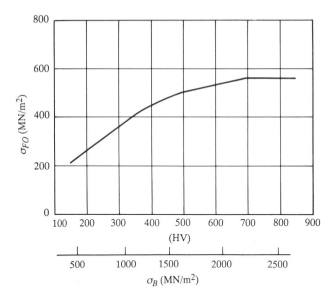

Figure 10.28   Values of σ_{FO}

Typical values of σ_R				
	Quality A or B		Quality C	
Hardening process	σ_R (MN/m²)	$\sigma_{R\ core}$ (MN/m²)	σ_R (MN/m²)	$\sigma_{R\ core}$ (MN/m²)
Carburized and hardened	−400	240	0	240
Nitride-hardened	−400	140	0	140
Induction-hardened	−140	450	0	450

Gear grinding may affect the residual stress at the immediate surface and, for guidance, the values in the table below may be added algebraically to those in the preceding table.

Change in residual stress due to post-hardening operations	
Operation	Algebraic change to σ_R
Very light grinding, carefully controlled	0
Light full-form grinding	+ 300 MN/m² (tensile)
Heavy abrasive grinding	+ 600 MN/m² (tensile)
Controlled shot-peening	− 500 MN/m² (compressive)

Shot-peening can be used to increase the surface residual compressive stress. Correct selection of shot and of intensity is extremely important and should be controlled by Almen strips. For guidance, a typical value of the change in residual stress after shot-peening with the correct technique is given in the table above.

4 Y_N, *Life factor for bending stress.* The life factor for bending stress accounts for the increase in permissible stress if the number of stress cycles is less than the endurance life.

If the gear is subject to variable duty (and the design torque has therefore been calculated using the variable duty procedure given on pages 192–194), then the value of Y_N is 1.0.

If the S/N curve of the material is known, this is used as the basis for the life factor, otherwise Y_N is obtained from Figure 10.29 or Figure 10.30 and 10.31, as appropriate:

(a) Figure 10.29 applies to through-hardened steels
(b) Figure 10.30 applies to surface-hardened steels, with case depth greater than or equal to the limiting case depth, and cast iron.
(c) Figure 10.31 applies to surface-hardened steels, with case depth less than the limiting case depth, grey cast iron and bronze.

For bath-nitrided steel, $Y_N = 1.0$ for all values of N, the number of tooth cycles.

Note: The values of the limiting case depth are given in Figure 10.16 (page 186).

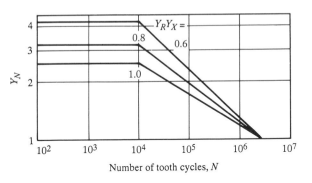

Figure 10.29 Y_N for through-hardened steels

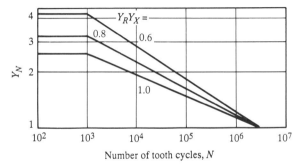

Figure 10.30 Y_N for thick-case surface-hardened steels and cast iron

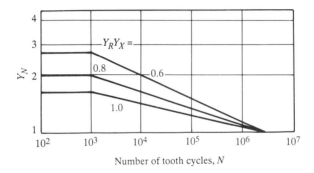

Figure 10.31 Y_N for thin-case surface-hardened steels, grey cast iron and bronze

5 Y_R – *Surface condition factor for bending stress.* The surface condition factor accounts for the reduction of endurance limit due to flaws in the material and the surface roughness of the tooth root fillets.

The values for the surface condition factor, Y_R, should be taken from Figure 10.32.

Notes:

(a) Material 1 (curve 1) applies to through-hardened steels, bronze and cast iron other than grey cast iron

(b) Material 2 (curve 2) applies to surface-hardened steels with case depth greater than or equal to the limiting case depth

(c) Material 3 (curve 3) applies to surface-hardened steels with case depth less than the limiting case depth

The values of the limiting case depth are given in Table 10.6, page 187.

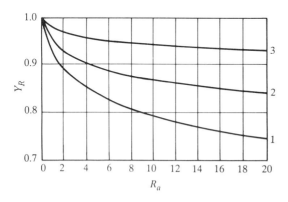

Figure 10.32   Values of Y_R

6 Y_X – *Size factor for bending stress.* The size factor is included to take into account possible influences of size on material quality and its response to heat treatment and other manufacturing processes.

The values for the size factor should be taken from Figure 10.33.

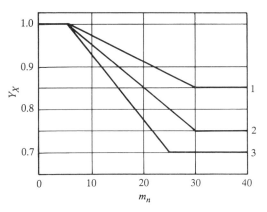

Figure 10.33   Values of Y_X

Note: The material grades shown in Figure 10.33 are explained in detail on page 210.

7   Y_M– *Material quality factor for bending stress.* Better quality control exercised in the manufacture of a material results in less scatter on the mechanical properties of the finished material. Hence for a given confidence level, better quality materials have a higher permissible stress and, conversely, lower quality materials a lower permissible stress. The material qualities are defined below.

Quality A. All tests applicable to quality A materials also apply to quality B, but random sampling applied to quality B is replaced by 100% testing. The inspection requirements are as follows:

(a) Chemical analysis: Supplier certification.
(b) Mechanical properties (in final condition): HB, HV or HRC (see BS 240: Part 1; BS 427: Part 1; and BS 891: Part 1). Ultimate tensile strength and Charpy or Izod (see BS 131: Parts 1 and 2).
(c) Crack detection: Magnetic particle inspection (see BS 6072).
(d) Ultrasonic inspection: 100% check (see BS 4080; BS 4124: Part 1; and BS 5996).
(e) Case depth: Hardness traverse check on a testpiece (the same material cast and heat-treatment condition) carburized with the gear. For induction- or flame-hardened gears, hardness traverse check at nominated positions across the facewidth on a sacrificial test gear, or segment-hardened under the same conditions as the gear.
(f) Surface structure (carburized steel): Check on testpiece, essentially fine martensite and specified retained austenite and carbide.
(g) Heat treatment: Furnace temperature chart records.

Quality B. For cast iron other than nodular cast iron, the permissible stresses for quality B materials are the same as for quality C, on the grounds of safety. The inspection requirements are therefore the same as for quality C. For other materials, the inspection requirements are as follows:

(a) Chemical analysis: Supplier certification.
(b) Mechanical properties (in final condition): HB, HV or HRC (see BS 240: Part

1; BS 427: Part 1; and BS 891). Ultimate tensile strength and Charpy or Izod (see BS 131: Parts 1 and 2).

(c) Crack detection: Magnetic particle inspection (100% inspection on surface-hardened, otherwise random samples) (see BS 6072).

(d) Weld repairs: For cast steels, permitted with an approved procedure. For other materials, not permitted in toothed area.

(e) Ultrasonic inspection: 100% checks on cast materials (see BS 4080).

(f) Case depth: Etch check on a testpiece carburized with the gear. For induction- or flame-hardened gears, etch check on tooth end-face and full tooth profile on a sample or every gear (dependent on batch size).

(g) Core structure (nodular irons): Sample check from batch for pearlite and ferrite content and graphite spheroidization.

(h) Heat treatment (carburized steel): Furnace fitted with atmosphere control instrumentation.

Quality C. The inspection requirements for quality C materials are as follows:

(a) Mechanical properties (in final condition): HB or HV only (see BS 240: Part 1; and BS 427: Part 1).

(b) Case depth: Etch-check on a testpiece carburized with the gear. For induction- or flame-hardened gears, etch-check on the tooth end-face on a sample gear.

(c) Weld repairs: For cast steels, permitted with an approved procedure. For other materials, not permitted in toothed areas.

In order to rate a pair of gears to a particular material quality level, a specification needs to be drawn up to define the level of inspection expected at different stages of the manufacture. Such a specification may be the subject of agreement between the gear manufacturer and the gear purchaser.

The details given on quality A, B and C materials are provided as guidance and are not intended to form the basis of a specification, but rather to be an aid to determining the quality level of a material manufactured to an existing specification.

The values of Y_M are given in the table below.

	Value of Y_M		
Material	Quality A	Quality B	Quality C
Surface-hardened steels	1.0	0.9	0.6
Through-hardened or normalized steels	1.0	0.9	0.6
Through-hardened or normalized cast steels	0.9	0.8	0.5
Nodular cast iron	0.7	0.6	0.5
Other cast irons	0.3	0.2	0.2

8 Y_δ – *sensitivity factor for bending stress.* The sensitivity factor accounts for the sensitivity of the gear material to the presence of notches, i.e. the root fillet.

The value of Y_δ at the endurance limit is calculated from the following equation:

$$Y_\delta = \frac{1+\sqrt{0.2p'(1+2q_s)}}{1+\sqrt{0.2p'}}$$

where

(A) p' should be taken from the table below.

Material		Values of p'	p' (mm)
Grey cast iron	—		0.310
Nitrided steel	—		0.100
Soft steel	$\sigma_F = 300 \, MN/m^2$		0.083
and bronze	$\sigma_F = 400 \, MN/m^2$		0.045
Through-hardened	$\sigma_{0.2} = 500 \, MN/m^2$		0.028
steel, cast steel	$\sigma_{0.2} = 600 \, MN/m^2$		0.019
and SG cast iron	$\sigma_{0.2} = 800 \, MN/m^2$		0.006
	$\sigma_{0.2} = 1000 \, MN/m^2$		0.001
Carburized, induction- and flame-hardened steels			0.003

Notes:
(a) When calculating a maximum gear rating for soft steel or bronze, a value of σ_F: – σ_{FP} – for the estimation of p' can be calculated from the permissible bending stress formula (page 206), using $Y_\delta = 1.17$.
(b) $\sigma_{0.2}$ is 0.2% proof stress.

(B) q_s – For the calculation of q_s, see formula on page 217.

Y_δ *at static strength – peak torque capacity.* The values of Y_δ are calculated as follows:

(a) For grey cast iron $Y_{\delta \, stat.} = 1.0$
(b) For nitrided steels $Y_{\delta \, stat.} = 0.27 Y_S + 0.72$
(c) For soft steels and bronze

$$Y_{\delta \, stat.} = 1 + 0.93(Y_S - 1) \times \left(\frac{200}{\sigma_F}\right)^{1.4}$$

(d) For through-hardened steel

$$Y_{\delta \, stat.} = 1 + 0.82(Y_S - 1) \times \left(\frac{300}{\sigma_{0.2}}\right)^{1.4}$$

where $\sigma_{0.2} = 0.2\%$ proof stress
(c) For carburized, induction- and flame-hardened steel $Y_{\delta \, stat.} = 0.77 Y_S + 0.22$

For the values of Y_S, see page 217.

Note: When calculating a maximum gear rating for soft steel or bronze, a value of σ_F can be calculated from the following formula:

$$\sigma_F = 1.5 K_A K_v \sigma_{FY} Y_M Y_S$$

where

K_A is obtained from the formula on page 195
K_v is obtained from the formula on page 196
σ_{FY} is yield strength for bending stress (MN/m²)
Y_M is obtained from the formula on page 211
Y_S is obtained from the formula on page 217

9 $S_{F\,min.}$ – *Minimum demanded safety factor on tooth root stress*. The choice of the minimum demanded safety factor is to be agreed between the gear manufacturer and the purchaser, as in the case for contact stress (see page 205).

Note: The value should reflect the confidence in the actual operating conditions and material properties being truly reflected in this British Standard. When the load histogram is not surely known or where high tooth loads are likely to occur due to circumstances outside the scope of this Standard, an appropriately high value of the minimum demanded safety factor should be used.
   The recommended ranges for $S_{F\,min.}$ are as follows:

(a) For normal industrial applications, $S_{F\,min.} = 1.4$–1.5
(b) For high reliability and critical applications (high consequential damage, loss of life, etc.), $S_{F\,min.} = 1.6$–3.0

10 F_t – *Nominal tangential force at reference circle*. See F_{Ht} – nominal tangential force for contact stress, page 192.
11 b – facewidth (mm).
12 m_n – normal module (mm).
13 Y_F, Y_S and Y_β – geometry factors for bending stress:

(a) Form factor Y_F. The form factor takes into account the influence of the tooth form on the nominal bending stress for application of load at the highest point of single tooth pair contact.
(b) Stress correction factor, Y_S. The stress correction factor takes into account the stress-increasing effect of the fillet and the proximity of the bending moment arm on the nominal bending stress for application of load at the highest point of single tooth pair contact.
(c) Helix angle factor for bending stress, Y_β. The helix angle factor for bending stress accounts for the fact that the conditions for tooth root stress in helical gears are more favourable as a result of the inclined line of contact than for the virtual spur gears on which the calculations are based.

   Geometrical equations. The parameters used for calculating the auxiliary parameters for Y_F, Y_S and Y_β are given below.
1   Base helix angle, β_b (rad.)

$$= \text{arc cos}\sqrt{1 - (\sin \text{ Helix angle } - \text{ normal} \times \cos \text{ Press. angle})^2}$$

2 Virtual transverse contact ratio, $\varepsilon_{\alpha n}$

$$= \frac{\text{Transverse contact ratio}}{\cos^2 \text{Base helix angle}}$$

For: Transverse contact ratio, see page 204
Base helix angle, see page 214

3 Virtual reference diameter, d_n (mm)

$$= \text{Normal module} \times \text{Virtual no. of teeth}$$

4 Virtual base diameter, d_{bn} (mm)

$$= \text{Virtual ref. dia.} \times \cos \text{Normal press. angle}$$

or

$$= \text{Module} - \text{normal} \times \cos \text{Virtual no. of teeth} \times \cos \text{Normal press. angle}$$

5 Virtual number of teeth, Z_V

$$= \frac{\text{No. of teeth}}{\cos^3 \text{Helix angle (radians)}}$$

6 Virtual tip diameter, d_{an} (mm)

$$= \text{Virtual ref. dia.} + \text{Tip dia.} - \text{Ref. dia.}$$

or

$$= \text{Normal module} \times \text{Virtual no. of teeth} + (\text{Tip dia.} - \text{Ref. dia.})$$

Auxiliary parameters θ, G, H and q_s for Y_F, Y_S and Y_β of external gears. For the calculation of these parameters the dimensions of the tool, i.e. h_{ao} – addendum of basic rack (mm), and p_{ao} – tip radius of tool (mm), are introduced. The nominal tooth form is taken as a basis, i.e. for this purpose the influence of backlash and grinding allowance is ignored.

7 $\theta = \dfrac{2G}{Z_V} \tan\theta - H$

Note: $\theta = \pi/6$ radians can be used as a starting point for the solution of the above equation.

where

$$G = \frac{p_{ao}}{m_n} - \frac{h_{ao}}{m_n} + x$$

(see Figure 10.27, page 203)

$$H = \frac{2}{Z_V}\left(\frac{\pi}{2} - \frac{D}{m_n}\right) - \frac{\pi}{3}$$

$$D = \frac{\pi}{4} m_n - h_{ao} \tan\alpha_n + h_{pr} \times (\tan\alpha_n - \tan\alpha_{pr}) - (1 - \sin\alpha_{pr}) \times \frac{p_{ao}}{\cos\alpha_{pr}}$$

p_{ao} = tip radius of tool (mm) (see Figure 10.27, page 203)
h_{ao} = basic rack addendum (mm) (see Figure 10.27, page 203)
m_n = normal module (mm)
x = addendum modification coefficient
Z_V = speed factor for contact stress (see Figure 10.17, page 187)
D = tool diameter (mm)
α_n = nominal pressure angle at reference diameter (rad)
h_{pr} = height of protuberance (mm)
α_{pr} = angle of protuberance (rad)

For tools without protuberance use $\alpha_{pr} = \alpha_n$.

$$\frac{S_{Fn}}{m_n} = Z_V \times \sin\left(\frac{\pi}{3} - \theta\right) + \sqrt{3} \times \left(\frac{G}{\cos\theta} - \frac{p_{ao}}{m_n}\right)$$

$$\frac{p_F}{m_n} = \frac{p_{ao}}{m_n} + \frac{2G^2}{\cos\theta(Z_V\cos^2\theta - 2G)}$$

$$d_{en} = 2\frac{Z}{|Z|}\sqrt{\left[\sqrt{\left(\frac{d_{an}}{2}\right)^2 - \left(\frac{d_{bn}}{2}\right)^2} - \left(\frac{\pi d\cos\beta\cos\alpha_n}{|Z|}\right) \times (\varepsilon_{an} - 1)\right]^2 + \left(\frac{d_{bn}}{2}\right)^2}$$

$$\alpha_{en} = \text{arc}\cos\left(\frac{d_{bn}}{d_{en}}\right)$$

$$\gamma_e = \left(\frac{\pi/2 + 2\times\tan\alpha_n}{Z_V} + \text{inv}\,\alpha_n - \text{inv}\,\alpha_{en}\right)$$

$$\alpha_{Fen} = \alpha_{en} - \gamma_e$$

$$\frac{h_F}{m_n} = 0.5Z_V \times \left[\frac{\cos\alpha_n}{\cos\alpha_{Fen}} - \cos\left(\frac{\pi}{3} - \theta\right)\right] + 0.5 \times \left(\frac{p_{ao}}{m_n} - \frac{G}{\cos\theta}\right)$$

Auxiliary parameters for Y_F, Y_S and Y_β of internal gears (approximated by a rack) are calculated as follows:

8

$$\alpha_{Fen} = \alpha_n$$

$$\frac{S_{Fn2}}{m_n} = 2\left[\left(\frac{\pi}{4} + \tan\alpha_n\right)\left(\frac{h_{f2} - p_{ao}}{m_n}\right) + \left(\frac{p_{ao} - pr}{m_n\cos\alpha_n}\right) - \left(\frac{p_{ao}}{m_n} \times \cos\frac{\pi}{6}\right)\right]$$

$$h_{f2} = \frac{d_2 - d_{f2}}{2}$$

$$\frac{h_{F2}}{m_n} = \left(\frac{d_{en2} - d_{fn2}}{2m_n}\right) - \left[\frac{\pi}{4} + \left(\frac{h_{f2}}{m_n} - \frac{d_{en2} - d_{fn2}}{2m_n}\right) \times \tan\alpha_n\right]$$

$$\times \tan\alpha_n - \frac{p_2}{m_n}\left(1 - \sin\frac{\pi}{6}\right)$$

9 *Tooth form factor, Y_F.* The value of Y_F is calculated as follows:

$$Y_F = \frac{6\dfrac{h_F}{m_n} \times \cos\,\alpha_{Fen}}{\left(\dfrac{S_{Fn}}{m_n}\right)^2 \times \cos\,\alpha_n}$$

10 *Stress correction factor, Y_S.* The value of Y_S is calculated as follows:

$$Y_S = (1.2 + 0.13\angle)q_s^{\left(\frac{1}{1.21+2.3}\right)/\angle}$$

where

$$\angle = \frac{S_{Fn}}{h_F}$$

q_s – notch parameter

$$= \frac{S_{Fn}}{2_{pF}}$$

11 *Helix angle factor, Y_β.* The value of Y_β is calculated as follows:

$$Y_\beta = 1 - \varepsilon_\beta \frac{\beta}{120}$$

when: $e_\beta > 1$ use $\varepsilon_\beta = 1$
and $\beta > 30°$ use $\beta = 30°$

where

S_{Fn} = thickness of virtual tooth at critical section (mm) (see page 216)
p_F = root fillet radius at critical section (mm) (see page 216)
d_{en} = Virtual diameter to highest point of single tooth pair contact (mm) (see page 216)
d_{an} = virtual tip diameter (mm) (see page 215)
d_{bn} = virtual base diameter (mm) (see page 215)
d = reference diameter (mm)
β = helix angle (rad)
ε_{an} = virtual transverse contact ratio (see page 204)
α_{en} = pressure angle at highest point of single tooth pair contact (rad) (see page 216)
α_{Fen} = angle for application of load at highest point of single tooth pair contact (rad) (see page 216)
h_{f2} = dedendum of internal gear (mm)
h_{F2} = bending moment arm (mm)
d_{fn2} = virtual root diameter of internal gear (mm)

12 K_A – Application factor (see page 195)
13 K_v – Dynamic factor (see page 196)

14 $K_{F\alpha}$ *and* $K_{F\beta}$ – *Load factors for bending stress.* The load factors for bending stress account for uneven distribution of bending moment across the facewidth caused by uneven loading across the face.

(A) $K_{F\alpha} = K_{H\alpha}$

For $K_{H\alpha}$ see page 198

(B) $K_{F\beta} = K_{H\beta} \left[\frac{1}{1 + h/b + (h/b)^2} \right]$

For $K_{H\beta}$ see page 198

where

h/b is the maximum of h_1/b_1 and h_2/b_2
h = tooth depth (mm)
b = facewidth (mm)
h_1 = tooth depth – pinion (mm)
b_1 = facewidth – pinion (mm)
h_2 = tooth depth – wheel (mm)
b_2 = facewidth – wheel (mm)

15 S_F – actual safety factor:

$$S_F = \frac{S_{F\,min.} \sigma_{FP}}{\sigma_F}$$

for: $S_{F\,min.}$ see page 214
σ_{FP} see page 206
σ_F see page 206

11
Bevel gear stress formulae

This chapter covers the various formulae available to the designer for calculating the load-carrying capacity of bevel gears.

Spiral bevel gears (BS 545: 1949)

1 Tangential load

$$= \frac{\text{Torque transmitted (lb/in)}}{\text{Pitch circle radius (in)}}$$

$$= \frac{63\,000 \times \text{Horse-power}}{\text{PC rad.} \times \text{rev/min}}$$

$$= \frac{33\,000 \times \text{Horse-power}}{\text{Pitch line velocity}}$$

$$= \text{Lewis form factor} \times \text{Facewidth} \times \text{Circ. pitch} \times \text{Safe working stress}$$

2 Horse-power for wear

$$= \frac{X_{\text{CP}} \times S_{\text{CP}} \times Z \times F \times \text{rev/min} \times n}{126\,000 \times K \times \text{DP} \times \Omega_c} \left(\frac{C-F}{1.1C} \right)$$

from Tangential load (E)

$$= \frac{63\,000 \times \text{hp}}{\text{PCR} \times \text{rev/min}}$$

$$\therefore \text{hp} = \frac{E \times \text{PC rad.} \times \text{rev/min}}{63\,000}$$

Tangential load (E)

$$= \text{Lewis form factor } (y) \times \text{Facewidth } (F) \times \text{CP} \times \text{Safe working stress } (f_w)$$

$$\therefore \text{hp} = \frac{y \times F \times \text{CP} \times f_w \times \text{PCR} \times \text{rev/min}}{63\,000}$$

$$\therefore \frac{y \times F \times \mathrm{CP} \times f_w \times \mathrm{PCR} \times \mathrm{rev/min}}{63\,000}$$

$$= \frac{X_{\mathrm{CP}} \times S_{\mathrm{CP}} \times Z \times F \times \mathrm{rev/min} \times n}{126\,000 \times K \times \mathrm{DP} \times \Omega_c} \left(\frac{C-F}{1.1C} \right)$$

$\therefore$ Safe working stress for wear, f_w

$$= \frac{X_{\mathrm{CP}} \times S_{\mathrm{CP}} \times Z \times n \times 63\,000}{126\,000 \times K \times \mathrm{DP} \times \Omega_c \times y \times \mathrm{PC}} \ \mathrm{rad.} \left(\frac{C-F}{1.1C} \right)$$

$$= \frac{X_{\mathrm{CP}} \times S_{\mathrm{CP}} \times Z \times n}{2 \times K \times \mathrm{DP} \times \Omega_c \times y \times \mathrm{PCR}} \left(\frac{C-F}{1.1C} \right)$$

3 Horse-power for strength

$$= \frac{X_{\mathrm{BP}} \times S_{\mathrm{BP}} \times Y_P \times F \times \mathrm{rev/min} \times n}{126\,000 \times K \times \mathrm{DP}^2 \times \Omega_b} \left(\frac{C-F}{1.1C} \right)$$

$\therefore$ Safe working stress for strength, f_s

$$= \frac{X_{\mathrm{BP}} \times S_{\mathrm{BP}} \times Y_P \times n \times 63\,000}{126\,000 \times K \times y \times \mathrm{CP} \times \mathrm{PCR} \times \mathrm{DP}^2 \times \Omega_b} \left(\frac{C-F}{1.1C} \right)$$

$$= \frac{X_{\mathrm{BP}} \times S_{\mathrm{BP}} \times Y_P \times n}{2 \times K \times y \times \mathrm{CP} \times \mathrm{PCR} \times \mathrm{DP}^2 \times \Omega_b} \left(\frac{C-F}{1.1C} \right)$$

where

X_{CP} = speed factor for wear – pinion (see Figure 11.1)
S_{CP} = surface stress factor – pinion (see Figure 10.2, page 148)
Z = zone factor (see Figure 11.2)
F = facewidth of tooth (in)
n = number of teeth – pinion
K = pitch factor (see Figure 11.3)
DP = diametral pitch
Ω_c = overlap ratio factor (see Figure 11.4)
y = Lewis form factor (see page 133)
CP = circular pitch (in)
X_{BP} = speed factor for strength – pinion (see Figure 11.5)
S_{BP} = bending stress factor – pinion (see Figure 10.2, page 148)
Y_P = strength factor – pinion (see Figure 11.6)
Ω_b = spiral angle factor (see Figure 11.7)

Note: The overlap ratio is the ratio of the greatest angle subtended at the apex of the developed pitch cone by any two points at the intersection of the tooth flank with the pitch cone, to the angle subtended at the apex of the developed pitch cone by two points equidistant from the apex on similar flanks of adjacent teeth (see Figure 11.8).

4 Spiral bevel gears are preferably made with an overlap ratio of at least unity, although it may not be practicable to do so in every case.

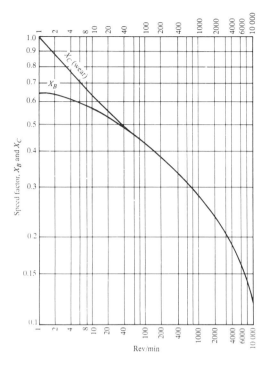

Figure 11.1 Speed factor, X_C (for wear)

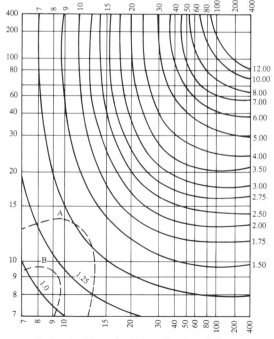

Number of teeth in gear for which zone factor is required

Figure 11.2 Zone factor, Z, for bevel gears

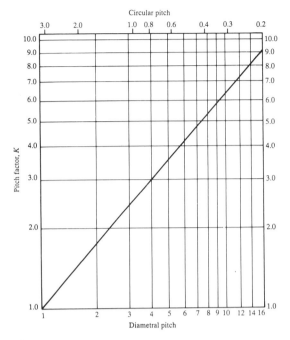

Figure 11.3   Pitch factor, *K*

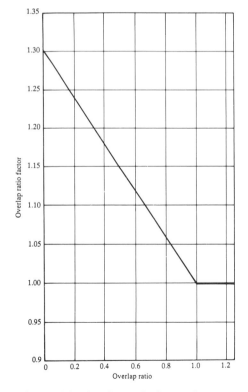

Figure 11.4   Overlap ratio factor, Ω_c

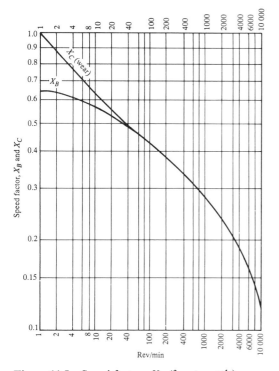

Figure 11.5   Speed factor, X_B (for strength)

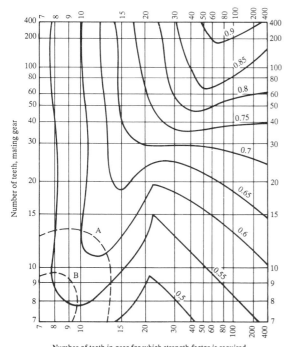

Number of teeth in gear for which strength factor is required

Figure 11.6   Strength factor, Y (for bevel gears)

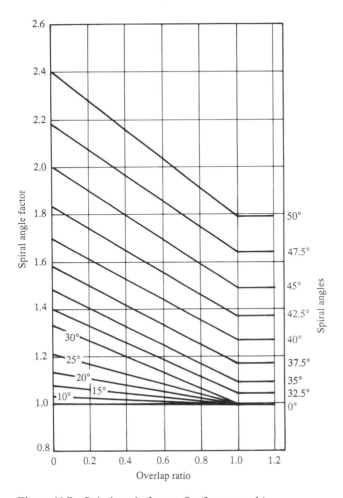

Figure 11.7   Spiral angle factor, Ω_b (for strength)

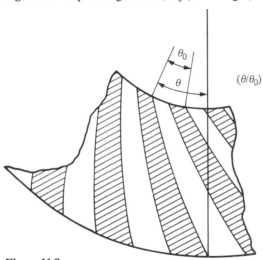

Figure 11.8

As a guide to the minimum value of spiral angle to ensure an overlap ratio of not less than unity, the following formula should be used:

$$\tan \text{Spiral angle} = \text{Circular pitch} \times \left(\frac{1}{\text{Facewidth}} - \frac{1}{(2 \times \text{Cone distance}) - \text{Facewidth}} \right)$$

In the case of straight bevel gears, the overlap ratio is always zero and

Ω_b – spiral angle factor $= 1.00$
Ω_c – overlap ratio factor $= 1.33$

Modified Lewis formulae for bevel gears

The Lewis formulae for spur gears (see page 132) can be modified for stressing bevel gears as follows:

1 Tangential load on teeth (lb)

1A $$= \frac{\text{Mean pitch rad.}^2}{\text{Pitch rad.}} \times \text{Lewis factor} \times \text{Tooth width} \times CP \times \text{Safe } W_s$$

or

1B $$= \frac{\text{Torque transmitted}}{\text{Mean pitch circle rad.}}$$

where

$CP = $ circular pitch
$W_s = $ working stress

2 From the above formula:
Safe working stress

$$= \frac{\text{Tangential load}}{\dfrac{\text{Mean pitch rad.}^2}{\text{Pitch rad.}} \times \text{Lewis form factor} \times \text{Tooth width} \times \text{Circ. pitch}}$$

where the Lewis form factor is based on the number of teeth in the equivalent spur gearwheel, which is calculated as follows:
No. of teeth – equivalent spur gearwheel

$$= \frac{\text{No. of teeth in bevel gear}}{\text{Pitch cone angle}}$$

3 Using the number of teeth – equivalent spur gearwheel, the Lewis form factor for various types of gear teeth is calculated from the following formulae:

$14\frac{1}{2}°$ pressure angle – full-depth teeth

$$= 0.124 - \frac{0.684}{\text{No. of teeth}}$$

20° pressure angle – full-depth teeth

$$= 0.154 - \frac{0.912}{\text{No. of teeth}}$$

20° pressure angle – stub teeth

$$= 0.175 - \frac{0.900}{\text{No. of teeth}}$$

4   Mean pitch radius

$$= \text{Pitch radius} - (0.5 \times \text{Facewidth} \times \cos \text{Pitch cone angle})$$

Gleason stress formulae

The Gleason Gear Co., Rochester, New York, USA, devised purely mathematical formulae for the calculation of the stresses in bevel gears as follows.

The recommendations and rating formulae given are designed specifically for bevel gears with tooth contact which has been developed to give the correct pattern in the final mountings under full load. The application of these formulae and recommendations to bevel gears in which this condition is not fulfilled require a modification in the ratings.

The extent of this modification is defined in the formulae for certain conditions.

The section 'Fundamental bending stress formulae' is intended for the calculation of bending stresses in a pair of gears when the power or torque is known. The section 'Fundamental power formulae' is intended for determining the power capacity of the pair of gears based on an assumed allowable bending stress. The appropriate section to suit the particular application should be used.

Fundamental bending stress formulae

The basic equation for the bending stress in a bevel gear is given as follows:

$$S_t = \frac{W_t K_o}{K_V} \frac{P_d}{F} \frac{K_s K_m}{J K_x}$$

where

S_t = calculated tensile stress (lb/in^2) at the tooth root
W_t = transmitted tangential load (lb)
K_o = overload factor
K_v = dynamic factor
P_d = diametral pitch at large end of teeth
F = tooth facewidth (in)
K_s = size factor
K_m = load distribution factor
J = geometry factor
K_x = cutter radius factor

The basic equation for the working stress in a bevel gear is given as follows:

$$S_W = \frac{S_{at}K_L}{K_T K_R}$$

where

S_W = working stress (lb/in^2)
S_{at} = allowable bending stress (lb/in^2)
K_L = life factor
K_T = temperature factor
K_R = factor of safety

Note: The calculated bending stress must be equal to or less than the working stress, i.e. $S_t \leq S_W$

Fundamental power formulae

The basic equation for the rated power of a pair of bevel gears is given by the following equation. The equation is for rating stock gears or for determining the capacity of an existing pair of gears:

$$P' = S_{at}\frac{n_p d}{126\,050}\frac{F}{P_d}\frac{JK_x}{K_s}$$

where

P' = rated power (hp) at n_p rev/min of pinion
n_p = rev/min – pinion
d = pitch dia. at large end of pinion teeth (in)
F = tooth facewidth (in)
P_d = diametral pitch at large end of teeth
J = geometry factor
K_x = cutter radius factor
K_s = size factor

The above-rated capacity of a pair of bevel gears operating at a specified speed (n_p) must be modified to suit the particular application. The resulting allowable power is calculated as follows:

$$P = \frac{P'K_L K_v}{K_o K_T K_R K_m}$$

where

P = allowable power (hp) which may be safely transmitted at n_p rev/ min of pinion
P' = rated power at n_p rev/min given by the previous equation
K_L = life factor
K_v = dynamic factor
K_o = overload factor

K_T = temperature factor
K_R = factor of safety
K_m = load distribution factor

To calculate the factors required to arrive at the stress and power figures, see formulae on pages 226 and 227 inclusive. The following formulae are provided.

1 *Transmitted tangential load,* W_t. The tangential load is calculated directly from the power or torque transmitted as follows:

$$W_t = \frac{126\,050P}{dn_p} = \frac{2T}{d}$$

where

P = power transmitted in horse-power. The maximum tangential load will depend upon the maximum torque rather than the maximum power. Therefore, consideration should be given to the torque characteristics of the driving motor

d = large end-pitch diameter of the pinion (in). Adjustment has been made in the geometry factor to correct the tangential load for the mean pitch diameter

n_p = pinion speed in rev/min corresponding to the power P

T = pinion torque (lb/in). In general, the calculated stress should be based on the maximum operating torque.

2 *Overload factor,* K_o. The overload factor makes allowance for the roughness or smoothness of operation of both the driving and driven units. In determining the overload factor, consideration should be given to the fact that many prime movers develop momentary overload torques which are very much greater than those determined by the rated output of the prime mover. Unless experience dictates otherwise (see paragraph 3, below), the values given in the table below may be used as a guide.

	Overload factors, K_o		
	Character of load on driven machine		
Prime mover	Uniform	Medium shock	Heavy shock
Uniform	1.00	1.25	1.75
Light shock	1.25	1.50	2.00
Medium shock	1.50	1.75	2.25

3 *Service factor.* Service factors are special factors which have been established by an industry for specific applications, where field data are available for determining more positively what factor should be used. The service factor includes not only the overhead factor, but also the life factor and factor of safety.

Service factors should be used whenever available. If a specific service is used in place of the overload factor, K_o, use a value of 1.00 for the life factor, K_L, and the factor of safety, K_R.

4   *Dynamic factor, K_v.* The dynamic factor reflects the effect of inaccuracies in profile, tooth spacing and runout.

The values of the dynamic factor can be obtained from Figure 11.9.

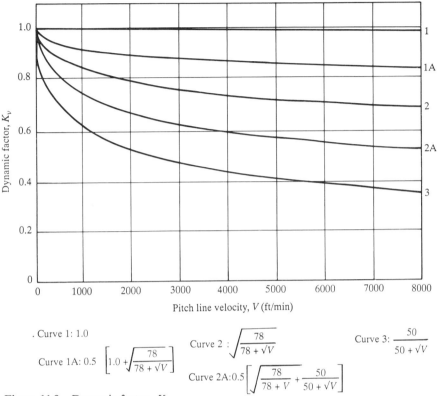

Curve 1: 1.0

Curve 1A: $0.5\left[1.0 + \sqrt{\dfrac{78}{78 + \sqrt{V}}}\right]$

Curve 2 : $\sqrt{\dfrac{78}{78 + \sqrt{V}}}$

Curve 2A: $0.5\left[\sqrt{\dfrac{78}{78 + V}} + \dfrac{50}{50 + \sqrt{V}}\right]$

Curve 3: $\dfrac{50}{50 + \sqrt{V}}$

Figure 11.9   Dynamic factor, K_v

Notes:

Curve 1. Spiral bevel gears cut to good commercial quality with accurate spacing and concentricity and quenching in a manner that maintains such accuracy

Curve 1A. Large spiral bevel gears on the same accuracy as in curve 1 but free-quenched

Curve 2. Spiral bevel gears of lower accuracy than in curve 1A, or large planed spiral bevel gears

Curve 2A. Straight bevel gears of good commercial quality

Curve 3. Straight bevel gears of lower accuracy than in curve 2A, or large planed straight bevel gears

On straight bevel or Zerol bevel gears when the profile contact ratio m_p is less than one, the value from Figure 11.9 should be multiplied by the value of

$$\frac{m_p}{(2.0 - m_p)}$$

5   *Diametral pitch, P_d.* This value is taken at the outer end of the tooth. In the stress formula, however, adjustment has been made in the geometry factor to correct for the mean diametral pitch.

6   Facewidth, F (in). In general, the facewidth will be equal on both gear and mating pinion. If, however, the facewidth is greater on one member than on its mating member, it will be conservative to use the smaller value. If the maximum capacity is to be calculated, it will be necessary to use the formulae in the geometry factor calculations.

7   Geometry factor, J. Within the formulae for the geometry factor are the formulae to allow the maximum capacity of the gears to be calculated when gear and pinion facewidths are unequal:

$$J = \frac{Y_K}{m_n K_1} \cdot \frac{R_t}{R} \cdot \frac{F_e}{F} \cdot \frac{P_d}{P_m}$$

To solve this equation the data given below must be used.

Note: Within the geometry factor are incorporated the tooth-form factors, the load location, the load sharing, the effective facewidth, the stress correction factor, and the inertia factor.

Y_K = tooth-form factor
m_n = load-sharing ratio
K_1 = inertia factor
R_t = mean transverse radius to point of load application
R = mean transverse pitch radius
F_e = effective facewidth
F = facewidth
P_d = diametral pitch
P_m = mean diametral pitch

In order to solve the geometry factor equation, the following data must be available for both gear and mating pinion:

A_o = outer cone distance
a_o = large end addendum
b_o = large end dedendum
D = large end-pitch diameter
F = actual facewidth (this may be different on the two members)
F' = net facewidth (if facewidths of gear and pinion are not equal, use the smaller value)
N = no. of teeth
P_d = large end diametral pitch (transverse)
r_t = tool edge radius
t_o = large end transverse circular tooth thickness
δ = dedendum angle
Γ = pitch angle
Γ_o = face angle
ϕ = normal pressure angle
ψ = mean spiral angle

In addition to the data given above, the following calculated quantities will be required for both gear and pinion, where subscripts '*P*' and '*G*' refer to pinion and gear, respectively, and subscript 'mate' refers to the value for the mating member.

(a) Mean cone distance, $A = A_o - 0.5F'$

(b) Addendum angle, $\alpha = \Gamma_o - \Gamma$

(c) Mean addendum, $a = a_o - 0.5F' \tan \alpha$

(d) Mean dedendum, $b = b_o - 0.5F' \tan \delta$

(e) $K = \dfrac{3.2N_G + 4.0N_P}{N_G - N_P}$

(f) Mean diametral pitch, transverse:

$$P_m = \frac{A_o}{A} P_d$$

(g) Large end transverse circular pitch:

$$p = \frac{\pi}{P_d}$$

(h) Mean normal circular pitch:

$$p_n = \frac{A}{A_o} p \cos \psi$$

(i) $p_2 = \dfrac{p_n}{\cos \phi \ (\cos^2 \psi + \tan^2 \phi)}$

(j) Mean transverse pitch radius:

$$R = \frac{D}{2 \cos \Gamma} \cdot \frac{A}{A_o}$$

(k) Mean normal pitch radius:

$$R_N = \frac{R}{\cos^2 \psi}$$

(l) Mean normal base radius:

$$R_{BN} = R_N \cos \phi$$

(m) Mean normal outside radius:

$$R_{ON} = R_N + a$$

(n) Mean normal circular tooth thickness:

$$t = \frac{A}{A_o} t_o$$

(o) $\Delta p_1 = \sqrt{R_{ON}^2 - R_{BN}^2} - R_N \sin \phi$

(p) Length of action in mean normal section:

$$Z_N = \Delta_{p1}{'}P{'} + \Delta_{p1}{'}G{'}$$

(q) $K_2 = \dfrac{F'}{A_o}\left[\dfrac{2 - \dfrac{F'}{A_o}}{2\left(1 - \dfrac{F'}{A_o}\right)}\right]$

(r) Transverse (profile) contact ratio:

$$m_p = \frac{Z_N}{P_2}$$

   For straight bevel and Zerol bevel gears this value must be greater than 1.0, otherwise these formulae cannot be used.

(s) Face contact ratio:

$$m_F = \frac{\left(K_2 \tan \psi - \dfrac{K_2^3}{3} \tan^3 \psi\right) A_o P_d}{\pi}$$

(t) Modified contact ratio:

$$m_o = \sqrt{m_p^2 + m_F^2}$$

(u) Distance in mean normal section from the beginning of action to the point of load application:

$$P_3 = P_2 \left(\frac{m_p}{m_o}\right)^2 \left(1 - \frac{m_o}{2} + \frac{m_o^2}{2m_p} \pm \frac{2m_F}{K_{mp}}\sqrt{m_o - 1}\right) \begin{array}{l}\text{concave} \\ \text{convex}\end{array}$$

where m_o is *less than* 2.0.

$$P_3 = P_2 \left(\frac{m_p}{m_o}\right)^2 \left(\frac{m_o^2}{2m_p} \pm \frac{m_F m_o}{K m_p}\right) \begin{array}{l}\text{concave} \\ \text{convex}\end{array}$$

where m_o is *greater than* 2.0.

(v) Distance from mean section to centre of pressure measured in the lengthwise direction along the tooth:

$$X_o'' = \frac{F' m_F}{m_o^2}\left[\frac{2m_p}{km_F}\sqrt{m_o - 1} \pm \left(\frac{m_o - 1}{2}\right)\right] \begin{array}{l}\text{pinion} \\ \text{gear}\end{array}$$

when *m* is less than 2.0.

$$X_o'' = \frac{F' m_p}{km_o} \begin{array}{l}\text{when } m_o \text{ is} \\ \text{greater than 2.0}\end{array}$$

(w) $\Sigma R_n = R_{N'P'} + R_{N'G'}$

(x) Pressure angle at point of load application:

$$\tan \phi h = \frac{P_3 + \Sigma R_n \sin \phi - \sqrt{(R_{ON}^2 - R_{bN}^2)_{mate}}}{R_{bN}}$$

(a1)   Rotation angle between point of load application and tooth centre line:

$$\theta_h = \frac{\dfrac{0.5t}{R_N} - \text{inv. } \phi_h + \text{inv. } \phi}{0.017\,453}$$

(b1)   Angle which the normal force makes with a line perpendicular to the tooth centre line:

$$\phi_N = \phi_h - \theta_h$$

(c1)   Radius in mean normal section to point of load application on the tooth centre line:

$$R_x = \frac{R_{bN}}{\cos \phi_N}$$

(d1)   Distance from pitch circle to point of load application on the tooth centre line:

$$\Delta R_N = R_x - R_N$$

(e1)   Fillet radius at root of tooth:

$$r_f = \frac{(b - r_T)^2}{R_N + b - r_T} + r_T$$

where $r_T = $ tool edge radius

(numbering system (a1)–(e1) from BS 545, 1949)

For Coniflex straight bevel gears and Zerol bevel gears with 20° and 25° pressure angles, and generated spiral bevel gears with 20° pressure angle and 35° spiral angle; 20° pressure angle, 25° spiral angle and 90° shaft angle; 20° pressure angle, 15° spiral angle and 90° shaft angle; 25° pressure angle; 35° spiral angle and 90° shaft angle; 20° pressure angle, 35° spiral angle and 60° shaft angle; 20° pressure angle, 35° spiral angle and 120° shaft angle:

$$r_T = \frac{0.120}{P_d}$$

For Coniflex straight bevel differential gears with $22\frac{1}{2}°$ pressure angle:

$$r_T = \frac{0.240}{P_d}$$

If tools with edge radius $r_T = 0.120/P_d$ are used for the differential gears, the value of the geometry factor, J, should be multiplied by 0.89.

For automotive spiral bevel gears with 20° pressure angle, 35° spiral angle and 90° shaft angle:

$$r_T = \frac{0.240}{P_d} \text{ for gear}$$

and

$$r_T = \frac{0.120}{P_d} \text{ for pinion}$$

Notes:

1　On 20° and 25° pressure angle Coniflex straight bevel gears the facewidth should not exceed:

> one-third of the cone distance or $10/P_d$

2　On Zerol bevel gears with 20° and 25° pressure angle, the facewidth should not exceed:

> one-quarter of the cone distance or $10/P_d$

3　On Coniflex straight bevel differential gears with $22\frac{1}{2}°$ pressure angle, the facewidth should not exceed:

> one-third of the cone distance

4　On generated spiral bevel gears with 20° pressure angle and 35° spiral angle, the facewidth should be within the following tolerances, along with spiral bevel gears with 20° pressure angle, 25° spiral angle and 90° shaft angle; 20° pressure angle, 15° spiral angle and 90° shaft angle; 25° pressure angle, 35° spiral angle and 90° shaft angle; 20° pressure angle, 35° spiral angle and 120° shaft angle; and automotive spiral bevel gears with 20° pressure angle, 35° spiral angle and 90° shaft angle:

facewidth should not exceed 0.3 of the cone distance or $10/P_d$, and is not less than 0.25 of the cone distance

5　On generated spiral bevel gears with 20° pressure angle, 35° spiral angle and 60° shaft angle, the facewidth should be within the following tolerances:

not greater than 0.3 of the cone distance or $10/P_d$ nor less than 0.20 of the cone distance

(f1)　Projected length of the line of contact contained within the ellipse of tooth contact in the lengthwise direction of the tooth:

$$F_K = \frac{F'm_F}{m_o^2} \left[\frac{2m_p}{m_F} \sqrt{m_o - 1} \right] \quad \begin{array}{l} \text{when } m_o \text{ is} \\ \text{less than 2.0} \end{array}$$

$$F_K = \frac{F'm_p}{m_o} \quad \begin{array}{l} \text{when } m_o \text{ is} \\ \text{greater than 2.0} \end{array}$$

(g1)　$Y_2 = b - r_T$

(h1)　$x_o = \dfrac{t}{2} + b \tan \phi + r_T (\sec \phi - \tan \phi)$

(numbering system (f1)–(h1) from BS 545, 1949)

The preceding values will now enable the factors in the geometry factor formula to be calculated (see page 230).

8 *Tooth form factor*, Y_K. The tooth form factor incorporates the components for both the radial and tangential loads, and the combined stress concentration and stress correction factor.

As the tooth form factor must be determined for the weakest section, an initial assumption must be made, and by trial a final solution obtained.

8A X_θ = assumed value; for an initial value, make $X_\theta = x_o + Y_2$.

8B $\theta = \dfrac{X_\theta}{R_N}$

8C $X_2 = X_\theta - x_o$
8D $Z_1 = Y_2 \cos \theta - X_2 \sin \theta$
8E $Z_2 = Y_2 \sin \theta + X_2 \cos \theta$

8F $\tan \xi = \dfrac{Z_1}{Z_2}$

8G $t_N = X_\theta - R_N(\theta - \sin \theta) - r_T \cos \xi - Z_2 =$ one-half the tooth thickness at the weakest section
8H $h_N = \Delta R_N + R_N(1 - \cos \theta) + r_T \sin \xi + Z_1 =$ distance along the tooth centre line from the weakest section to the point of load application

Note:

8I Change X_θ until $\dfrac{t_N \cot \xi}{h_N} = 2.0$

then proceed as follows:

8J Tooth strength factor, X_N

$$= \dfrac{t_N^2}{h_N}$$

8K Combined stress concentration factor and stress correction factor (Dolan and Broghamer), K_f

$$= H + \left(\dfrac{2t_N}{r_f}\right)^J \left(\dfrac{2t_N}{h_N}\right)^L$$

For coefficients, see the table below.

Pressure angle	H	J	L
14° 30′	0.22	0.20	0.40
20° 0′	0.18	0.15	0.45

8L   Tooth form factor, Y_K

$$= \frac{2}{3} \frac{P_d}{K_f \left(\dfrac{1}{X_N} - \dfrac{\tan \phi_N}{3 - t_N} \right)}$$

9   *Load-sharing ratio, m_N.* The load-sharing factor determines what proportion of the total load is carried on the most heavily loaded tooth:

$$m_N = 1.0 \quad \begin{array}{l} \text{when } m_o \text{ is} \\ \text{less than } 2.0 \end{array}$$

$$m_N = \frac{m_o^3}{m_o^3 + 2\sqrt{(m_o^2 - 4)^3}} \quad \begin{array}{l} \text{when } m_o \text{ is} \\ \text{greater than } 2.0 \end{array}$$

10   *Inertia factor, K_i.* The inertia factor allows for the lack of smoothness of rotation in gears with a low contact ratio:

$$K_i = \frac{2.0}{m_o} \quad \begin{array}{l} \text{when } m_o \text{ is} \\ \text{less than } 2.0 \end{array}$$

$$K_i = 1.0 \quad \begin{array}{l} \text{when } m_o \text{ is} \\ \text{greater than } 2.0 \end{array}$$

11   Mean transverse radius to point of load application, R_t

$$= R\left(\frac{A + x_o''}{A} \right) + \Delta R_N$$

12   Mean transverse pitch radius, R (see item (j), page 231)

13   *Effective facewidth, F_e.* This value evaluates the effectiveness of the tooth in distributing the load over the root cross-section:

$$\Delta F_T' = \frac{F - F_K}{2 \cos \psi} + \frac{x_o}{\cos \psi} = \text{toe increment}$$

$$\Delta F_H' = \frac{F - F_K}{2 \cos \psi} - \frac{x_o''}{\cos \psi} = \text{heel increment}$$

$$\Delta F_T = \Delta F_T' \quad \begin{array}{l} \text{when } \Delta F_T' \text{ and } \Delta F_H' \\ \text{are both positive} \end{array}$$

$$\Delta F_T = \frac{F - F_K}{\cos \psi} \quad \begin{array}{l} \text{when } \Delta F_H' \text{ is positive} \\ \text{and } \Delta F_T' \text{ is negative} \end{array}$$

$$\Delta F_T = 0 \quad \begin{array}{l} \text{when } \Delta F_H' \text{ is negative} \\ \text{and } \Delta F_T' \text{ is positive} \end{array}$$

$$\Delta F_H = \Delta F_H' \quad \begin{array}{l} \text{when } \Delta F_T' \text{ and } \Delta F_H' \text{ are} \\ \text{both positive} \end{array}$$

$$\Delta F_H = \frac{F - F_K}{\cos \psi} \quad \begin{array}{l} \text{when } \Delta F_H' \text{ is positive and} \\ \Delta F_T' \text{ is negative} \end{array}$$

$$\Delta F_H = 0 \quad \begin{array}{l} \text{when } \Delta F'_H \text{ is negative and} \\ \Delta F'_T \text{ is positive} \end{array}$$

Effective facewidth, F_e

$$= h_N \cos \psi \left(\tan^{-1} \frac{\Delta F_T}{h_N} + \tan^{-1} \frac{\Delta F_H}{h_N} \right) + F_K$$

14 Diametral pitch, P_d
15 Facewidth, F
16 Mean diametral pitch, P_m – see item (f), page 231.
17 Size factor, K_s:
  gears coarser than 16 DP – $K_s = P_d^{-0.25}$
  gears finer than 16 DP, see Figure 11.10.

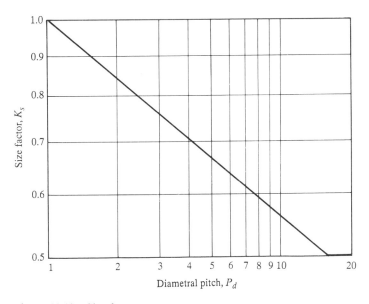

Figure 11.10 Size factor, K_s

18 *Load distribution factor, K_m.* As the performance of bevel gears depends to a considerable degree upon their alignment under operating conditions, the load distribution factor is used, the factor being based on the magnitude of the displacements of the gear and pinion from their designed correct locations.

If the assumed or known deflections or displacements are available, the load distribution factor can be taken from Figure 11.11.

If the deflections are larger than allowed for in the design and manufacture of the gears, the tooth contact may not be favourable, and this will increase the stresses in the gear teeth. In Figure 11.11, use the value of displacement from the position for which the tooth contact is developed together with the corresponding load. Vertical displacement refers to a change in the perpendicular distance between the gear and pinion axis. Axial displacement refers to movement of the gear or

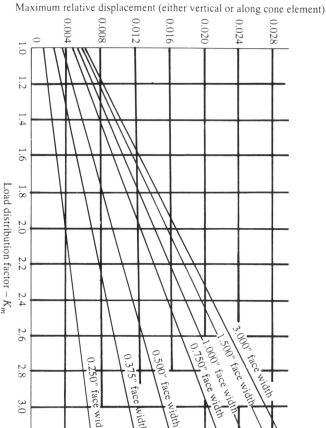

Figure 11.11 Load distribution factor for bevel gears

pinion along their axis, and in order to obtain the amount of displacement along the cone element, the axial displacement should be multiplied by the cosine of the pitch angle.

Where the estimated or actual displacements are not known, an estimate of this factor can be taken from the table below. Where mountings are carefully designed for maximum rigidity use the smaller factor from the table, but where the mounting rigidity is questionable the larger factor should be used.

Although the table indicates that lower factors are obtained with straddle mountings, it is often true that overhung mountings are just as good or better than straddle mountings. Because of the lower bearing loads in the straddle mounting, the overall design may be somewhat smaller and lighter. Regardless of the type of mounting, the size and type of bearings and their supports should provide rigidity as well as adequate life.

19   *Cutter radius factor*, K_x. This factor reflects the effect of the cutter radius (lengthwise curvature of the tooth) on the calculated bending stress.

Using K_x in the bending stress formula decreases the calculated stress as the cutter diameter is decreased.

	Load distribution factors, K_m		
Application	Both members straddle mounted	One member straddle mounted	Neither member straddle mounted
General industrial	1.00–1.10	1.10–1.25	1.25–1.40
Automotive	1.00–1.10	1.10–1.25	–
Aircraft	1.00–1.25	1.10–1.40	1.25–1.50

Recommended design practice is to select the cutter radius on the basis of the following equation:

$$\text{Cutter radius} = 1.1 A_G \sin \psi_G$$

(*Note*: Use the next larger nominal size)

where

A_G = gear mean cone distance
ψ_G = gear mean spiral angle

For the values of the cutter radius factor, K_x, see Figure 11.12.

20   *Allowable bending stress, S_{at}.* The maximum allowable bending stress (lb/in^2) is based upon the properties of the material. It varies with the material, heat treatment and surface treatment. Nominal values for the allowable bending stress in gear teeth for commonly used gear materials and heat treatments are given in Table 11.1.

Table 11.1   Allowable bending stress, S_{at}

Material	Heat treatment	Hardness (Brinell)	Hardness (Rockwell C)	Bending stress
Steel	Carburized (case-hardened)	–	55 min.	30 000
Steel	Flame- or induction-hardened (unhardened root fillet)	–	50 min.	13 500
Steel	Hardened and tempered	450 min.	–	25 000
Steel	Hardened and tempered	300 min.	–	19 000
Steel	Hardened and tempered	180 min.	–	13 500
Steel	Normalized	140 min.	–	11 000
Steel	Nitrided	–	–	22 000
Nodular iron	Hardened and tempered	450 min.	–	18 500
Nodular iron	Hardened and tempered	300 min.	–	14 000
Nodular iron	Hardened and tempered	180 min.	–	10 000
Nodular iron	Normalized	140 min.	–	8 000
Cast iron	As cast	200 min.	–	7 000
Cast iron	As cast	175 min.	–	4 600
Cast iron	As cast	–	–	2 700

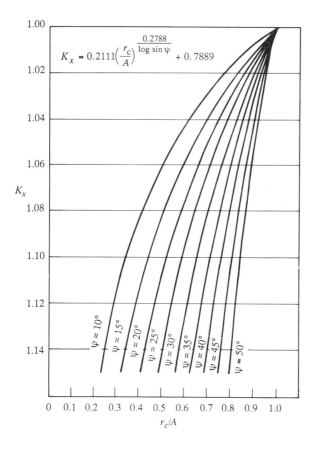

Figure 11.12   Cutter radius factor, K_x, vs. ratio of cutter radius to mean cone distance (A, gear mean cone distance; ψ, gear mean spiral angle; r_c, cutter radius)

Note: The values given in Table 11.1 are only approximate and are subject to considerable variation. Higher stresses may be permitted in some cases by careful gear design, manufacturing procedures, choice of steels and the use of the best heat-treating procedure. Likewise, lower values may be required if the steel composition and heat treatment are not suited to the application.

Carburized case-hardened gears require a core hardness of approximately 260–350 BHN (26–37 RC) and a total case depth in the range shown in Figure 11.13 to develop the greatest strength. The case must also be free of surface decarburization or grinding cracks and burns (if ground), and must have a carbon content near the eutectoid composition.

Flame- and induction-hardening have given excellent results in instances where there is sufficient control over the process. However, these processes require close control for satisfactory results, and can be detrimental in circumstances where they are employed improperly.

Nitrided steels usually have strengths very similar to through-hardened steels

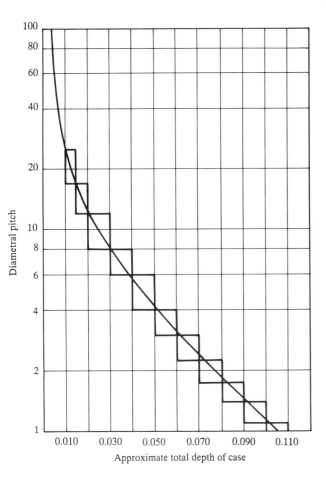

Figure 11.13 Diametral pitch vs. total case depth (In case of choice, use the greater depth on ground gears or on short facewidths. On fine-pitch gears (25 DP and finer) consult metallurgical department)

of the same hardness as the core hardness. In fine pitches it is sometimes possible to obtain higher strength with nitriding.

Use 70% of the values given in the table for idler gears and other gears where the teeth are loaded in both directions.

21   *Life factor, K_L.* The life factor, K_L, should be taken from Figure 11.14. This factor is dependent upon the required life, in cycles. For a single mesh, the number of revolutions and the number of cycles are the same.

For a gear which has more than one mating member, the life must be equal to the required number of revolutions multiplied by the number of mating gears. Where the required life is less than 6 000 000 cycles on the pinion, the life factors for gear and pinion will be different.

In cases where the load varies, it is possible to determine the equivalent life at maximum torque mathematically as follows:

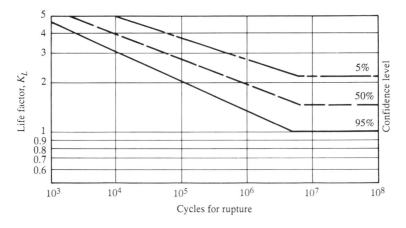

Figure 11.14   Life factor for bevel gears

Required equivalent life in pinion cycles at maximum torque

$$= 60L_H \left[k_1 n_{p1} + k_2 n_{p2} \left(\frac{T_2}{T_1} \right)^{5.68} + k_3 n_{p3} \left(\frac{T_3}{T_1} \right)^{5.68} + k_n n_{pn} \left(\frac{T_n}{T} \right)^{5.68} \right]$$

where

L_H = required total life in hours
$k_1, k_2, k_3 \ldots k_n$ = proportion of time at torque loads $T_1, T_2, T_3 \ldots T_n$, respectively
$n_{p1}, n_{p2}, n_{p3} \ldots n_{pn}$ = pinion rev/min corresponding to torque loads $T_1, T_2, T_3 \ldots T_n$, respectively
$T_1, T_2, T_3 \ldots T_n$ = torque loads, where T_1 is the maximum torque and T_n is the minimum torque which will produce a stress above the endurance limit

The required equivalent life in gear cycles at maximum torque may be obtained by multiplying the life in pinion cycles by the gear ratio:

$$L_{CG} = L_{CP} \frac{N_P}{N_G}$$

where

L_{CG} = equiv. life in gear cycles at max. torque
L_{CP} = equiv. life in pinion cycles at max. torque
N_P = no. of teeth – pinion
N_G = no. of teeth – gear

22 *Factor of safety, K_R.* The factor of safety has been introduced into this equation to offer the designer an opportunity to design for maximum safety or in some instances to design for a calculated risk. In the formula, the factor of safety is applied to the fatigue strength of the material rather than to the tensile strength.

As a result of this, the safety factors are much smaller than the values used in general machine design. Failure in the following table does not mean an immediate failure under the applied load, but rather a shorter life than the minimum specified.

The factors of safety should be as follows:

Requirements of application	Factor of safety, K_R
Maximum safety	2.0
Fewer than 1 failure in 100	1.0
Fewer than 1 failure in 3	0.8

12
Hypoid gear stress formulae

The Gleason formulae for bending and contact stresses in hypoid gear teeth will be covered in this chapter.

Under ideal operating conditions, hypoid gear teeth have a tooth contact pattern which utilizes the full working profile of the tooth without load concentration in any area and with gradual fading of the tooth contact pattern at the tips and ends of the teeth. Under such conditions, the gears will have the greatest load capacity and will function most smoothly and quietly.

In actual practice, however, it is impossible to obtain this ideal tooth contact pattern under all operating conditions, and therefore the gears are usually called upon to operate over a wide range of conditions. Thus the design and manufacture of the gears and mountings must be based on a compromise. Working and assembly tolerances limit the usable length and width of the tooth contact pattern.

The recommendations and rating formulae given in this chapter are prepared specifically for hypoid gears in which the tooth contact pattern has been developed to give the optimum results in the final mountings under full load. The application of these rating formulae to hypoid gears in which this condition is not fulfilled requires careful selection of the factors used in the formulae.

When designing hypoid gears, it is essential that both the strength – bending stress, and durability – contact stress are within acceptable limits.

To this point, the following formulae should be adhered to.

1 Bending stress, S_{tG}, in a hypoid gear

$$= \frac{2T_G K_o}{K_v} \cdot \frac{P_d}{F_G D} \cdot \frac{K_s K_m}{J_G}$$

2 Bending stress, S_{tP}, in mating hypoid pinion

$$= \frac{2T_P K_o}{K_v} \cdot \frac{P_d}{F_G D} \cdot \frac{N}{n} \cdot \frac{K_s K_m}{J_P'}$$

3 Contact stress, S_c in a hypoid gear or pinion

$$= C_P \sqrt{\frac{2T_{Pmx} C_o}{C_v} \cdot \frac{1}{F_G D^2} \cdot \left(\frac{N}{n}\right)^2 \cdot \frac{C_s C_m C_f}{I}} \sqrt[3]{\frac{T_P}{T_{Pmx}}}$$

4 Working bending stress, S_{wt}, in a hypoid gear or pinion

$$= \frac{S_{at} K_L}{K_T K_R}$$

5 Working contact stress, S_{wc}, in a hypoid gear or pinion

$$= \frac{S_{ac} C_L C_H}{C_T C_R}$$

where

S_{tP}, S_{tG} = calculated tensile bending stresses at the root of the tooth for pinion and gear, respectively (lb/in^2)

S_c = calculated contact stress at point on tooth where its value will be a maximum (lb/in^2)

S_{Wt}, S_{Wc} = working tensile bending stress and working contact stress, respectively (lb/in^2)

T_P, T_G = transmitted torque – pinion and gear, respectively (lb/in)

K_o, C_o = overload factors for strength and durability, respectively

K_v, C_v = dynamic factors for strength and durability, respectively

P_d = gear transverse diametral pitch at outer end of tooth (teeth/in)

F_P, F_G = facewidths of pinion and gear, respectively (in)

D = gear outer pitch diameter (in)

K_s, C_s = size factors for strength and durability, respectively

K_m, C_m = load distribution factors for strength and durability, respectively

J_G = geometry factor for strength – gear

n, N = numbers of teeth – pinion and gear, respectively

J_P' = modified pinion geometry factor for strength

C_P = elastic coefficient for gear and pinion materials combinations (lb$^{\frac{1}{2}}$/in)

T_{Pmx} = maximum transmitted pinion torque (lb.in)

C_f = surface condition factor for durability

I = geometry factor for durability

S_{at}, S_{ac} = allowable tensile bending stress and allowable contact stress, respectively (lb/in^2)

K_L, C_L = life factors for strength and durability, respectively

K_T, C_T = temperature factors for strength and durability, respectively

K_R, C_R = factors of safety for strength and durability, respectively

C_H = hardness ratio factor for durability.

The calculated tensile bending stresses must be equal to or less than the working tensile bending stress: $S_{tP}, S_{tG} \leq S_{Wt}$.

Also, the calculated contact stress must be equal to or less than the working contact stress: $S_c \leq S_{Wc}$.

The following formulae provide the details required to calculate the factors used in the stress calculations.

6 *Overload factors, K_o, C_o*. The overload factor makes allowance for the roughness or smoothness of operation of both the driving and driven units. When determining the overload factor, consideration should be given to the fact that many prime movers develop momentary overload torques which are very much greater than those determined by the rated output of the prime mover. If these peak overload torques are known, their values should be used as the transmitted torques when making the analysis. If they are not known, the values given in the table below may be used as a guide.

Prime mover	Character of load on driven machine		
	Uniform	Medium shock	Heavy shock
Uniform	1.00	1.25	1.75
Medium shock	1.25	1.50	2.00
Heavy shock	1.50	1.75	2.25

The figures given in the table are speed-decreasing drives; for speed-increasing drives add the following to the above factors:

$$0.01 \left(\frac{\text{No. of teeth} - \text{gear}}{\text{No. of teeth} - \text{pinion}} \right)^2$$

7 *Service factors.* Service factors are special factors which have been established by industry for specific applications, where field data are available for determining more positively what factors should be used.

The service factor includes not only the overload factor, but also the life factor and factor of safety. Service factors should be used whenever available. If service factors are used in place of the overload factors, K_o and C_o, use a value of 1.0 for the life factors, K_L and C_L, and factors of safety, K_R and C_R. In general, the service factors for strength and durability will not be equal.

8 *Dynamic factors, K_v, C_v.* The dynamic factor reflects the effect of inaccuracies in profile, tooth spacing, and runout, on instantaneous tooth loading. For hypoid gears having the preferred tooth contact pattern and accurate tooth spacing and concentricity, the dynamic factor may be taken as unity (see curve 1 in Figure 12.1 for gears of AGMA Class 11 or higher). Values of the dynamic factor for hypoid gears of lower accuracy or for large planed hypoid gears are given by curve 2.

9 *Size factors, K_s, C_s.* The size factor is introduced in the formulae for strength and durability to take into account the fact that the allowable stress is a function of the size of specimen and the hardenability of the material. The effect of specimen size has shown up most clearly on the allowable bending stress; it is far less noticeable on the allowable contact stress.

The size factor for strength can be taken from Figure 12.2 or calculated as follows;

$$K_s = \frac{1}{P_d^{0.25}} \text{ when } P_d \text{ is coarser than } 16 \, \text{DP}$$

or

$$K_s = 0.5 \text{ when } P_d \text{ is finer than } 16 \, \text{DP}$$

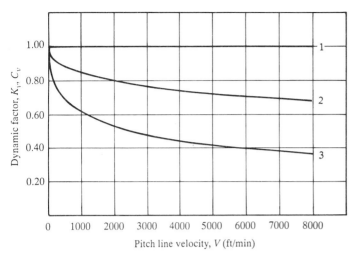

Figure 12.1 Dynamic factors, K_v, C_v

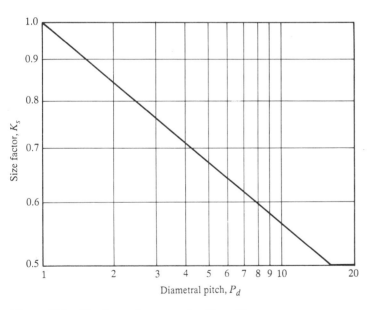

Figure 12.2 Size factor for strength of hypoid gears

Because of lack of test data, no values are available to show the effect of surface hardness and tooth size on surface durability. Therefore, the size factor for durability, $C_s = 1.0$, unless individual experience dictates otherwise.

10 *Load distribution factors*, K_m, C_m. As hypoid gear performance is dependent to a considerable degree upon their alignment under operating conditions, a load distribution factor is introduced in the rating formulae to make allowance for this effect. This factor is based on the magnitude of the relative displacements of both gear and pinion.

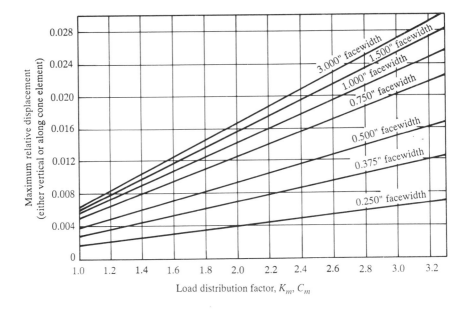

Figure 12.3 Load distribution factors for hypoid gears

Where assumed or known deflections or displacements are available, the load distribution factor can be taken from Figure 12.3.

It is usual to assume that the tooth contact has been developed to give a suitable pattern in the finalized mountings under normal operating loads. If the deflections of the mountings are larger than allowed for, the tooth contact pattern may not be favourable. Just as if the deflections of the mountings allowed for are large under heavy loads, the tooth contact pattern will not be favourable under lighter operating loads, and the deflections created in such instances may increase the stresses in the gear teeth. The values used from Figure 12.3 should be taken to suit the value of displacement from the position for which the tooth contact pattern was developed, along with the corresponding load.

Vertical displacement refers to a change in the perpendicular distance between the gear and pinion axes, i.e. the hypoid offset, and axial displacement refers to movement of the gear or pinion along its axis. To obtain the amount of displacement along the cone element, the axial displacement should be multiplied by the cosine of the pitch angle.

If the estimated or actual displacements are unknown, an estimated factor may be taken from the table below.

Application	Both members straddle mounted	One member straddle mounted	Both members overhung mounted
General industrial	1.00–1.10	1.10–1.25	1.25–1.40
Automotive	1.00–1.10	1.10–1.25	–
Aircraft	1.00–1.25	1.10–1.40	1.25–1.50

Where mountings are designed for maximum rigidity use the smaller factor from the table, and where mounting rigidity is doubtful use the larger factor.

Although the table indicates that the lowest factors are obtained with straddle mountings on both members, in practice it has been found that overhung mountings carefully designed are as good as or better than a poorly designed straddle mounting. Because of the lower bearing loads encountered in straddle mountings, the overall design should be more compact and lighter in weight than an overhung-type mounting. It is essential that, regardless of the type of mounting used, the size and type of bearing selected along with their supports should provide adequate rigidity and life.

11 *Geometry factors for strength, J_P, J'_P, J_G.* The geometry factor incorporates the tooth form factor, the load location, the load sharing between pairs of gear teeth, the effective facewidth, the stress concentration and stress correction factors, and the inertia factor resulting from a low contact ratio. The basic geometry factors for pinion and gear strength are J_P and J_G, respectively. J'_P is a modified geometry factor for the hypoid pinion and is related to the basic pinion geometry factor by the following expression:

$$J'_P = J_P \cdot \frac{F_P}{F_G}$$

where

F_P = pinion facewidth
F_G = gear facewidth

Figures 12.4(a) to 12.4(f) give the geometry factors for strength for some of the more common hypoid gear designs. The upper curves on the graphs give the geometry factor for the gear, J_G, while the lower curves give the geometry factor for the pinion, J'_P. These two values are used in the equations for both the bending stress in a hypoid gear and the bending stress in the mating hypoid pinion.

The graphs are based on the following:

(a) Gear facewidth, F_G: $0.155D$
(b) Pinion mean spiral angle, ψ_P:

$$25° + 5° \sqrt{\frac{N_G}{N_P}} + 90° \frac{E}{D}$$

(c) Gear cutter edge radius, r_{TG}:

$$\frac{0.240}{P_d}$$

(d) Pinion cutter edge radius, r_{TP}:

$$\frac{0.120}{P_d}$$

(e) Gear cutter diameter, D_c: $0.85D$
(f) Strength balance: 0.100 except when ratio of gear to pinion toplands in the mean section exceeds 1.5

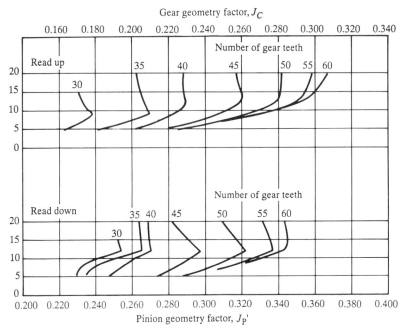

Figure 12.4 (a) Geometry factor for strength of hypoid gears with 19° average pressure angle and E/D ratio of 0.10

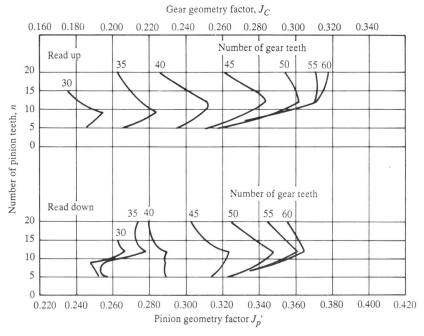

Figure 12.4 (b) Geometry factor for strength of hypoid gears with 19° average pressure angle and E/D ratio of 0.15

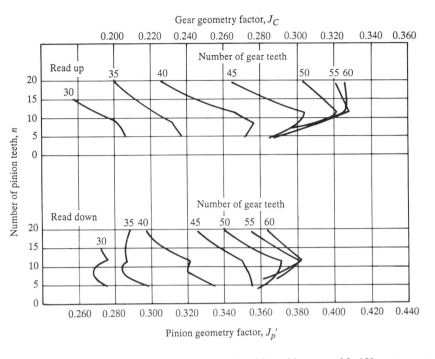

Figure 12.4 (c) Geometry factor for strength of hypoid gears with 19° average pressure angle and E/D ratio of 0.20

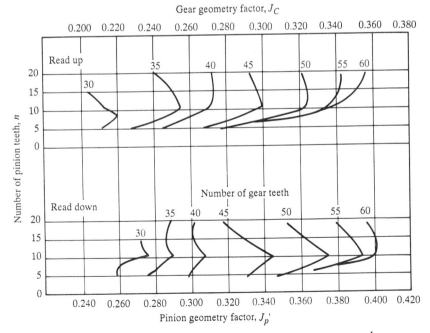

Figure 12.4 (d) Geometry factor for strength of hypoid gears with $22\frac{1}{2}°$ average pressure angle and E/D ratio of 0.10

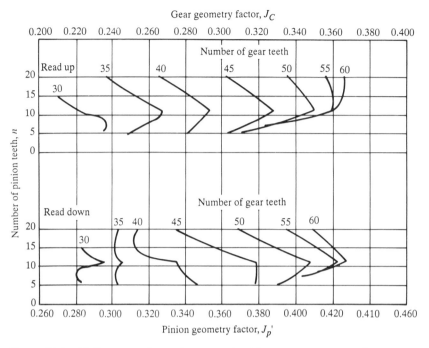

Figure 12.4   (e) Geometry factor for strength of hypoid gears with $22\frac{1}{2}°$ average pressure angle and E/D ratio of 0.15

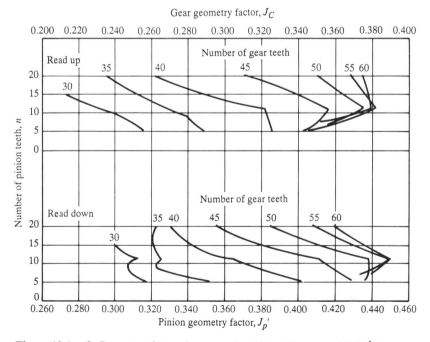

Figure 12.4   (f) Geometry factor for strength of hypoid gears with $22\frac{1}{2}°$ average pressure angle and E/D ratio of 0.20

(g) Tooth proportions: designed in line with the 'Gleason method for designing hypoid gear blanks' (see Chapter 8)
(h) Tooth taper: tilted root lines about mean point
(i) Average pressure angle, ϕ_a: 19° or $22\frac{1}{2}°$
(j) Hypoid pinion offset, E/D: 0.10, 0.15 or 0.20 divided by pitch diameter.

The illustrations tabulated below are included on pages 250–252.

Page	Figure no.	Average pressure angle, ϕ_a	$\dfrac{\text{Offset}}{\text{Gear PC dia.}} = \dfrac{E}{D}$
250	12.4(a)	19°	0.10
250	12.4(b)	19°	0.15
251	12.4(c)	19°	0.20
251	12.4(d)	$22\frac{1}{2}°$	0.10
252	12.4(e)	$22\frac{1}{2}°$	0.15
252	12.4(f)	$22\frac{1}{2}°$	0.20

12 *Elastic coefficient, C_P.* The elastic coefficient for hypoid gears with localized tooth contact pattern is calculated using the following equation:

$$C_P = \sqrt{\frac{3}{2\pi} \cdot \frac{1}{\dfrac{1-\mu_P^2}{E_P} + \dfrac{1-\mu_G^2}{E_G}}}$$

where

$\mu_P, \mu_G =$ Poisson's ratio for materials of pinion and gear, respectively (use a value of 0.3 for ferrous materials)

$E_P, E_G =$ Young's modulus of elasticity (lb/in²) for materials of pinion and gear, respectively (see table below).

		Elastic coefficients, C_P	
		Gear materials	
		Steel	Cast iron
Pinion material	Young's modulus, E	30.0×10^6	19×10^6
Steel	30.0×10^6	2800	2450
Cast iron	19.0×10^6	2450	2250

13 *Maximum pinion torque, T_{Pmx}.* This is the value of maximum transmitted pinion torque in pound-inches. It is calculated using the following formula:

$$\frac{63\,000P}{n_p}$$

by selecting the corresponding values of power, P, and pinion speed, n_p, which result in the maximum value. It is assumed that the tooth contact pattern has been developed to produce a full pattern at this maximum torque value.

14   *Surface condition factor,* C_f. The surface condition factor for durability depends on surface finish as affected by cutting, lapping, grinding, shot-peening, etc. It also depends on surface treatments such as lubrizing, copper plating, etc. In the absence of test values, the surface condition factor, C_f, may be taken as unity, provided that first-class gear manufacturing practice has been followed.

15   *Geometry factor for durability,* I. Within the geometry factor for durability are incorporated the relative radius of curvature between mating tooth surfaces, the load location, the load sharing between pairs of teeth, the effective facewidth and the inertia factor resulting from a low contact ratio.

Figures 12.5(a) to 12.5(f) give the geometry factors for durability for some of the more common hypoid gear designs. These values are used in the equation for the contact stress in a hypoid gear and its mating pinion. All the charts are based on the same criteria listed for the geometry factors for strength (see pages 250 and 252).

The illustrations tabulated below are included on pages 255–257.

Page	Figure no.	Average pressure angle, ϕ_a	$\dfrac{\text{Offset}}{\text{Gear PC dia.}} = \dfrac{E}{D}$
255	12.5(a)	19°	0.10
255	12.5(b)	19°	0.15
256	12.5(c)	19°	0.20
256	12.5(d)	$22\frac{1}{2}°$	0.10
257	12.5(e)	$22\frac{1}{2}°$	0.15
257	12.5(f)	$22\frac{1}{2}°$	0.20

Notes:

(a) The calculated bending stresses for gear and pinion must not exceed the working tensile bending stress

(b) The calculated contact stress between gear and pinion must not exceed the working contact stress

16   *Allowable bending stress,* S_{at}. The maximum allowable tensile bending stress (lb/in^2) is based upon the physical properties of the material. It varies with the material composition, heat treatment and surface treatment. Table 12.1 (page 258) gives nominal values for the allowable bending stress in a hypoid gear for the commonly used air-melt steels and heat treatments. (*Note*: These values are only approximate and are subject to considerable variations, as described in the following pages. The bending stresses listed are not directly related to the usual tensile strength of the material, but are based on the fatigue properties of actual gear teeth when calculated by the preceding formulae.)

Higher stresses may be permitted in some cases by careful gear design,

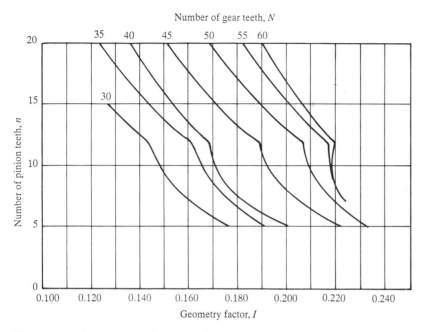

Figure 12.5   (a) Geometry factor for durability of hypoid gears with 19° average pressure angle and E/D ratio of 0.10

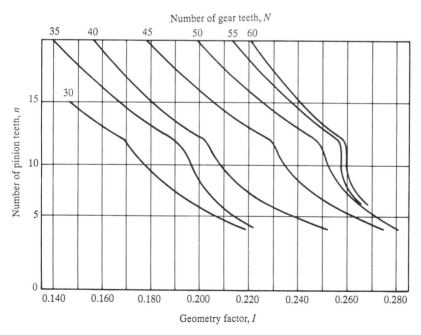

Figure 12.5   (b) Geometry factor for durability of hypoid gears with 19° average pressure angle and E/D ratio of 0.15

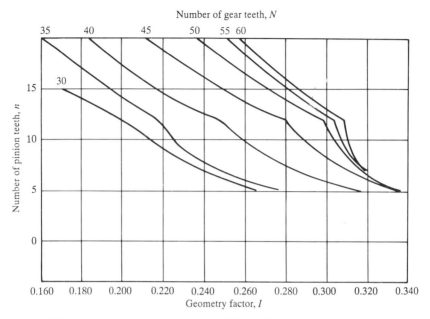

Figure 12.5   (c) Geometry factor for durability of hypoid gears with 19° average pressure angle and E/D ratio of 0.20

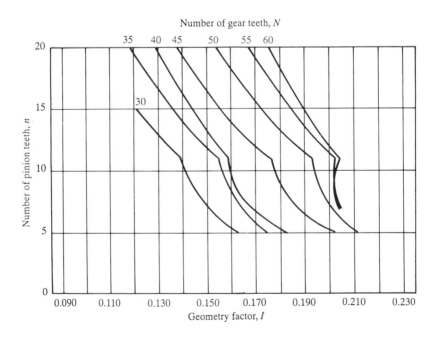

Figure 12.5   (d) Geometry factor for durability of hypoid gears with $22\frac{1}{2}°$ average pressure angle and E/D ratio of 0.10

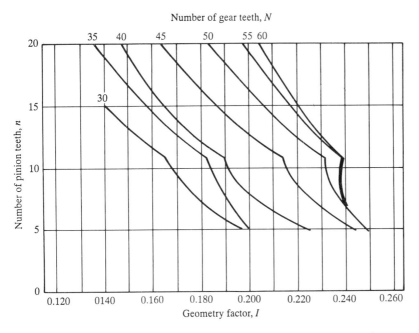

Figure 12.5   (e) Geometry factor for durability of hypoid gears with $22\frac{1}{2}°$ average pressure angle and E/D ratio of 0.15

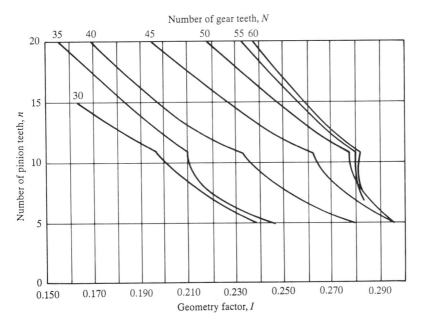

Figure 12.5   (f) Geometry factor for durability of hypoid gears with $22\frac{1}{2}°$ average pressure angle and E/D ratio of 0.20

Table 12.1 Allowable stresses for air-melt steel

Material	Heat treatment	Surface hardness		Endurance limit			
		Brinell	Rockwell C	Bending, S_{at}		Contact, S_{ac}	
				lb/in^2	kg/mm^2	lb/in^2	kg/mm^2
Steel	Carburized (case-hardened)		60 min.	30 000	21.0	250 000	175
Steel	Carburized (case-hardened)		55 min.	27 500	19.2	200 000	140
Steel	Flame- or induction-hardened		50 min.	13 500	9.5	190 000	133
Steel	Hardened and tempered	440 min.		25 000	17.5	190 000	133
Steel	Hardened and tempered	300 min.		19 000	13.3	135 000	95
Steel	Hardened and tempered	180 min.		13 500	9.5	95 000	66
Steel	Nitrided	Core 300 min.	60 min.	22 000	15.4	160 000	112

manufacturing procedures, choice of materials, and use of the best heat-treatment procedures. Lower values must be used if the steel composition and quality and the heat treatment are not suited to the application.

Carburized case-hardened gears require a core hardness in the range of 260–350 Brinell (26–37 Rockwell) and an effective case depth in line with Figure 12.6, to develop the greatest strength. The case must also be free from surface decarburization, grinding cracks or burns, and must have a carbon content near the eutectoid composition.

Flame and induction hardening have given excellent results in instances where there is sufficient control over the process, but these processes require extremely close control for satisfactory results, and can prove detrimental if not used correctly.

Nitrided steels usually have strengths very similar to through-hardened steels of the same hardness as the core hardness. In fine pitches where the nitrided case depth is approximately the same as the carburized case depth, the strength of the nitrided steels will approach that of case-hardened steels.

For idler gears and any gears where the teeth are subjected to a reversal of load in each cycle, the value given in Table 12.1 should be reduced by 30%.

17   *Allowable contact stress, S_{ac}.* The maximum allowable contact stress (lb/in²) is based on the physical properties of the material; it varies with the material composition, heat treatment and surface treatment.

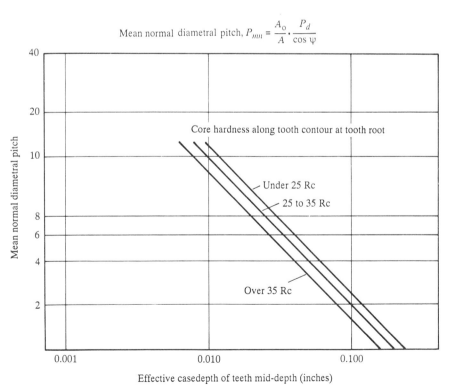

$$\text{Mean normal diametral pitch, } P_{mn} = \frac{A_0}{A} \cdot \frac{P_d}{\cos \psi}$$

Core hardness along tooth contour at tooth root

Under 25 Rc

25 to 35 Rc

Over 35 Rc

Mean normal diametral pitch

Effective casedepth of teeth mid-depth (inches)

Figure 12.6   Diametral pitch vs. effective case depth

Table 12.1 (page 258) gives nominal values for the allowable contact stress on hypoid gear teeth for the more commonly used air-melt steels and heat treatments. (*Note*: These values are only approximate and are subject to considerable variations, as discussed in the following paragraphs.)

Higher stresses may be permitted in some cases by careful gear design, manufacturing procedures, choice of materials, and use of the best heat-treatment procedures. Lower values must be used if the steel composition and quality or the heat treatment are not suited to the application.

Carburized case-hardened gears must be free from surface decarburization or grinding cracks or burns. The effective case depth should be in line with Table 12.1 to minimize case crushing and pitting.

18   Life factors, K_L, C_L. Both strength and durability are fatigue phenomena and therefore display a relationship between stress and life. The life factor for strength can be obtained from Figure 12.7 and the life factor for durability can be obtained from Figure 12.8. The life factor is dependent upon the required life in cycles. For a single mesh, the number of revolutions and the number of cycles are equal. For a gear which has more than one mating member, the life must be equal to the required number of revolutions multiplied by the number of mating gears.

In cases where the load is not constant, it may be necessary to determine the equivalent life at maximum torque. The following formulae based on the cumulative damage theory may be used:

Strength, L_{CPt}

$$= 60 L_H \left[k_1 N_{P1} + k_2 N_{P2} \left(\frac{T_2}{T_1} \right)^{5.68} + k_3 N_{P3} \left(\frac{T_3}{T_1} \right)^{5.68} + \ldots + k_n N_{Pn} \left(\frac{T_N}{T_1} \right)^{5.68} \right]$$

Durability, L_{CPC}

$$= 60 L_H \left[k_1 N_{P1} + k_2 N_{P2} \left(\frac{T_2}{T_1} \right)^{6} + k_3 N_{P3} \left(\frac{T_3}{T_1} \right)^{6} + \ldots + k_n N_{pN} \left(\frac{T_N}{T_1} \right)^{6} \right]$$

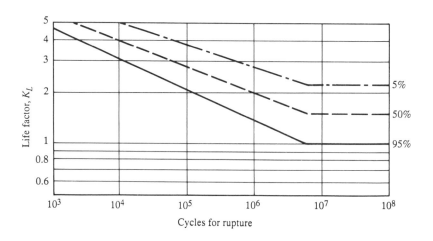

Figure 12.7   Life factor for strength

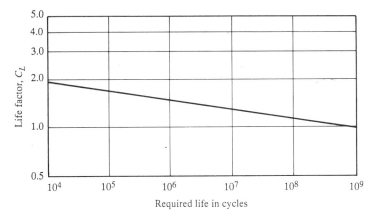

Figure 12.8 Life factor for durability

where

(a) L_{CPt}, L_{CPC} = required life in pinion cycles at maximum torque for strength and durability, respectively
(b) L_H = required total life (hours)
(c) $k_1, k_2, k_3 \ldots k_n$ = proportion of time of operation at torque loads $T_1, T_2, T_3 \ldots T_n$, respectively
(d) $N_{P1}, N_{P2}, N_{P3} \ldots N_{PN}$ = pinion speed (rpm) corresponding to torque loads $T_1, T_2, T_3 \ldots T_n$, respectively.
(e) $T_1, T_2, T_3 \ldots T_N$ = torque loads, where T_1 is the maximum torque and T_n is the minimum torque which will produce a stress above the endurance limit. Note that T_n for strength and durability may differ from one another.

The required equivalent life in gear cycles at maximum torque may be obtained by multiplying the life in pinion cycles by the gear ratio:

$$L_{CG} = L_{CP} \frac{N_P}{N_G}$$

As the contact stresses on both gear and mating pinion are equal, the equivalent life in gear cycles is of no particular concern for durability. However, the bending stresses on gear and mating pinion are frequently different and therefore the equivalent life in gear cycles may be of concern.

Where the calculated tensile bending stress, S_t, or calculated contact stress, S_c, is known, the life factors can be calculated using the following formulae:

$$K_L = \frac{S_t}{S_{at}}$$

$$C_L = \frac{S_c}{S_{ac}}$$

Using these life factor values and Figures 12.7 and 12.8, the life in cycles for the corresponding member may be estimated for both strength and durability.

19 *Hardness ratio factor, C_H.* The hardness ratio factor for durability depends on the gear ratio and relative material hardness of pinion and gear. For gear ratios above $8:1$ where pinion and gear are made from materials of unequal hardness, it may be necessary to give consideration to this factor. Otherwise use a value of 1.0.

20 *Temperature factors, K_T, C_T.* Under normal conditions use a temperature factor of 1.0 for both strength and durability. For conditions involving case-hardened steel and oil discharge temperatures between 160 °F and 300 °F, one accepted basis for correction is as follows:

$$K_T = C_T = \frac{460 + T_F}{620}$$

where

$$T_F = \text{peak operating oil temperature (°F).}$$

21 *Factors of safety, K_R, C_R.* The factors of safety are introduced in the equations for working bending stress and working contact stress, to allow the designer the choice of designing for maximum safety or for a calculated risk, depending upon the application.

The factor of safety for strength, K_R, is applied to the fatigue strength of the material rather than to the tensile strength. For this reason the values are much smaller than customarily used in other branches of machine design.

The factor of safety for durability, C_R, is likewise applied to the fatigue strength of the material to resist contact fatigue. Because the rate of propagation of contact fatigue failures is relatively slow, actual tooth breakages may not occur. Contact fatigue failure is considered to occur when at least one pit on the tooth surface grows to 0.187 in diameter and is 0.008 in deep.

Suggested factors of safety are given in the table below.

Application requirements	Strength, K_R	Durability, C_R
Maximum safety	2.0	1.25 or higher
Fewer than 1 failure in 100	1.0	1.0
Fewer than 1 failure in 3	0.8	0.8

Failure in the table does not refer to an immediate failure under the applied load, but rather a shorter life than the minimum specified.

13
Worm gear stress formulae

This chapter covers the British Standard method for stress calculations for both diametral pitch and metric module worm gears, which is one of the best methods available and is widely accepted in industry.

Diametral pitch worm gears

1 *Determination of load capacity.* The permissible torque capability of a pair of worm gears is limited either by the surface stress in the gear teeth or the bending stress. This refers to both the worm threads and the wormwheel teeth. Therefore the determination of the load capacity of a pair of worm gears involves four calculations, i.e. both the surface stress and bending stress for the worm threads and the wormwheel teeth, the permissible load capacity being the lowest of the four values.

1A *Permissible load for wear.* For the normal rating the permissible torque on the wormwheel is limited by surface stress, i.e. wear, by the lower of the following values:

(a) $X_{CP}S_{CP}ZD_f^{1.8}m$ (lbf. in)
(b) $X_{CW}S_{CW}ZD_f^{1.8}m$ (lbf. in)

where

$$X_{CP} = \text{speed factor for wear – worm}$$
$$S_{CP} = \text{surface stress factor – worm}$$
$$Z = \text{zone factor (Table 13.1)}$$
$$D_f = \text{wormwheel reference circle diameter (PC dia.) (in)}$$
$$m = \text{axial module (in)}$$
$$X_{CW} = \text{speed factor for wear – wormwheel}$$
$$S_{CW} = \text{surface stress factor – wormwheel}$$

The speed factor for wear, X_C, corresponding to the combination of both the rotational and the rubbing speed, should be in accordance with Figure 13.1, where the rubbing speed in feet per minute is calculated as follows:

(a)
(b)

Table 13.1   Worm gear zone factors, Z

No. of threads	Diam. factor														
	6	6.5	7	7.5	8	8.5	9	9.5	10	11	12	13	14	17	20
1	1.045	1.048	1.052	1.065	1.084	1.107	1.128	1.137	1.143	1.160	1.202	1.260	1.318	1.402	1.508
2	0.991	1.028	1.055	1.099	1.144	1.183	1.214	1.223	1.231	1.250	1.280	1.320	1.360	1.447	1.575
3	0.822	0.890	0.989	1.109	1.209	1.260	1.305	1.333	1.350	1.365	1.393	1.422	1.442	1.532	1.674
4	0.826	0.883	0.981	1.098	1.204	1.301	1.380	1.428	1.460	1.490	1.515	1.545	1.570	1.666	1.798
5	0.947	0.991	1.050	1.122	1.216	1.315	1.417	1.490	1.550	1.610	1.632	1.652	1.675	1.765	1.886
6	1.132	1.145	1.172	1.220	1.287	1.350	1.438	1.521	1.588	1.675	1.694	1.714	1.733	1.818	1.928
7			1.316	1.340	1.370	1.405	1.452	1.540	1.614	1.704	1.725	1.740	1.760	1.846	1.950
8					1.437	1.462	1.500	1.557	1.623	1.715	1.738	1.753	1.778	1.868	1.960
9							1.573	1.604	1.648	1.720	1.743	1.767	1.790	1.880	1.970
10									1.680	1.728	1.748	1.773	1.798	1.888	1.980
11										1.732	1.753	1.777	1.802	1.892	1.987
12											1.760	1.780	1.806	1.895	1.992
13												1.784	1.806	1.898	1.998
14													1.811	1.900	2.000

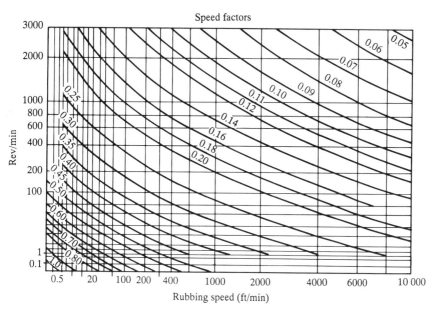

Figure 13.1   Speed factors for worm gears (for wear), X_C

Rubbing speed, V_S (ft/min) $=0.262 d_f n \sec \lambda$

or

$$V_S = 0.262 m.n.\sqrt{t^2 + q^2}$$

where

d_f = worm reference circle diameter (PC diameter) (in)
n = speed of worm (rpm)
λ = worm thread lead angle
m = axial module (in)
t = no. of threads – worm
q = diameter factor (see page 114)

The surface stress factor, S_C, corresponding to the combination of materials used can be obtained from Table 13.2 (page 271)
1B *Permissible load for strength.* For the permissible torque on the wormwheel at normal rating, the lower of the values obtained from the following formulae for strength should be used:

(a) $1.8 X_{bp} S_{bp} m l_r D_f \cos \lambda$ (lbf. in)
(b) $1.8 X_{bw} S_{bw} m l_r D_f \cos \lambda$ (lbf. in)

where

X_{bp} = speed factor for strength – worm
S_{bp} = bending stress factor – worm
m = axial module (in)

l_r = length of root – wormwheel teeth
D_f = wormwheel reference circle diameter (PC dia.) (in)
λ = worm thread lead angle
X_{bw} = speed factor for strength – wormwheel
S_{bw} = bending stress factor – wormwheel

The bending stress factor, S_b, for the material used should be taken from Table 13.2 (page 271).

The speed factor for strength, X_b, corresponding to the rotational speed only should be in accordance with Figure 13.2.

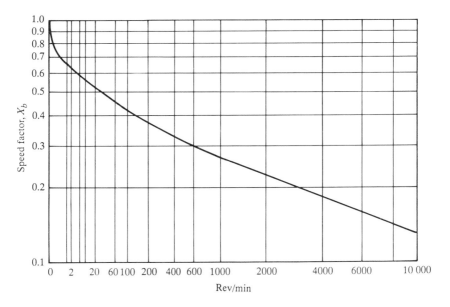

Figure 13.2   Speed factors for worm gears (for strength), X_b

1C   *The horse-power rating.* The normal horse-power rating of the wormwheel is obtained by the following formula:

$$\frac{M_w N}{63\,000}\,\text{(hp)}$$

where

M_w is the smallest of the four values obtained in items 1A and 1B
N = revolutions per minute of wormwheel

Note: The continuous rating of worm gearing operating in still air may be limited by consideration of temperature rise, rather than by resistance to bending or surface stresses.

Where the working oil temperature of 200°F is exceeded, the maximum permissible torque on the wormwheel may be less than that calculated in items 1A and 1B.

1D   *Expected life.* The permissible torque or horse-power obtained in accordance with items 1A to 1C inclusive is the loading to which the gears may safely be subjected for a total running time of 26 000 hours. If it is specified or deemed desirable that worm gears shall be designed on the basis of any other life, the permissible horse-power, or wormwheel torque, shall be multiplied by the following:

$$\left(\frac{27\,000}{1000+U_{ec}}\right)^{1/3} \text{ for wear}$$

or

$$\left(\frac{26\,200}{200+U_{eb}}\right)^{1/7} \text{ for strength}$$

where

U_{ec} = total equivalent running time for wear (h)
U_{eb} = total equivalent running time for strength (h)

respectively, corresponding to the expected life. Values of these factors may be obtained from Figure 13.3.

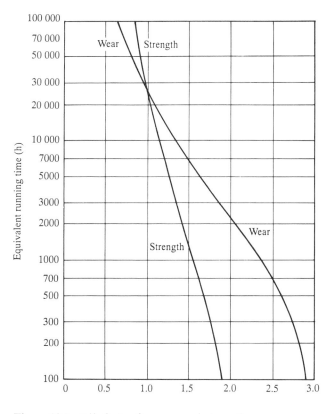

Figure 13.3   Life factor for wear and strength

Unless otherwise specified or determinable, the normal rating (e.g. the continuous load capacity of the motor) shall be deemed to apply continuously throughout the expected total running time.

1E   *Factor of safety.* The factor of safety is calculated from the following formula:

$$\frac{\text{Ultimate tensile strength of worm or wheel}}{\text{Working stress}}$$

Note: Use the lower ultimate tensile strength for the worm or wormwheel material.

Working stress

$$= \frac{\text{Actual torque on wormwheel (lbf. in)}}{1.8 m l_r D_f \cos \lambda}$$

where

m = axial module (in)
l_r = length of root – wormwheel teeth
D_f = wormwheel reference circle diameter
λ = lead angle of worm thread

2   Determination of equivalent running time for loading conditions other than a steady load.

2A   *Cycles of different uniform loads at different speeds.* If the load cycle on the wormwheel comprises a maximum torque, M_1, acting for U_1 hours at a mean speed, N_1, and smaller torques, M_2, M_3, etc., acting for U_2, U_3, etc., hours at mean speeds N_2, N_3, etc., the equivalent running time per cycle for wear at torque, M_1, and speed, N_1, is given by the following equation:

$$U_c = U_1 + U_2 \left(\frac{N_2}{N_1}\right)\left(\frac{M_2}{M_1}\right)^7 + U_3 \left(\frac{N_3}{N_1}\right)\left(\frac{M_3}{M_1}\right)^7 + \text{etc.}$$

in which each term represents the equivalent running time for the corresponding part of the cycle.

The total equivalent running time for wear at torque M_1 and wormwheel speed N_1 is given by:

$$U_{ec} = U_c \times \text{No. of complete cycles expected during life of gears}$$

The equivalent running time for strength at torque M_1 and wheel speed N_1 is then given by:

Running time per cycle for strength, U_b

$$= U_1 + U_2 \left(\frac{N_2}{N_1}\right)\left(\frac{M_2}{M_1}\right)^7 + U_3 \left(\frac{N_3}{N_1}\right)\left(\frac{M_3}{M_1}\right)^7 + \text{etc.}$$

in which each term represents the equivalent running time for the corresponding part of the cycle.

The total equivalent running time for strength at torque M_1 and wormwheel speed N_1 can then be calculated as follows:

$$U_{cb} = U_b \times \text{No. of complete cycles expected during life of gears}$$

2B *Irregular variation of load and variable speed.* The equivalent running time for a period of the load cycle, as calculated in section 2A during which load and speed vary other than uniformly, may be determined by subdividing it into periods during none of which the torque varies by more than $0.25M_1$ and then calculating the equivalent running time for wear and strength corresponding to each such period on the basis of the mean load and mean speed during the period in line with section 2A.

2C *Uniform variation of load and variable speed.* If, during any period, W, of the load cycle under section 2A, the torque changes uniformly from M_{W1} to M_{W2}, at mean speed N_W, the expression for the equivalent running time for that period for wear at torque M_1 and speed N_1 is given by:

$$U_{CW} = \frac{U_W}{4}\left(\frac{N_W}{N_1}\right)\left[\frac{M_{W1}}{M_1} + \frac{M_{W2}}{M_1}\right]\left[\left(\frac{M_{W1}}{M_1}\right)^2 + \left(\frac{M_{W2}}{M_1}\right)^2\right]$$

The equivalent running time for strength at torque M_1 and speed N_1 is calculated as follows:

$$U_{bW} = \frac{U_W}{8}\left(\frac{N_W}{N_1}\right)\left[\frac{M_{W1}}{M_1} + \frac{M_{W2}}{M_1}\right]\left[\left(\frac{M_{W1}}{M_1}\right)^2 + \left(\frac{M_{W2}}{M_1}\right)^2\right]\left[\left(\frac{M_{W1}}{M_1}\right)^4 + \left(\frac{M_{W2}}{M_1}\right)^4\right]$$

Note: Sections 2A, 2B and 2C will be applicable if the speed is uniform:

$$\frac{N_2}{N_1} \text{ or } \frac{N_W}{N_1}, \text{ etc.,}$$

then become unity

2D *Load varying in a cycle which is repeated a whole number of times in one revolution of the wormwheel.* If a whole number of load cycles are completed in exactly one revolution of the wormwheel, then the gears shall be designed to transmit the maximum torque continuously for an equivalent time equal to the expected running life of the gears.

3A *Momentary overload capacity.* A momentary load shall be considered as one whose duration is too short to be defined with certainty and which acts for a period of not more than 15 seconds or 0.004 hours.

Worm gears designed in accordance with this standard are capable of transmitting occasional momentary loads not exceeding either of the following:

For wear: $2S_{CW}ZD_f^{1.8}m$ (lbf. in)

For strength: $4S_{bW}l_rD_fm \cos \lambda$ (lbf.in)

where

S_{CW} = surface stress factor – wormwheel
Z = zone factor
D_f = wormwheel reference circle diameter (in)
m = axial module
S_{bW} = bending stress factor – wormwheel
l_r = length of root wormwheel tooth
λ = lead angle of worm thread

4   Axle transmission gears

4A   The torque transmitted by an axle transmission wormwheel can be calculated using the following formula:

$$M \times R_1 \times R_2 \text{ (lbf. in)}$$

where

$M =$ maximum engine torque (lbf. in)
$R_1 =$ gearbox ratio giving lowest road speed
$R_2 =$ rear axle ratio

4B   The roadwheel torque necessary to cause skidding when the vehicle is fully laden can be calculated using the following formula:

$$\text{Min. torque} = W_1 \mu r \text{ (lbf. in)}$$

where

$W_1 =$ load on driving axle when vehicle is fully laden (lb)
$\mu =$ coefficient of friction between tyres and ground
$r =$ rolling radius of tyres (in)

The corresponding wormwheel torque to the above is calculated as follows:

$$W_1 \mu r \times \frac{\text{Speed of roadwheels (rev/min)}}{\text{Speed of wormwheel (rev/min)}} \text{ (lbf. in)}$$

4C   The maximum torque which the axle transmission wormwheel may be called upon to transmit is equal to the lower of the two values given by the calculations in 4A and 4B.

4D   *Permissible load for wear.* The permissible wormwheel torque shall be limited by wear to the lower of the following values:

(a) $\dfrac{15+G}{30K} S_{CP} D_t^{1.8} mZ$ (lbf. in)

(b) $\dfrac{15+G}{30K} S_{CW} D_t^{1.8} mZ$ (lbf. in)

(c) $3000 D_t^{1.8} mZ$ (lbf. in)

when the worm and wormwheel materials are in group E and A, respectively, in Table 13.2, where

$$G = \frac{100}{Wr} \times \text{Roadwheel torque (lbf. in)}$$

$W =$ gross laden weight of vehicle including trailer
$r =$ rolling radius of tyre (in)
$K =$ duty factor, depending on type of vehicle (see Table 13.3)
$S_{CP} =$ surface stress factor – worm (see Table 13.2)
$D_t =$ reference circle diameter of wormwheel (in)
$m =$ axial module (in)
$Z =$ zone factor (see Table 13.1, page 264)
$S_{CW} =$ surface stress factor wormwheel (see Table 13.2)

Table 13.2

Material	BS ref.	Bending stress factor, S_b	Surface stress factor, S_C, when running with:				
			A	B	C	D	E
A Dyn. metal GZ14						2 000	2 900
Phosphor-bronze (centrifugally cast)	1400 PB2-C	10 000	–		1 200^b	1 200	1 300	2 200
Phosphor-bronze (sand-cast and chilled)	–	9 100	–		900^b	900	1 000	1 800
Phosphor-bronze (sand-cast)	–	7 200	–		660^b	660	770	1 500
B Grey cast iron	1452, Grade 12	5 800	900^b	600^b	600^c	600^c	750^c
C 4% carbon steel (normalized)	970 En 8	20 000	1 550	1 000	–	–	–
D 0.55% carbon steel (normalized)	970 En 9	25 000	2 200	1 200^c	–	–	–
0.55% carbon steel (flame-hardened)	970 En 9	30 000	6 000	–	–	–	–
E Carbon case-hardening steel	970 En 32	40 000	7 000	4 400^c	–		–	2 200^c
Nickel and nickel molybdenum case-hardening steels	En 33 En 34 En 35 $\}^a$	47 000	7 700	4 400	–		–	2 200^c
E Nickel chromium and nickel chromium molybdenum case-hardening steels	En 36 En 39 $\}$	50 000	8 800	4 400	–		–	2 200^c

^{a}Equivalent grades of steel are permissible.
^{b}Maximum permissible rubbing speed, 500 ft/min.
^{c}Permissible for hand motions only.

4E *Permissible load for strength*. The permissible wormwheel torque shall be limited by strength to the lower of the following two values:

(a) $\dfrac{15+G}{16.67\,K} S_{bp} m l_r D_t \cos \lambda$ (lbf. in)

(b) $\dfrac{15+G}{16.67\,K} S_{bw} m l_r D_t \cos \lambda$ (lbf. in)

where

$G =$ can be obtained from 4D
K is obtained from Table 13.3
$S_{bp} =$ bending stress factor – worm (see Table 13.2)
$m =$ axial module (in)
$l_r =$ length of root – wormwheel teeth (in)
$D_t =$ reference circle diameter – wormwheel (in)
$\lambda =$ lead angle of worm thread
$S_{bW} =$ bending stress factor – wormwheel (see Table 13.2)

Table 13.3. Duty factor, K

Type of vehicle	K
Long-distance goods vehicles which run for long periods in top gear	0.9
Goods vehicles	1.0
Goods vehicles with trailers	1.1
Long-distance passenger coaches	0.9
Urban passenger transport buses	1.15
Private motor cars	1.25
Trolley buses	1.25
Dumpers	2.0

It is assumed that the axle gear casings are made as stiff as reasonably possible and that the bearing caps are spigoted into the casing.

Metric module worm gears

1 *Determination of load capacity.* The permissible torque for a pair of worm gears is limited either by consideration of surface stress – wear, or bending stress – strength, in both the worm threads and wormwheel teeth. Consequently the load capacity of a pair of gears is determined using four calculations, concerned with wear and strength of worm and wormwheel. The permissible torque on the wormwheel should be the lowest of the four values.

1A *Permissible load for wear.* For the normal rating, the permissible torque on the wormwheel should be limited by wear to the lower of the following values:

(a) $0.001\,91 X_{C1} . \sigma_{CM1} . Z . d_2^{1.8} . m$ (N.m)
(b) $0.001\,91 X_{C2} . \sigma_{CM2} . Z . d_2^{1.8} . m$ (N.m)

where

$X_{C1} =$ speed factor for wear – worm
$\sigma_{CM1} =$ surface stress factor – worm
$Z =$ zone factor (see Table 13.1, page 264)

d_2 = reference circle diameter – wormwheel (PC dia.) (mm)
m = axial module (mm)
X_{C2} = speed factor for wear – wormwheel
σ_{CM2} = surface stress factor – wormwheel

The speed factor for wear, X_C, corresponding to the combination of rotational and rubbing speed, should be in accordance with Figure 13.4, where the rubbing speed, in metres per second, is calculated as follows:

Rubbing speed, V_S (m/s)
$$= 0.000\,052\,4d_1 . n_1 . \sec \gamma$$

or

$$= 0.000\,052\,4m . n_1\sqrt{z_1^2 + q^2}$$

where

d_1 = reference circle diameter – worm (mm)
n_1 = speed of the worm (rpm)
γ = worm thread lead angle
m = axial module (mm)
z_1 = number of threads – worm
q = diameter factor (see page 114)

The surface stress factor, σ_{CM}, corresponding to the combination of materials used, can be obtained from Table 13.4.

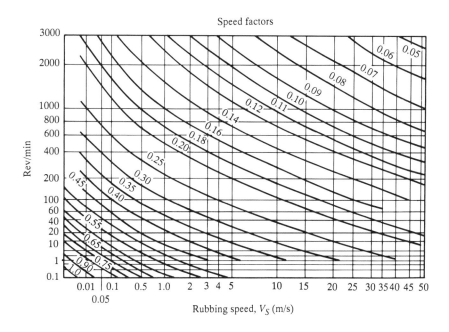

Figure 13.4   Speed factor for worm gears (wear), X_C

Table 13.4

Material	British Standard reference	Bending stress factor, σ_{bM}	Surface stress factor, σ_{CM}, running with:				
			A	B	C	D	E
A Phosphor-bronze (centrifugally cast)	BS 1400, PB2	69	–	8.3	8.3	9.0	15.2
Phosphor-bronze BS 1400, chilled	(sand-cast and PB2	63	–	6.2	6.2	6.9	12.4
Phosphor-bronze (sand-cast)	BS 1400 PB2	49	–	4.6^a	4.6	5.3	10.3
B Grey cast iron	BS 1452, GR180	40	6.2^a	4.1^a	4.1^b	4.1^b	5.2^b
C 0.40% carbon steel (normalized)	BS 970, Pt 1, 080.M40	138	10.7	6.9	–	–	–
D 0.55% carbon steel (normalized)	BS 970, Pt 1, 070.M55	173	15.2	8.3^b	–	–	–
E Carbon case-hardening steel	BS 970, Pt 1, 080.A15	276	48.3	30.3^b	–	–	15.2^b
Nickel and nickel molybdenum case-hardening steels	BS 970, Pt 1, 665M.17^c 805M20	325	53.1	30.3^b	–	–	15.2^b
Nickel chromium and nickel Chromium Molybdenum case-hardening steels	BS 970, Pt 1 655M13 835M15	345	60.7	30.3^b	–	–	15.2^b

[a]Maximum permissible running speed $= 2.54$ m/s.
[b]Permissible for hand motions only.
[c]Equivalent grades of steel are permissible.

1B *Permissible load for strength.* For the normal rating, the permissible torque on the wormwheel shall be limited by strength to the lower of the following values:

(a) $0.001\,8X_{b1} \cdot \sigma_{bM1} \cdot l_{f2} \cdot d_2 \cdot \cos\gamma \cdot m$ (N.m)
(b) $0.001\,8X_{b2} \cdot \sigma_{bM2} \cdot l_{f2} \cdot d_2 \cdot \cos\gamma \cdot m$ (N.m)

where

$$X_{b1} = \text{speed factor for strength – worm}$$
$$\sigma_{bM1} = \text{bending stress factor – worm}$$
$$l_{f2} = \text{length of root – wormwheel teeth (mm)}$$
$$d_2 = \text{wormwheel reference circle diameter (PC dia.) (mm)}$$
$$\gamma = \text{worm thread lead angle}$$

m = axial module (mm)
X_{b2} = speed factor for strength – wormwheel
σ_{bM2} = bending stress factor – wormwheel

The speed factor, X_b, corresponding to the rotational speed only, should be in accordance with Figure 13.5 (below).

The bending stress factor, σ_{bM}, corresponding to the material used, can be obtained from Table 13.4.

The continuous rating of worm gearing operating in still air may be limited by considerations of temperature rise rather than by resistance to bending or surface stresses. Where a working oil temperature of 95°C is exceeded, the maximum permissible torque on the wormwheel may be less than that calculated in sections 1A and 1B.

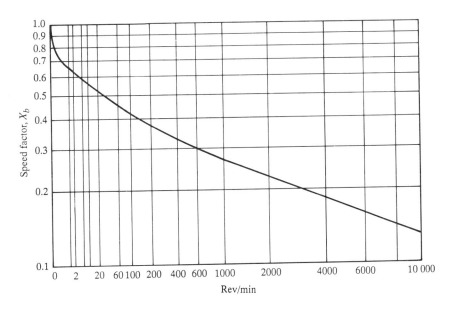

Figure 13.5 Speed factor for worm gears (strength), X_b

1C *Power.* Subject to adequate lubrication, the normal power rating of the wormwheel is calculated as follows:

$$\frac{Mn_2}{9550}$$

where

M = the smallest of the four values obtained in sections 1A and 1B
n_2 = revolutions per minute – wormwheel

1D *Expected life.* The permissible power or wormwheel torque obtained in accordance with sections 1A to 1C inclusive should apply to an expected total running life of 26 000 hours.

Where worm gears are designed on the basis of any other life, the permissible power or wormwheel torque should be multiplied by the following:

$$\left(\frac{27\,000}{1000+H_{ec}}\right)^{1/3} \quad \text{for wear}$$

$$\left(\frac{26\,200}{200+H_{eb}}\right)^{1/7} \quad \text{for strength}$$

where

H_{ec} = total equivalent running time for wear (h)
H_{eb} = total equivalent running time for strength (h)

respectively, corresponding to the expected life. Values of these factors may be obtained from Figure 13.6.

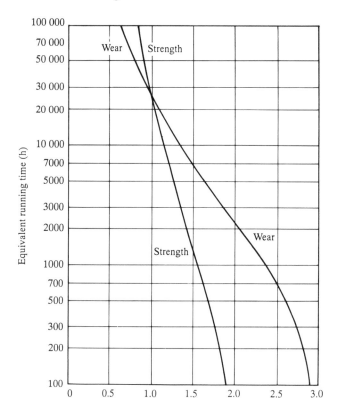

Figure 13.6 Total equivalent running time and related life factors for wear and strength

Unless otherwise specified, the normal rating (e.g. the continuous load capacity of the motor) shall apply continuously throughout the expected total tunning time.
1E *Factor of safety.* The factor of safety is calculated from the following formula:

$$\frac{\text{Tensile strength of worm or wheel material}}{\text{Working stress}}$$

Note: Use the lower ultimate tensile strength of the material for the worm or wormwheel.

Working stress

$$= \frac{\text{Actual torque on wormwheel (N.m)}}{0.001\,8m\,.\,l_{f2}\,.\,d_2\,.\,\cos\,\gamma}$$

where

m = axial module (mm)
l_{f2} = length of root – wormwheel teeth (mm)
d_2 = wormwheel reference circle diameter (PC dia.) (mm)
γ = worm thread lead angle

2 Determination of equivalent running time for loading conditions other than a steady load

2A *Cycles of different uniform loads at different speeds.* If the load cycle on the wormwheel comprises a maximum torque M_1, acting for a period H_1 at a mean speed $n_{2.1}$, and smaller torques M_2, M_3, etc., acting for periods H_2, H_3, etc., at mean speeds $n_{2.2}$, $n_{2.3}$, etc., the equivalent running time per cycle for wear at torque M_1 and speed $n_{2.1}$ is given by the following equation:

$$H_c = H_1 + H_2 \frac{(n_{2.2})(M_2)^3}{(n_{2.1})(M_1)} + H_3 \frac{(n_{2.3})(M_3)^3}{(n_{2.1})(M_1)} + \text{etc.}$$

where each term represents the equivalent running time for the corresponding part of the cycle.

The total equivalent running time for wear at torque M_1 and wormwheel speed $n_{2.1}$ is then given by:

$$H_{ec} = H_c \times \text{Number of complete cycles expected during life of gears}$$

The equivalent running time per cycle for strength at torque M_1 and wormwheel speed $n_{2.1}$ can be calculated using the following formula:

$$H_b = H_1 + H_2 \left(\frac{n_{2.2}}{n_{2.1}}\right)\left(\frac{M_2}{M_1}\right)^7 + H_3 \left(\frac{n_{2.3}}{n_{2.1}}\right)\left(\frac{M_3}{M_1}\right)^7 + \text{etc.}$$

where each term represents the equivalent running time for the corresponding part of the cycle.

The total equivalent running time for strength at torque M_1 and wormwheel speed $n_{2.1}$ is then given by:

$$H_{eb} = H_b \times \text{Number of complete cycles expected during life of gears}$$

2B *Irregular variation of load (variable speed).* The equivalent running time for a period of the load cycle as calculated in section 2A, during which load and speed vary other than uniformly, should be determined by subdividing it into periods during none of which the torque changes by more than $0.25M_1$. The equivalent running time for wear and strength corresponding to each such period on the basis of the mean load and the mean speed during the period should be calculated in accordance with section 2A.

2C *Uniform variation of load (variable speed).* If, during any period W of the load cycle specified in section 2A, the torque changes uniformly from M_{w1} to M_{w2} at mean speed N_{2w}, the expression for the equivalent running time for that period for wear at torque M_1 and speed $N_{2.1}$ is given by the expression

$$H_{cw} = \frac{H_w}{4}\left(\frac{N_{2w}}{N_{2.1}}\right)\left(\frac{M_{w1}}{M_1} + \frac{M_{w2}}{M_1}\right) \times \left[\left(\frac{M_{w1}}{M_1}\right)^2 + \left(\frac{M_{w2}}{M_1}\right)^2\right]$$

The equivalent running time for strength at torque M_1 and speed $N_{2.1}$ is calculated as follows:

$$H_{bw} = \frac{H_w}{8}\left(\frac{N_{2w}}{N_{21}}\right)\left(\frac{M_{w1}}{M_1} + \frac{M_{w2}}{M_1}\right) \times \left[\left(\frac{M_{w1}}{M_1}\right)^2 + \left(\frac{M_{w2}}{M_1}\right)^2\right]$$

$$\times \left[\left(\frac{M_{w1}}{M_1}\right)^4 + \left(\frac{M_{w2}}{M_1}\right)^4\right]$$

Note: Sections 2A, 2B and 2C will also be applicable if the speed is uniform, in which case:

$$\frac{N_{2.2}}{N_{2.1}} \text{ or } \frac{N_{2w}}{N_{2.1}} \text{ etc.}$$

then become unity

2D *Load varying in a cycle that is repeated a whole number of times in one revolution of the wormwheel.* If a whole number of load cycles are completed in exactly one revolution of the wormwheel, the gears shall be designed to transmit the maximum torque continuously for an equivalent time equal to the expected running life of the gears.

3A *Momentary overload capacity.* A momentary overload shall be considered as one whose duration is too short to be defined with certainty but does not exceed 15 seconds.

Worm gears shall be capable of transmitting occasional momentary overloads (in N.m) not exceeding values calculated from the following expressions:

For wear: $0.003\,82\sigma_{CM2}Zd_2^{1.8}m$

For strength: $0.004\sigma_{BM2}l_{f2}d_2m \cos\gamma$

where

σ_{CM2} = surface stress factor – wormwheel
Z = zone factor (see Table 13.1, page 264)
d_2 = wormwheel reference circle diameter
m = axial module
σ_{BM2} = bending stress factor – wormwheel
l_{f2} = length of root of wormwheel teeth
γ = lead angle of worm thread

4 Vehicle axle transmission gears

4A Torque (in N.m) transmitted by an axle transmission wormwheel can be calculated as follows:

$$M_e R_1 R_2$$

where

M_e = maximum engine torque (N.m)
R_1 = gearbox ratio giving the lowest road speed
R_2 = rear axle ratio

4B The roadwheel torque (in N.m) necessary to cause wheel spin/skidding when the vehicle is fully laden is given by the following expression:

$$W_1 \mu R_1$$

where

W_1 = load on driving axle when vehicle is fully laden (kN)
μ = coefficient of friction between tyres and ground
R_1 = rolling radius of tyres (mm)

The wormwheel torque (in N.m) corresponding to this is given by the following expression:

$$W_1 \mu R_1 \times \frac{\text{Speed of roadwheel (rev/min)}}{\text{Speed of wormwheel (rev/min)}}$$

4C The maximum torque that the axle transmission wormwheel may be called upon to transmit is given by the smaller of the two values obtained in accordance with 4A and 4B.

4D *Permissible load for wear.* The permissible wormwheel torque (in N.m) should be limited by wear to the lowest of the three values obtained from the following expressions when the worm and wormwheel materials used are as given in groups E and A, respectively, of Table 13.4, page 274:

(a) $0.001\,91 \left(\dfrac{15+G}{30K_A} \right) \sigma_{CM1} d_2^{1.8} mZ$

(b) $0.001\,91 \left(\dfrac{15+G}{30K_A} \right) \sigma_{CM2} d_2^{1.8} Z$

(c) $0.035\,9 d_2^{1.8} mZ$

where

$G = \dfrac{100}{WR_t} \times$ Roadwheel torque (Nm) corresponding to the maximum wormwheel torque obtained in accordance with 4C

$\sigma_{CM1}, \sigma_{CM2}$ = surface stress factors for worm and wormwheel, respectively, from Table 13.4, page 274
d_2 = reference circle diameter of the wormwheel (mm)

m = axial module (mm)

Z = zone factor (see Table 13.1, page 264)

K_A = application factor, dependent on type of vehicle (see Table 13.3, page 272)

W = gross laden weight of vehicle including any trailer (kN)

R_t = rolling radius of tyres (mm)

Note: Equations (a) and (b) may also be expressed in N.m as follows:

(a) $\dfrac{15+G}{15\,710K_A}\sigma_{CM1}d_2^{1.8}mZ$

(b) $\dfrac{15+G}{15\,710K_A}\sigma_{CM2}d_2^{1.8}mZ$

4E *Permissible load for strength.* The permissible wormwheel torque (in N.m) shall be limited by strength to the lower of the two values obtained from the following expressions:

(a) $\dfrac{15+G}{16\,670K_A}\sigma_{BM1}ml_{t2}d_2\cos\gamma$

(b) $\dfrac{15+G}{16\,670K_A}\sigma_{BM2}ml_{t2}d_2\cos\gamma$

where

G can be obtained from section 4D

K_A is obtained from Table 13.3, page 272

$\sigma_{BM1}, \sigma_{BM2}$ = bending stress factors for worm and wormwheel, respectively (see Table 13.4)

m = axial module (mm)

l_{t2} = length of root – wormwheel teeth (mm)

d_2 = reference circle diameter of wormwheel (mm)

γ = lead angle of worm thread

14
Summary

Apart from the formulae given in the previous chapters, other Standards are available to the gear designer. These include the following:

1 American Gear Manufacturers' Association Standards
2 ISO Standards
3 DIN Standards,
   together with various gear company Standards such as:
   (a) Gleason Gear Corporation
   (b) MAAG Gear Company
   (c) Klingelnberg Gear Company
   (d) Oerlikon Gear Company

which would form the basis of another book. However, between all the companies involved in the gear industry, the many years of experience, experiments and service results have shown that the load capacity of a pair of gears increases with the accuracy of the gears and the hardness of the tooth flanks. Since the loading capacity of the gears directly influences the weight and volume of the gear unit, the price and subsequent cost to the customer for the unit will also be affected.

The analysis of gears has reached a very high level and the modern aids available to the designer have made it possible to apply this theory profitably and economically, since the time-consuming work of calculations can be carried out on computers.

The increasing call for higher load capacities has led to increased use of harder materials for gears and subsequently to the development of tooth flank and root hardening, along with a thorough review of hardening techniques.

With the call for increased speeds for gear drives, the resultant dynamic forces have risen, but these can be reduced along with the noise in operation, the heat generated and vibration by using the most accurate tooth forms possible. Each pair of teeth in a high-speed gear-drive transmitting power engage and disengage within a few microseconds and, in this period of time, the nature and magnitude of the physical occurrences in the mesh change rapidly. The forces and torques being transmitted cause elastic deformation of all the components in the gear drive, with subsequent malalignment and displacements. Therefore, to ensure the smoothest possible mesh under load, the geometric form of the tooth flanks must deviate from the purely theoretical profile by a strictly specified but minute amount.

Such deliberate corrections must be observed not only for every tooth of the gear but for the teeth on all the gears in the gear train.

By the more profound knowledge of the process of meshing, the new and more reliable treatments of the gear materials, the use of more effective lubricants and, more importantly, the improved accuracy of gear-cutting techniques have all combined to raise the endurance strength and durability of gears appreciably during the past decade.

Thus the limitations of the modern high-capacity gear drives are frequently no longer dictated by the running properties of the gears themselves, but by totally different factors. Therefore, it is obvious that the more experience the designer has with gear design problems, the better the results that should be expected.

This statement can be verified by taking the stress formulae given in Chapter 10 for spur and helical gears and, using a known spur gear as a basis, calculate the allowable loadings and stresses. The results will, as stated in the introduction to Chapter 10, show a wide scatter. These will show as much as 300% variation, and the designer must then make the decision whether to use the loading and stress, giving him the largest factor of safety with its inherent weight penalty and extra cost, or to use a higher loading and stress value thus reducing the factor of safety and subsequently the weight and cost of the gear train.

With industry today, and in particular the automotive industry, becoming more weight-, space- and overall cost-conscious, gear drives have had to become more compact which, in return, has resulted in the higher load capacities and the increased use of better grade materials with tighter quality control during heat-treatment processes. Thus the gear and transmission designer is gradually being forced into a position where he makes the ultimate decision.

Fortunately, as the demands become greater so the steel industry and the heat-treatment processes have been making steps forward, and therefore better materials with improved hardenability are making harder tooth surfaces available.

My own particular experiences in recent years have produced the following results with the varying stress formulae. The results given are based on the torque figures and gear ratios of a well-known automotive gearbox which has been on the market for some time following the company's rigorous test programme, and to my knowledge no failures have been reported. However, a lot of praise has been forthcoming for the gearbox from both professional engineers and members of the public who have been privileged to drive the particular vehicle to which the gearbox is fitted.

Stressing comparisons for spur and helical gears

The figures given in the following pages are the actual safety factors that have been calculated from the known details.

First gear
Lewis formula: safety factor $0.4435 - 1$
Buckingham formula:
   Bending stress: safety factor $0.3143 - 1$
   Contact stress: safety factor $0.2111 - 1$

British Standard 436: 1986:
  Bending stress: safety factor 0.6557 – 1
  Contact stress: safety factor 0.6676 – 1
AGMA 170.01 – 1976:
  Bending stress: safety factor 0.4611 – 1
  Contact stress: safety factor 0.6005 – 1

The Lewis formula is used to calculate the shear strength of the gear tooth and relate it to the yield strength of the material. The Buckingham stress formula compares the dynamic load with the beam strength of the gear tooth and gives a limit load for wear.

Although both of these formulae include form factors, it is difficult to see from the figures to date how these are allied to the tooth contact ratio between the gear pairs.

British Standard 436: Part 3: 1986 compares the permissible contact stress with the calculated actual contact stress, and the permissible tooth root bending stress with the calculated actual tooth root bending stress.

AGMA 170.01 – 1976 Standard Design Guide for Vehicle Spur and Helical Gears provides comparisons between the calculated root bending stress and the design limit for bending stress, along with the calculated contact stress and the design limit for contact stress.

The figures given, plus the following safety factors, which should always be greater than 1.00 to 1.00, prove that regardless of the empirical formula used and its age – the Lewis formula dating back to the 1890s and the Buckingham formula dating back to the mid-1920s – it is not the actual answers that are obtained. However, even with the modern formulae it is the designer's responsibility to arrive at the correct interpretation of the results to suit the particular application.

To assist the automotive gear designer, the following figures give the safety factors for the rest of the gears in the gearbox, for which first-gear safety factors have already been given.

Second gear
Lewis formula: safety factor 0.7976 – 1
Buckingham formula:
  Bending stress: safety factor 0.4498 – 1
  Contact stress: safety factor 0.3903 – 1
British Standard 436:
  Bending stress: safety factor 1.4264 – 1
  Contact stress: safety factor 1.1713 – 1
AGMA 170.01:
  Bending stress: safety factor 0.717 – 1
  Contact stress: safety factor 1.0571 – 1

Third gear
Lewis formula: safety factor 0.8258 – 1
Buckingham formula:
  Bending stress: safety factor 0.4016 – 1
  Contact stress: safety factor 0.5608 – 1

British Standard 436:
  Bending stress: safety factor 1.2208 − 1
  Contact stress: safety factor 1.1096 − 1
AGMA 170.01:
  Bending stress: safety factor 0.6182 − 1
  Contact stress: safety factor 1.2117 − 1

Fourth gear
Lewis formula: safety factor 0.9028 − 1
Buckingham formula:
  Bending stress: safety factor 0.4471 − 1
  Contact stress: safety factor 0.5492 − 1
British Standard 436:
  Bending stress: safety factor 1.0319 − 1
  Contact stress: safety factor 1.0716 − 1
AGMA 170.01:
  Bending stress: safety factor 0.7269 − 1
  Contact stress: safety factor 1.144 − 1

Fifth gear
Lewis formula: safety factor 0.9608 − 1
Buckingham formula:
  Bending stress: safety factor 0.458 − 1
  Contact stress: safety factor 0.5756 − 1
British Standard 436:
  Bending stress: safety factor 0.8861 − 1
  Contact stress: safety factor 0.9478 − 1
AGMA 170.01:
  Bending stress: safety factor 0.7646 − 1
  Contact stress: safety factor 1.1191 − 1

Final drive gear
Lewis formula: safety factor 0.3603 − 1
Buckingham formula:
  Bending stress: safety factor 0.2841 − 1
  Contact stress: safety factor 0.2913 − 1
British Standard 436:
  Bending stress: safety factor 1.0105 − 1
  Contact stress: safety factor 0.797 − 1
AGMA 170.01:
  Bending stress: safety factor 0.3104 − 1
  Contact stress: safety factor 0.7816 − 1

Reverse gear
Lewis formula: safety factor 0.4276 − 1
Buckingham formula:
  Bending stress: safety factor 0.2806 − 1
  Contact stress: safety factor 0.0873 − 1

British Standard 436:
  Bending stress: safety factor 0.3443 – 1
  Contact stress: safety factor 0.6436 – 1
AGMA 170.01:
  Bending stress: safety factor 0.1439 – 1
  Contact stress: safety factor 0.4204 – 1

The calculations for the safety factors given were based on the following torque figures:

(a) The first gear is based on the vehicle wheel-slip torque
(b) The final drive gear calculations use maximum engine torque in first gear
(c) The remaining gears are calculated using maximum engine torque

The results produced illustrate the point made previously in this chapter, regarding the wide scatter of results that can be obtained and, when interpreted correctly, can be used successfully regardless of the age of the formula.

The ISO Standard, which is more comprehensive than the new British Standard, is at the moment in its infancy when compared with some of the Standards described earlier in this book. As sufficient comparative figures are not available at present, it would appear to be prudent to await a broader spectrum of results before any judgement of the Standard's accuracy is made. The ISO Standard has been received by both the professional engineer and the engineering universities with great enthusiasm, and everyone involved in the gear design industry is pinning great hopes on the accuracy and repeatability of the results obtained.

From the design and stressing formulae given, it is obvious that the calculation of any one of these formulae can be simplified and the time taken to obtain the results vastly reduced by creating a program and running the gear data through a computer. The program should be written to accept the known input data and produce the results in the same order and format as used on the company gear detail drawings, thus reducing the chances of errors being made when transferring computer results to the detail drawings. Thus, although many gear design computer programs are available on the open market at this time, my own experience has shown that many of them do not give results that I actually require. Therefore, it has proved to be more practical to have a computer program produced within the company that is specifically designed to suit the particular needs of the types of application that are to be tackled, rather than try to utilize one of the standard commercial programs. Although the writing of the program will take some time, once prepared it is always available in the form required and therefore over a period the time invested will be reclaimed.

In recent years, a large amount of research work has been carried out in the use of finite element analysis to solve the gear stressing problems in various applications, but to date this system is reliant on some empirical formulae, which as shown earlier in this chapter, need not produce the answers required but rely on the correct interpretation. Therefore, the finite element analysis system is, in the majority of instances, being used as a check or back-up system to the empirical stressing formula which has been in use much longer and has more comparative results available. Although a number of engineering papers on the finite element analysis system have already been published, as with the ISO Standard insufficient results are available for a comprehensive comparison of the accuracy of the system to be made.

During my years as a gear designer, the improvement made in both gear design and the accuracy of the stressing formulae has moved forward very slowly, but from the gear users' point of view the old motto 'slow but sure' is an absolute necessity – and thorough research is a slow process.

Bibliography

AGMA Standard 170-01 – 1976 Standard Guide for Vehicle Spur and Helical Gears. American Gear Manufacturers' Association

British Standard 436: 1940 Strength and Horse Power Capacity of Gears. British Standards Institution, London.

British Standard 436: Part 1 (1967) and Part 2 (1970) Spur and Helical Gears. British Standards Institution, London.

British Standard 436: Part 3: 1986 Strength and Load Carrying Capacity of Gears. British Standards Institution, London.

British Standard 545: 1949 Bevel Gears. British Standards Institution, London.

British Standard 721, Part 1 (1963) and Part 2 (1983) Worm Gearing. British Standards Institution, London.

Buckingham, E. (1925) *Manual of Gear Design*. Industrial Press, New York, USA.

Dudley, D.W. (1976) *Practical Gear Design*. McGraw-Hill, New York, USA.

Gleason Gear Co. Ltd (1971, 1980, 1983) *Bevel and Hypoid Gear Design*. Rochester, New York, USA.

MAAG Gear-Wheel Co. Ltd (1963) *Gear Book*. Zurich.

Merritt, H.E. *Gears*. Pitman, London.

Merritt, H.E. (1965) *Gear Engineering*. Pitman, London.

National Broach and Machine Co. (1972) *Modern Methods of Gear Manufacture*. Detroit, Michigan, USA.

Tuplin, W.A. (1962) *Gear Design*. Machinery Publishing Co., London.

Index